T210
Environmental control and public health

Block 3
Water pollution control

The Open U

This publication forms part of an Open University course T210 Environmental Control and Public Health. Details of this and other Open University courses can be obtained from the Student Registration and Enquiry Service, The Open University, PO Box 197, Milton Keynes MK7 6BJ, United Kingdom: tel. +44 (0)845 300 60 90, email general-enquiries@open.ac.uk

Alternatively, you may visit the Open University website at http://www.open.ac.uk where you can learn more about the wide range of courses and packs offered at all levels by The Open University.

To purchase a selection of Open University course materials visit http://www.ouw.co.uk, or contact Open University Worldwide, Michael Young Building, Walton Hall, Milton Keynes MK7 6AA, United Kingdom for a brochure. tel. +44 (0)1908 858793; fax +44 (0)1908 858787; email ouw-customer-services@open.ac.uk

The Open University
Walton Hall, Milton Keynes
MK7 6AA

First published 2002. Second edition 2003. Third edition 2007

Edited and designed by The Open University.

Typeset by SR Nova PVT. Ltd, Bangalore, India.

Printed and bound in the United Kingdom by Hobbs the Printers, Brunel Road, Totton, Hampshire.

ISBN 978 0 7492 2379 3

3.1

T210 Course Team

Dr Suresh Nesaratnam	course chair/author
Judith Anderson	course manager
Dr Rod Barratt	author
Sylvan Bentley	picture researcher
Philippa Broadbent	print buying controller
Dr Stephen Burnley	author
Roger Busby	author
Dr Keith Cavanagh	author/editor
Dr Sally Crompton	author
Jim Frederickson	author
Pam Furniss	author
Keith Horton	external consultant/author
Caryl Hunter-Brown	subject information specialist
Dr Alan Kirkwood	external consultant/author
Jo Lambert	learning projects manager
Roy Lawrance	graphic artist
Karen Lemmon	compositor
Vicki McCulloch	graphic designer
James McLannahan	consultant
Katie Meade	rights executive
Dr Dick Morris	consultant
Dr John Newbury	consultant
Stewart Nixon	software developer
Dr Julian Parfitt	author
Dr Shirley Payne	consultant
Dr Michael Peet	BBC (OU Production Centre)
Prof. Andrew Porteous	consultant
Janice Robertson	editor
Dr David Sharp	consultant
Dr Shahram Taherzadeh	author
Mark Thomas	software developer
Marjorie Thompson	course secretary
Dr James Warren	author
Rob Westcott	editor

In addition the Course Team wishes to thank the following for reviewing the material:

External assessor	Prof. Douglas Probert
Block 2	Jenny Morris
Block 3	Prof. Hugh Tebbutt, Cynthia Blackwell
Block 4	Dr Jan Gronow, Pat Wheeler
Block 5	Oliver Hetherington
Block 6	Michael Gittins

Contents of the course

CONTENTS

LEARNING OUTCOMES

The aims of this block are:

■ to give an overview of the biological, physical and chemical characteristics of rivers and lakes, and how each of these affects the other;

■ to give an overview of water treatment, water supply and water demand;

■ to give an indication of the different sources of pollution and how pollutants affect the aquatic environment;

■ to give an overview of sewage treatment together with the options available for biological treatment;

■ to give examples of methods by which the various water quality parameters can be measured;

■ to consider the various pollutants that can arise from farms and how these can be controlled.

After studying this block, reviewing the associated DVD, carrying out the relevant home experiments, and referring to the Set Book, you should be able to demonstrate the following learning outcomes.

Knowledge and understanding
You should be able to:

1 describe the operation and mechanisms of the hydrological cycle (SAQs 5–10);

2 list and describe the major physical, chemical and biological characteristics of clean fresh water, and explain their effects on aquatic organisms (SAQs 11–17);

3 explain the mode by which potable water is produced through the processes of screening, microstraining, aeration, coagulation and flocculation, sedimentation, flotation, filtration and disinfection (SAQs 18–24);

4 explain how the issues of nitrates, trace organics, fluoridation and plumbo-solvency can be dealt with in potable water supply (SAQs 25–6);

5 describe the main desalination processes used to produce potable water from saline or brackish sources (SAQ 27);

6 explain the function of transmission mains, ring mains, service reservoirs and water towers, and discuss the merits and disadvantages of different types of piping materials (SAQs 28–30);

7 identify the principal demands for water in society (SAQs 31–3);

8 describe a variety of means by which the usage of potable water can be reduced in the home, in gardens and in offices, and list the pollutants present in greywater (SAQ 34);

9 identify the pollutants that can be present in rainwater harvested from roofs and describe ways of eliminating these (SAQ 35);

10 list the major sources of water pollution and give examples of the types of pollutants they discharge;

11 list the main physical, chemical and biological pollutants, and describe their effects on a river ecosystem (SAQs 36–41);

12 explain the concept of biochemical oxygen demand (BOD), and describe how it can be used as a measure of pollution (SAQs 42–6);

13 select an appropriate method of analysis for each of the major pollutants and water quality parameters (SAQs 47–51);

14 describe the various stages involved in sewage treatment (SAQs 52–63, 76, 77);

15 describe the various pretreatment processes that may have to be applied to industrial effluents to render them suitable for discharge to sewers, for treatment at a domestic sewage treatment plant (SAQ 64);

16 describe various tests to assess treatability, and explain the process of bioaugmentation (SAQ 65);

17 give examples and characteristics of the variants of the biological oxidation system for treating effluents, and indicate the type of effluent or situation for which each type would be most appropriate (SAQs 66–71);

18 give examples of tertiary treatment processes to reduce the level of suspended solids, ammonia, nitrates and phosphates in a secondary-treated effluent (SAQs 72–5);

19 list the sources and characteristics of sewage sludge, and describe the various methods by which it may be treated and disposed of, together with their applicability (SAQs 78–83);

20 describe the likely sources of pollution on farms, and devise systems to ensure that the surroundings are protected from likely harm (SAQs 84–8);

21 be familiar with UK and European Union legislation covering water and water pollution control.

Thinking (cognitive) skills

You should have the skills to:

22 undertake design calculations related to settling tanks (SAQs 18, 19 and 25), water storage (SAQ 29), sewage flows (SAQs 55 and 56), biological filters (SAQ 60), sludge settlement (SAQ 61) and activated sludge treatment (SAQ 62);

23 undertake calculations related to inhibition of biological activity (SAQ 65);

24 determine the area of reedbed required for a desired level of treatment (SAQ 69);

25 determine the quantity of sludge generated in the biological treatment of domestic sewage (SAQ 82);

26 determine the volume of storage required to contain farm effluent (SAQ 84);

27 be able to suggest appropriate treatment processes for given effluents (SAQ 70).

Professional and practical skills, through the Home Experiments

You should have the skills to:

28 measure the pH of different liquids;

29 determine the quantity and pH of rainfall over a month, and estimate your water usage;

30 determine the solubility of sodium bicarbonate using titration;

31 determine the hardness of a sample of water;

32 determine the BOD of a given wastewater;

33 determine the quality of a river in terms of oxygen demand, pH, ammonia, nitrate, nitrite and hardness.

Key skills

You should have the skills to:

34 manipulate and sort data (SAQs 5–7, 29);

35 present data in a variety of ways (SAQs 29 and 65);

36 use scientific evidence-based methods in the solution of problems (SAQs 15, 17, 26, 31, 36, 42–46, 52, 65, 67, 74, 77, 86);

37 communicate effectively through the TMAs associated with this block;

38 use an engineering approach to the solution of problems (SAQs 18, 19, 29, 55, 56, 59–62, 65, 69, 82, 84, 85).

INTRODUCTION

We can all relate to water. We know we need it to survive – indeed all the great civilizations of the world (the Egyptian, Greek, Mesopotamian, etc.) were centred around river valleys where there was a plentiful supply of fresh, clean water.

When we take water into our bodies, it is used in several ways – as a coolant (keeping our body at a temperature of 98.4 °F or 36.9 °C), as a waste disposal medium, as a conductor for nerve impulses, and as a component in the digestion of food.

You can see from the above that even if you didn't move an inch, your body would still need water to keep you alive. A survival handbook I read recently says that people can live for 21 days without food but for only 10 days without water. I suspect this must be for a temperate climate. In the desert, in summer, the limit might only be a day or two.

Water is a fascinating subject, encompassing chemistry, biology and physics. Apart from keeping us all alive, water is used extensively in industrial processes, and for recreation and transport. It is something we can't do without. The water we use for domestic purposes has to be free of contaminants – more than 25 000 people are said to die each *day* from ingesting poor-quality water!

In this block, we start from the basics – the hydrological cycle and the natural aquatic environment. Then we gently glide into water treatment, water supply and water conservation. As a society, we are getting more and more water-hungry – one of the signs of affluence!

Of course, what goes in must come out, and so we have effluents to deal with. Effluent treatment, as you can imagine, is a vast subject in itself. We will try to cover the main topics, looking at aquatic pollutants and the treatment options available to us. I hope you'll find the block enlightening.

Well, to get started, try the following 'refresher' questions, covering basic biology and chemistry. If you find them difficult, it might be best to have another look at Block 0: *Biology* and Block 0: *Chemistry*.

SAQ 1

Which of the following is a definition of a food chain?

A   The nutritional links between producers and primary, secondary and tertiary consumers.

B   The cycling of biomass through a particular environment.

C   The cycling of nutrients via producers, consumers and decomposers/ scavengers within an ecosystem.

SAQ 2

Which one of the following is *not* an act of pollution?

A   The production of CO_2 (carbon dioxide) by the burning of fossil fuels.

B   The production of CO_2 by green plants in a river.

C   Discotheque noise heard in neighbouring houses.

D   Excess noise at work.

E   The dispersion of treated sewage effluent in a river.

F   The dispersion of vegetable washing wastes in a river.

SAQ 3

Complete the following sentence with one of the options below.

The process of photosynthesis in green plants results in ...

A   the release of carbon dioxide.

B   the breakdown of carbohydrates.

C   the breakdown of carbon dioxide.

D   the production of carbohydrates and oxygen.

E   the production of carbohydrates and carbon dioxide.

SAQ 4

Write down the names of the following and note whether they are ions or molecules.

(a) NH_4^+

(b) N_2

(c) OH^-

(d) NO_3^-

(e) $MgCl_2$

(f) HCO_3^-

(g) CO_2

1 THE HYDROLOGICAL CYCLE

1.1 Introduction

The hydrological cycle, the continuous cycling of water between land, open water surfaces and the sea, either directly or indirectly, is an extremely complex process which has been known for a long time (Figure 1). The identifiable mechanisms of the cycle are complicated not only by the characteristics of air–water–land interfaces across which the cycle operates, but also by climatic factors which vary in both time and space. The various operations and mechanisms within the cycle are illustrated in Figure 2 and are described below.

Figure 1 Probably the oldest reference to the hydrological cycle, the Chandogya, one of the principal Upanishads, says 'rivers ... lead from sea to sea'. It reveals that as early as 1000 BCE, attempts were being made to interpret and explain recurrent phenomena on the basis of direct experience. (Cartoon by Ajit Nunan)

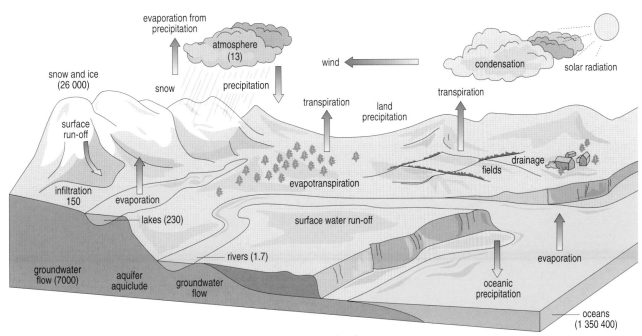

Figure 2 The hydrological cycle (volumes are in $Tm^3 = 10^{12} m^3$)

1.2   Evaporation

At an interface with the atmosphere, water changes its state from a liquid to a vapour in response to an increase in temperature caused by an external heat source. This temperature change is normally the result of solar radiation. The transfer of moisture into the air is called evaporation. The process is also controlled by the relative humidity, or level of vapour saturation, of the air. The greater the relative humidity of the air, the less likely it is that evaporation will take place for a given temperature. In addition to the direct controls of temperature and humidity, the rate of evaporation is also influenced by wind velocity, since continuous wind currents will carry away saturated air from the water surface, allowing more water to evaporate from the surface.

Evaporation is variable with both time and place because the controlling factors themselves provide transient conditions. It will occur almost continuously from stretches of permanent open water and intermittently, but usually at a lower rate, from land surfaces.

Over land surfaces, the rate of evaporation varies with the extent to which the ground is saturated. If the soil saturation level (i.e. the level to which all the voids are filled with water) is low, water moves up to the surface by the effect of capillary action. This controls the rate at which water will evaporate. Evaporation takes place from a sandy soil saturated up to the surface as quickly as it will from a lake, but the evaporation rate from saturated loam and clay soils is only 75–90% of that from an open body of water.

As it begins to rain, a large proportion of the water droplets is intercepted by the leaves of trees and other vegetation before reaching the ground. By this process of interception, water held on leaves and branches is returned rapidly to the atmosphere by evaporation. In forested areas, as much as 40% of light rain may be intercepted by foliage, although overall the fraction is probably nearer to 10–25%.

1.3   Transpiration

If there were no vegetation, the rate of evaporation from land surfaces after rain would diminish rapidly to a very low value. Plants increase this rate by transpiration. In this process, water is transferred from the soil through the roots to the leaves by osmosis and capillary action. Water evaporates from the surface of the leaves and the resulting vapour diffuses into the atmosphere. For hydrological measurements, this phenomenon is frequently lumped with evaporation because the two processes are not truly distinguishable using simple observational techniques over an area of mixed land use. The complete process of removal of moisture to the atmosphere from land surfaces by evaporation and transpiration is then termed evapotranspiration.

1.4   Condensation

As air rises it expands, owing to the decrease in pressure with height, and as it expands, in theory it cools at an average rate of 1 °C for every 100 m of altitude. As the air cools, it becomes saturated with water vapour which condenses around small particles in the air. These particles may occur naturally, such as soil particles or salt particles residual to evaporation of sea spray, or they may be produced artificially during combustion. A measure of the necessary cooling to produce condensation is the *dew-point*, which is the temperature at which air of a given absolute humidity and at a given pressure begins to give up its water as drops of dew. When moist air is chilled to a temperature below its dewpoint, in the presence of suitable minute particles, a cloud or mist will form.

1.5 Air circulation

At this stage, air circulation enters and plays a dual role. Firstly, winds transmit moisture horizontally from one location to another. In this way, moisture derived from oceanic evaporation can be transported many miles to a land mass. Secondly, convective or vertical currents arising from unequal heating or cooling can transmit moisture upwards. When it cools, some of the water vapour condenses. It is from these currents that most precipitation develops.

1.6 Precipitation

Precipitation is defined as the depth of rainfall, or the water equivalent of snow, sleet and hail falling during a given measurement period. It may be in the form of rain, snow, sleet or hail, or in minor forms such as dew and hoar frost, but existing theories do not yet satisfactorily account for all the observed characteristics. In tropical climates, precipitation occurs as a result of the gradual coalescence of the tiny condensed droplets as they collide within the cloud layer. In cooler climates, the formation of ice crystals in the upper levels of the cloud in turn is followed by crystal growth at the expense of water droplets, and this results in snow or hail. When sufficient growth has occurred, the large water drops or ice crystals have a larger ratio of mass to surface area than the small water drops or ice crystals.

SAQ 5

Verify the above statement that large drops have a larger mass surface area ratio than small ones, by considering two rain drops of equivalent diameter 1 mm and 3 mm, respectively. Take the density of the rainwater to be 998 kg m^{-3}.

Note: For a sphere of radius r, the volume $= \dfrac{4}{3} \pi r^3$ and the surface area $= 4 \pi r^2$.

The increased mass to surface area ratio allows the large drops to fall more rapidly than the small drops and they separate from the cloud. The small drops with very low velocity remain in the air currents associated with the cloud.

The large-scale cooling needed to give significant amounts of precipitation is achieved by lifting the air. There are three lifting processes (Figure 3) and these are used to describe the type of precipitation. They are:

(a) frontal (or cyclonic) – resulting from warm moist air meeting cooler air;

(b) orographic – upward deflection of warm air streams by mountains;

(c) convective (or convectional) – uplift associated with local heating by solar radiation.

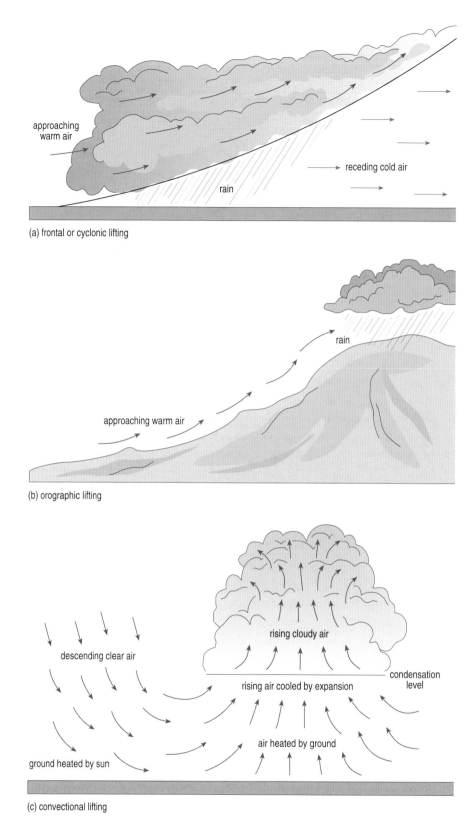

(a) frontal or cyclonic lifting

(b) orographic lifting

(c) convectional lifting

Figure 3   Lifting processes leading to precipitation

In the hydrological cycle, the total volume of water remains constant. The volume of water precipitated must necessarily balance the volume evaporated (when considered over a sufficiently long period of time to make variation in atmospheric storage of moisture insignificant).

1.7 Infiltration

Entry of precipitation through the soil surface and on downwards, by gravity, is known as infiltration. The rate at which this process can take place is governed by the permeability (a measure of the ease with which water can flow through the subsurface layer) and by the existing degree of saturation of the soil. Infiltration can be impeded by outcropping impermeable rocks or by paved areas, and also by the presence of fine-grained soils with a low permeability (such as clay). At certain times it will be inhibited by frozen ground or saturated soil, and in Arctic areas by frozen subsoil the whole year round.

The total amount of infiltration will depend upon the rate at which it can take place, and upon the time available for water to seep into the ground. You should appreciate that rapid run-off of water will reduce the time available for infiltration and decrease the total amount taken into the ground.

1.8 Surface run-off

In some inland drainage areas, all water is removed by evaporation and infiltration. However, precipitation not penetrating the land surface usually runs off the surface along defined channels which have been produced by geological processes, previous storms, or possibly by people. This accelerates the process. Its eventual destination is the ocean, except, of course, where it runs to inland seas such as the Dead Sea. It is in the run-off phase of the cycle that physical intervention by humans has been greatest. People have (Figure 4):

- harnessed the potential energy of rivers to provide power;
- curbed erosion in order to protect dwellings and avoid the loss of fertile soil;
- impounded water for supply schemes;
- diverted flow for the irrigation of crops and to facilitate navigation; and
- drained land to improve its agricultural value.

Figure 4 Water in our lives: (a) Itaipu Dam in Brazil

Figure 4   Water in our lives: (b) irrigation channels

1.9   Percolation

Movement of infiltrated water downwards through the zone of aeration (Figure 5) is known as percolation. The infiltrated water which does not remain held by capillary forces in the surface soils moves by the action of gravity through the unsaturated layers of soil or rock until it arrives at the water table. Here the percolated water joins the body of groundwater which seeps slowly to the sea.

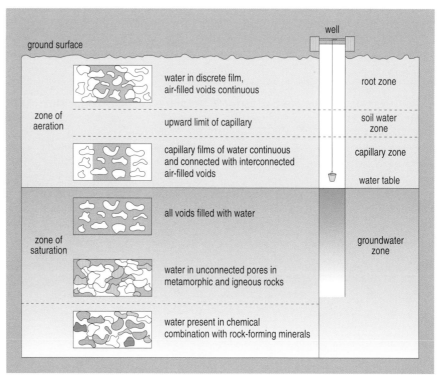

Figure 5   Zones of subsurface water

1.10   Aquifers

Groundwater is water that, after infiltrating and percolating through surface soils, flows into an *aquifer*, an underground water-bearing layer of porous rock. About one-third of the UK's drinking water is drawn from aquifers.

To permit economic development, an aquifer must be able to transmit large quantities of water from one point to another and therefore it must have a high permeability. The groundwater contained in aquifers is released from springs and can be responsible for the bulk of river flows.

Usually, aquifers are alluvial sands (sands which have been carried in suspension by rivers or floods) and gravels, the coarser sedimentary rocks such as sandstone, and rocks such as limestone in which chemical action has increased the water-bearing capacity. The strata of relatively impermeable rocks that lie either above or below confined aquifers (aquifers trapped between two impervious layers of rock) are called aquicludes.

The flow of groundwater takes place through the layer that is completely saturated. This layer, not surprisingly, is called the zone of saturation (see Figure 5).

1.11   Storage

In a given fixed space at any phase of the hydrological cycle, there is an inflow and an outflow of water, the rates of which vary with time. The total cumulative difference between inflow and outflow is the storage. So within that space there is a body of water whose mass is not directly controlled by instantaneous values of inflow and outflow. For example, in river flow the movement of the whole body of water in the channel is generally downstream, yet a given reach contains a volume whose size may not change very much over a period of settled, fairly dry weather. Also, water may be abstracted from this reach at a greater rate than the inflow.

The storage element is most stable when it is large in relation to input and output quantities. This implies that the stored volume of water is stable in large lakes and reservoirs and also in aquifers, where the inflow and outflow rates are naturally low. As the size of the system increases, so also does the stability.

In our discussion of the hydrological cycle we have presumed that the system is completely stable, so both inflow and outflow are zero. This assumes that water present in the hydrological cycle was formed at a very early stage in geological time. However, there is a theory that suggests that water is continuing to form in the Earth's core. Water is formed in small quantities, of course, by a number of artificial processes (e.g. in car exhausts). We have also assumed that no water is lost to the system by escaping from the Earth's gravitational pull.

The concept of storage is vital to the supply of water, since a major problem of supply revolves around the provision of water at the right time. Water is, of course, in highest demand in dry weather and we seek constantly to exploit or increase the existing storage potential in the cycle.

The relative contributions to total storage are summarized in Figure 6 and Table 1. The oceans of the world hold the bulk of the water on Earth. Thus the water resources of the world are largely saline (salty).

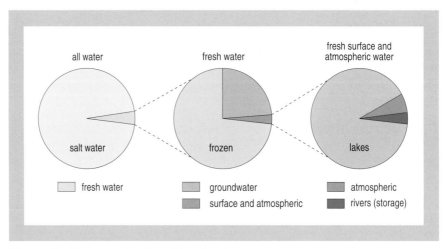

Figure 6   Components of world water storage

Table 1   Total available water in the various storage components of the hydrological cycle

Storage component	Volume of water (10^{12} m^3)	Volume (%, approx.)
Oceans	1 350 400	97.6
Ice caps and glaciers	26 000	1.9
Groundwater and soil moisture	7150	0.5
Freshwater lakes	125	0.009
Saline lakes	105	0.008
Rivers	1.7	0.0001
Atmosphere	13	0.001

From Table 1, it can be seen that only 2.4% of the Earth's water is non-saline, and that much of this is locked up as ice.

SAQ 6

Calculate the volume of surface fresh water available in the non-polar regions using the figures in Table 1. What percentage of the total water available is this?

One thing which is not shown in Table 1, but which I'm sure you have thought about, is the unevenness in the distribution of fresh water throughout the world. When I was working in Kuwait we had a proposal from an organization representing oil tanker owners. They wanted to sell fresh water from Norway and Wales, brought as ballast in the tankers coming to collect crude oil. For a variety of reasons, the proposals were rejected.

1.12   Summary

The hydrological cycle is a complex process involving evaporation, transpiration, condensation, air circulation, precipitation, infiltration, surface run-off and percolation. Aquifers are an important source of fresh water supplying about one-third of the UK's potable water demand. Most of the world's water is present as saline water in the oceans.

SAQ 7

What fraction of the total volume of water that circulates in the Earth's hydrological cycle does river water represent?

SAQ 8

What are the components of the hydrological cycle which can modify the volume of groundwater resources?

SAQ 9

Which of the following is the best description of evapotranspiration?

A The transfer of water from the oceans, seas and land surface to the air.

B The accelerated process of transfer of moisture to the air at a water–air interface caused by an external heat source.

C The transfer of moisture from soil to the air through roots and leaves of plants.

D Items **B** and **C** together.

E The total removal of moisture to the atmosphere from land surfaces.

SAQ 10

How do the following affect infiltration?

(a) Dense vegetation.

(b) Steeply sloping land surface.

(c) Cultivated land.

(d) Roads and buildings.

2   THE NATURAL AQUATIC ENVIRONMENT

2.1   Water, the medium of life

Referring back to Block 0: *Biology*, you will recall the list of necessities for the provision of life, which includes various nutrients and water: water is one of the basic resources needed for the process of photosynthesis. Since it is an excellent solvent, water, even in its 'natural' state, is never pure H_2O but contains a variety of soluble inorganic and organic compounds. Water can also carry large amounts of insoluble material in suspension. The amounts and types of impurities vary with location and time of year, and determine some of the characteristics of a particular watercourse.

One of the most important determining factors is the presence of organic material in solution or in suspension. Organic material can be used as 'food' by the organisms living in natural water, provided the material is biodegradable. *Biodegradable materials* are those organic substances which can be decomposed by micro-organisms (usually bacteria and fungi) into inorganic substances. We have met the idea of food chains and webs and the cycling of nutrients. The basis of a trophic system in a river is the content of inorganic and organic materials in it, the *biodegradation* of these by decomposer organisms, and the products of the photosynthetic activities of the primary producers.

In a water environment, as on land, the primary producers (green plants and algae) are eaten by herbivores (primary consumers) and these in turn are devoured by the secondary consumers (carnivores). The interdependence of these organisms gives a complex food web within which there are many food chains, the successive links in the chains being composed of different species in a predator–prey relationship.

For a river a typical food chain could be

algae $\longrightarrow$ rotifer $\longrightarrow$ mayfly $\longrightarrow$ small fish (minnow) $\longrightarrow$ large fish (pike)

Scavengers eat bottom debris, including dead organisms. If the latter are not eaten immediately, the decomposers (bacteria and fungi) break them down, releasing nutrients which can be taken up by plants.

Through this cyclic movement of nutrients, the water environment achieves an ecological equilibrium. In a given stretch of water a balance occurs between total production of living material and the occurrence of death and decomposition over a period of time. The river neither becomes choked with living organisms nor devoid of them – although, depending on location and geological conditions, the numbers and varieties of the biota vary enormously. The maintenance of equilibrium is dependent on the complexity of biota and the interlinking of food chains and webs.

A typical river has several sources in high ground which are characterized by steep gradients, swift current velocities, and erosion of the surrounding rocks and soil. As the gradient lessens, the current velocity decreases and the river deepens and widens. The river then tends to deposit stones, gravel and sand. This variation in the flow downhill has a direct influence on the types of organisms and substratum to be found at different points along the river. The whole length of the river can be subdivided into different zones, each characterized by its own typical fauna and flora.

In contrast to rivers, standing bodies of water such as lakes and reservoirs may be affected by thermal *stratification*. Figure 7 illustrates this effect for a typical lake. In the summer, there is very little mixing between the cooler, denser water at the bottom of the lake (hypolimnion) and the warmer, less dense water at the lake surface (epilimnion). Thus, stream and river water running into the lake will tend to stay in the upper layer. This water carries nutrients, so organisms flourish in the epilimnion and there is a high rate of primary production. In the hypolimnion, the dead remains of primary production settle out, forming a layer of bottom sediment. The lack of mixing between the layers (stratification) together with the absence of light penetration to the bottom of the lake determine the ecological characteristics of a deep lake or reservoir. In a deep lake, the absence of light prevents the growth of plant life in the bottom layers, although decomposer and scavenger micro-organisms can live on, and in, the bottom sediment.

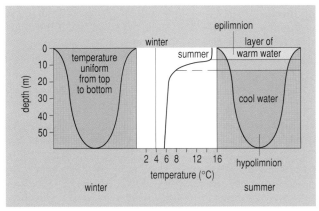

Figure 7   Thermal stratification of a lake

In contrast to summer conditions, Figure 7 shows that in winter, thermal stratification is absent. This is because the density of fresh water is greatest at 3.98 °C (about 4 °C). Thus, when the temperature of the surface layer falls to this temperature, the layer will descend to the bottom of the lake, displacing any colder (but less dense) water which will now rise to the surface. The lake 'turns over' and mixing occurs at all levels, leading to uniform temperature and uniform conditions throughout. This mixing process can bring partially decomposed bottom sediments to the surface, where further biodegradation can occur. This can also cause a significant deterioration in water quality.

Thus water carrying the organic and inorganic nutrients supports and maintains the aquatic ecosystem. Where there is very little biomass, the conditions are said to be *oligotrophic* (nutrient impoverished). This may occur when the physical and chemical characteristics of the land through which the water passes are such that nutrients are sparse or are not dissolved out of the soil and rocks. The opposite situation is *eutrophication*; this is the gradual increase with time of nutrients and biota in a body of water, eventually leading to parts of lakes (especially) and rivers becoming choked with plants.

2.2   Dissolved oxygen

Organic and inorganic nutrients are the basic food supply essential for maintaining the plants and animals in natural watercourses. Equally essential to aquatic life is a supply of oxygen, needed for respiration. Oxygen dissolved in the water is also needed in the biodegradation of organic matter by aerobic (oxygen-consuming) bacteria. A measure of this *oxygen demand* can be obtained experimentally and is defined as the *biochemical oxygen demand* (BOD). The BOD is a measure of the polluting capacity of an effluent due to the oxygen taken up by micro-organisms as they decompose the organic matter it contains. The procedure for its determination is given in Section 8.1.1.

Oxygen dissolved in natural waters arises from two main sources – the atmosphere and the process of *photosynthesis* (discussed in Block 0: *Biology*). Atmospheric air containing 21% oxygen by volume can dissolve in water up to a limit. Green plants in the presence of sunlight generate oxygen. These two sources replenish the oxygen used up in aerobic processes by aquatic organisms. The solubility of oxygen in water depends on the temperature, pressure, and the amount of dissolved solids present.

Table 2 shows the solubility of oxygen from air at atmospheric pressure in pure water at various temperatures. This is calculated using the expression $C_s = 14.65 - 0.41022T + 0.00791T^2 - 0.00007774T^3$ where C_s is the solubility of oxygen in water at 1 atmosphere pressure, and T is the temperature in degrees Celsius. As can be seen, the solubility decreases with an increase in water temperature (see also Block 0: *Chemistry*).

The solubility C_s is expressed in grams per cubic metre. (This is the same as mg l^{-1}, mg/l or ppm, parts per million. You may like to verify this for yourself.) C_s is the maximum amount of oxygen in grams which can be held in one cubic metre of solution – called the saturation concentration. A value of 5 g m^{-3} of dissolved oxygen is considered to be the minimum required to support a balanced population of desirable aquatic flora and fauna. When you consider from Table 2 that the saturation concentration of dissolved oxygen at 15 °C is only 10.01 g m^{-3}, it is evident that oxygen concentrations need not fall very much before the balance of aquatic life is threatened.

Decreasing the atmospheric pressure above the water decreases the saturation concentration of dissolved oxygen. Therefore, streams at high altitudes are unable to dissolve as much oxygen as those at the same temperature nearer sea level.

Increasing the concentration of dissolved salts also lessens the saturation concentration of dissolved oxygen in water, and the correction which must be subtracted for each gram of total salts per 1000 g of water is also shown in Table 2. It is for this reason that the amount of oxygen needed to saturate sea water is less than that required to saturate fresh water at the same temperature and pressure.

Table 2 Saturation concentration of oxygen in water at different temperatures

Temperature (°C)	Solubility of oxygen in water C_s (g m^{-3}) in equilibrium with air at 1 atmosphere (1.013×10^5 N m^{-2} or 101.3 kPa)	Correction to be subtracted for each degree of salinity (expressed as g total salts per 1000 g water)
0	14.65	0.0925
1	14.25	0.0890
2	13.86	0.0857
3	13.49	0.0827
4	13.13	0.0798
5	12.79	0.0771
6	12.46	0.0745
7	12.14	0.0720
8	11.84	0.0697
9	11.54	0.0675
10	11.26	0.0653
11	10.99	0.0633
12	10.73	0.0614
13	10.48	0.0595
14	10.24	0.0577
15	10.01	0.0559
16	9.79	0.0543
17	9.58	0.0527
18	9.38	0.0511
19	9.18	0.0496
20	8.99	0.0481
21	8.80	0.0467
22	8.63	0.0453
23	8.45	0.0440
24	8.29	0.0427
25	8.12	0.0415
26	7.97	0.0404
27	7.81	0.0393
28	7.66	0.0382
29	7.51	0.0372
30	7.36	0.0362

EXERCISE

A sample of sea water from the Arabian Gulf, at 30 °C, has a total salt content of 44 g per 1000 g water. If the sample is found to be 25% saturated with oxygen, what is the oxygen content in g m^{-3}?

ANSWER

At 30 °C, saturated pure water contains (from Table 2) 7.36 g m^{-3} of oxygen.

Since the sample is highly saline sea water, a correction has to be applied.

Correction $= 44 \times 0.0362$

$$= 1.59 \text{ g m}^{-3} \text{ oxygen}$$

Thus, if the sea water were saturated at 30 °C, it would have

$$7.36 - 1.59 = 5.77 \text{ g m}^{-3} \text{ oxygen}$$

But since it is only 25% saturated, the oxygen present

$$= 5.77 \times \frac{25}{100} \text{ g m}^{-3}$$

$$= 1.44 \text{ g m}^{-3}$$

The rate at which oxygen dissolves in water is dependent on several factors. One of these, the oxygen deficit (D), is the difference between the saturation concentration of oxygen (C_s) and the concentration of oxygen actually present (C) i.e. $D = C_s - C$. The oxygen deficit is the driving force for the replenishment of oxygen used up in polluted water. The greater the oxygen deficit is, the greater the transfer rate of oxygen into the water. Other factors important in the dissolution of oxygen in water include the turbulence of the water, its ratio of surface area to volume, the presence of animals and plants in the water, and any chemicals present. These will be discussed later.

EXERCISE

A river at a certain location has a dissolved oxygen content of 8.1 g m^{-3}. Using the data given in Table 2, calculate the oxygen deficit, if the river water has a temperature of 10 °C.

ANSWER

Oxygen deficit $D = C_s - C$.

From Table 2, $C_s = 11.26$ g m^{-3} at 10 °C.

From information given above, $C = 8.1$ g m^{-3}.

Therefore, $D = 11.26 - 8.1$ g m^{-3}

$$= 3.16 \text{ g m}^{-3}$$

Figure 8 illustrates how the oxygen concentration varies between the water surface and the interior of a water body when oxygen is consumed in the water. The resultant oxygen deficit causes oxygen to be transferred from the surface into the water body. As mentioned earlier, the greater the deficit, the greater the rate of oxygen transfer into the water.

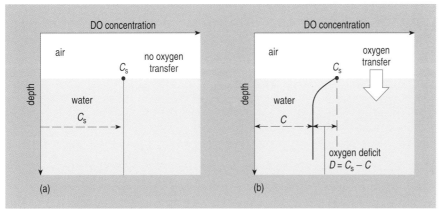

Figure 8 (a) Water body at equilibrium, with no consumption of oxygen; (b) consumption of oxygen in a water body resulting in an oxygen deficit being created, and oxygen consequently being transferred into the water body

The rate of oxygen transfer into a water body also depends on the *turbulence* of the water, since this helps transport oxygen from the surface layers to the main body of the water. Rapidly flowing turbulent streams are therefore able to take up oxygen more rapidly than smoothly flowing, slow ones.

Another factor governing the transfer of oxygen into a watercourse is the ratio of surface area to volume. A large surface area permits a greater diffusion of oxygen into the water. Hence shallow, wide rivers are reoxygenated more rapidly than deep, narrow ones. Agitation increases the ratio of surface area to volume, as, for example, when water flows over dams and weirs, and when waves are produced by strong winds. A further advantage of agitation is the entrainment of air bubbles as air is drawn into the water body.

The amount of oxygen in a water body at any given time depends not only on the characteristics mentioned above but also on biological and other factors. Almost all aquatic animals and plants use oxygen in carrying out their metabolic processes and so are constantly tending to increase the oxygen deficit. If organic pollutants are present, the oxygen deficit is increased further as biodegradation takes place. At the same time as oxygen is being consumed, oxygen replenishment via photosynthesis and natural aeration takes place.

Figure 9 shows graphically the processes of oxygen demand and replenishment. Curve (a) shows the oxygen demand of a polluted water sample. Curve (b) shows the reaeration process observed when oxygen is forced to dissolve in the water due to the oxygen deficit created by the biodegradation taking place. The net result of the oxygen demand and replenishment processes is illustrated by curve (c), which is called the dissolved oxygen sag curve. This is in effect the difference between the demand and replenishment curves.

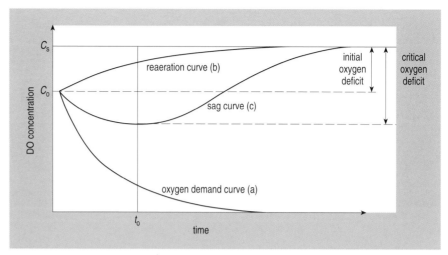

Figure 9   The dissolved oxygen sag curve

There are diurnal and seasonal differences in oxygen concentration. Figure 10 illustrates the diurnal variation that may occur. This variation is related to plant growth, light intensity and temperature. The amount of dissolved oxygen rises to a maximum during the day because of photosynthesis occurring in daylight. It decreases through the night because none is produced by photosynthesis, but respiration (using up oxygen) continues as it does during the daylight hours. This extreme diurnal variation occurs mainly between April and October because the lower temperatures during the rest of the year tend to slow down or inhibit the metabolic processes and plants become dormant.

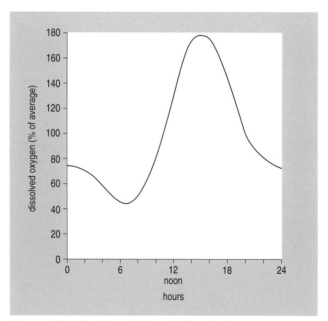

Figure 10   Hourly variation of dissolved oxygen

Figure 11 illustrates seasonal changes in dissolved oxygen. An increase occurs in the summer months because of longer days (more daylight) and therefore increased photosynthetic activity.

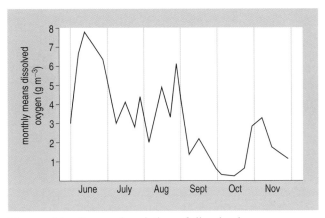

Figure 11   Seasonal variation of dissolved oxygen

In some circumstances, oxygen supersaturation can occur, i.e. more oxygen is dissolved in the water than the saturation concentration allows. This occurs because plants produce pure oxygen (whereas air contains 21%). Therefore, when photosynthesis is responsible for the oxygenation of the water, rather than atmospheric aeration, up to five times the saturation concentration is theoretically possible at the same temperature and pressure. In practice, 500% is never attained, but up to 200% has been recorded, in a shallow river with profuse plant growth, on bright sunny days.

SAQ 11

Which of the following events would not affect the rate of transfer of oxygen from the atmosphere to a body of water?

A   Doubling the oxygen deficit.

B   Large amounts of salts being discharged into the water.

C   A slight breeze blowing over the water.

D   Water flowing over a weir.

E   Raising the temperature of the water by 10 °C.

SAQ 12

When is the level of dissolved oxygen in a river likely to be at its highest and at its lowest?

2.3   Physical characteristics of natural waters

A river's physical characteristics include:

- clarity/turbidity

- colour

- speed of flow/turbulence

- odour

- the presence of plants and macroscopic animal life.

The physical characteristics are determined by location, geology and climate of the catchment area. In turn they influence the chemical and biological characteristics of the watercourse.

You will be asked to do a river water quality survey as part of your home experimental work and you will be expected to describe the river in physical, biological and chemical terms. The physical appearance may give you initial clues to the condition of the river. Figure 12 shows how the aquatic ecosystem is a complex set of physical, chemical and biological interrelationships. Nutrients and dissolved oxygen may be essential to aquatic life but other conditions must also be satisfactory.

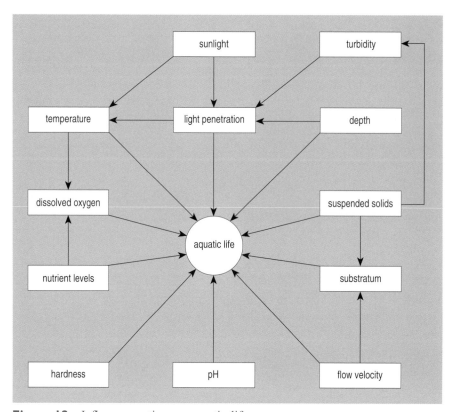

Figure 12   Influences acting on aquatic life

2.3.1   Turbidity, colour and suspended solids

As water runs off the land, there are some substances which do not dissolve but are taken along as *suspended solids*. Then, depending on their sizes and the velocity of the river, the solid particles may settle out at a certain point or be carried on further. Quantities are affected by seasonal changes and tend to be higher in winter because of increased storm *run-off* due to higher rainfall and melting snow.

The quantity of suspended solids (measured in $g\ m^{-3}$) affects the *turbidity* or cloudiness of the water. Suspended solids may also contribute colour to the water. Turbidity is measured in nephelometric turbidity units (NTU).

Nephelometric means that the measurement has been arrived at through the estimation of light absorption.

Particles of all sizes tend to reduce light penetration; this reduces the rate of photosynthesis and therefore causes a reduction in the growth of plant life. Very small particles which settle out on the bottom of the stream may have a blanketing effect, thereby preventing certain bottom dwellers from living there and green plants from photosynthesizing.

2.3.2   Speed of flow/turbulence

To get nutrients and dissolved oxygen to all parts of a body of water, good mixing is important. We have had one example in the thermal stratification in deep lakes in summer, where poor mixing and reduced sunlight lead to the bottom layers not being supplied with the necessary conditions for plant growth. The same principle applies to rivers and streams. Fast-moving turbulent streams mix and agitate the water, aiding the transfer of oxygen from the atmosphere to the river, and carry nutrients more efficiently to the plants and animals in the river. Small, rapidly flowing streams are nearly always saturated with dissolved oxygen; large sluggish rivers may have oxygen concentrations well below saturation conditions.

2.3.3   Temperature

All aquatic organisms have a fairly well-defined temperature tolerance range and this determines their distribution. Temperature affects the saturation concentration of dissolved oxygen (as seen in Table 2). An increase in water temperature will reduce the oxygen solubility as well as increase the metabolic activity of aquatic organisms. The combination of these two effects means that oxygen demand by organisms increases just when oxygen supply is being reduced.

Coarse fish such as perch, roach and chub can tolerate water temperatures up to 30 °C and dissolved oxygen levels as low as 3 g m^{-3}. However, game fish such as salmon or trout die if the oxygen concentration drops below 5 g m^{-3} or if the water temperature moves outside the 5–20 °C range.

2.4   Chemical characteristics of natural waters

Since water is such a good solvent, it is not surprising to find many different chemical substances present in it. Water, on reaching a river, will contain inorganic and organic compounds which were dissolved as rainwater percolated through the soil and rocks. In addition, some gases will dissolve in rainwater during its passage through the air.

The substances present in water may be conveniently grouped into:

1   those from dissolved gases such as oxygen and carbon dioxide;

2   those involved in the bicarbonate–carbonate equilibrium derived from carbon dioxide;

3   other dissolved substances.

All gases will dissolve to a greater or lesser extent in water. As we have seen, oxygen has a low solubility in water, as do nitrogen, argon and some of the other gases present in the atmosphere.

Carbon dioxide, by contrast, is very soluble in water: 1 m^3 of water at 20 °C will hold 878 g of pure carbon dioxide. However, carbon dioxide is special for another reason. When carbon dioxide dissolves, it reacts with the water to form bicarbonate and carbonate ions.

The chemical equation describing the process is called the bicarbonate–carbonate equilibrium.

$$CO_2 + H_2O \rightleftharpoons H^+ + HCO_3^- \rightleftharpoons 2H^+ + CO_3^{2-} \qquad (1)$$

dissolved carbon dioxide — hydrogen ion — bicarbonate ion — hydrogen ions — carbonate ion

Because all the reactions are reversible, the whole system reaches equilibrium, so that natural waters will contain various proportions of carbon dioxide, bicarbonate and carbonate.

How does the acidity (hydrogen ion concentration) of the water affect the equilibrium in Equation (1)?

For a reversible reaction, a change in the concentration of one of the chemical species in the reaction will produce a corresponding shift in the concentrations of other species in order to 'compensate' for the change. So in Equation (1), if the concentration of hydrogen ions (H^+) increases, the reactions move towards the left to compensate. A new equilibrium is reached with higher concentrations of CO_2 and bicarbonate, and a lower concentration of carbonate. Conversely, a decrease in hydrogen ions shifts the reactions in Equation (1) to the right. Figure 13 illustrates the relationship between pH and the concentrations of CO_2, HCO_3^- and CO_3^{2-}. The definition of pH in Block 0: *Chemistry* stated that low values (lower than a numerical value of 7) of pH correspond to 'acid' (high H^+) conditions, whereas high values (greater than 7) of pH correspond to 'alkaline' (low H^+) conditions. Figure 13 shows that in high-pH water, most of the carbon dioxide ends up as bicarbonate and carbonate, whereas in low-pH water, the carbon dioxide stays in solution without reacting further.

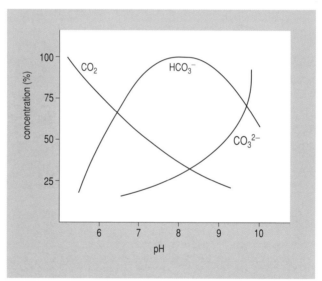

Figure 13   The bicarbonate–carbonate equilibrium

The bicarbonate–carbonate equilibrium is important in the process of photosynthesis, in which aquatic plants take up the inorganic carbon in carbon dioxide in the presence of sunlight for synthesizing new cell material. All plants can use dissolved CO_2 for this purpose, but none apparently can use carbonate directly. Blue-green algae can also use bicarbonate for photosynthesis. Thus, low-pH waters, with available carbon dioxide, are more favourable for photosynthesis.

The supply of carbon dioxide to the aquatic environment comes from the atmosphere through diffusion and as the product of aerobic and anaerobic metabolism, and is consumed during photosynthesis.

Apart from substances derived from the atmosphere, there are usually other substances dissolved in natural waters. *Salinity* is a general term which means the concentration of ionic constituents dissolved in water. These include the carbonates, sulphates and chlorides of sodium, calcium, potassium and magnesium. It may also mean specifically the sodium chloride content which comes from either sewage effluent or sea water intrusion. High chloride contents can also arise in watercourses receiving run-off from salted roads in winter.

The pH of natural water usually varies from approximately 6.0 to 8.0 depending on the types of rocks and substrate surrounding the watercourse, although in some drainage areas this can be as low as 4.0. There has been growing interest and concern regarding the acidity of rainwater in Europe and North America. Acidic precipitation (*acid rain*) can reach lakes and streams either directly or indirectly after interaction with the vegetation and soils. The magnitude of the effects depends on the buffering capacity of the water.

You might be familiar with hard water, from seeing scale deposited in kettles. As well as scale formation, both temporary and permanent hardness make lathering with ordinary soap difficult. The result is the formation of scum that floats on the surface of washing water. On the benefit side, the dissolved solids or minerals often give hard water a pleasant taste, and they are of nutritional importance to plants and micro-organisms, and may have various medicinal functions for humans.

Hardness in water is mainly due to the presence of ions of the metals calcium (Ca^{2+}), magnesium (Mg^{2+}), and iron (Fe^{2+}). Rivers and lakes fed by water that has run from chalky areas and limestone ($CaCO_3$) contain an abundance of calcium. Calcium and magnesium account for at least 70% of the total cations in water.

If calcium, magnesium and iron are present in water as bicarbonate salts, e.g. $Ca(HCO_3)_2$, and the water is boiled or heated above 70 °C, carbonate salts of the metals are precipitated. Such water is said to possess temporary or carbonate hardness because the carbonate salts (e.g. calcium carbonate) are largely insoluble, and are thus removed from the water and deposited as scale:

$$Ca(HCO_3)_2 \xrightarrow{\text{heat}} H_2O + CO_2 + CaCO_3$$

calcium
bicarbonate

calcium carbonate
(scale)

If the scale deposits on heating elements, it shortens their life and makes them less efficient.

When calcium, magnesium and iron are present as chloride or sulphate salts (e.g. $CaCl_2$), the hardness is called permanent or non-carbonate hardness. Although this type of hardness also contributes to scaling, in this case the precipitate is due to the decreased solubility of these metal salts at higher temperatures and not to the formation of new insoluble compounds.

The extent of hard water in the UK tends to follow a north to south-east gradient; the softest water being in Scotland, north England and Wales, and the hardest in East Anglia and south-east England. Also, groundwaters are more likely than surface waters to be hard. Mortality from cardiovascular (CV) disease (heart disease and stroke) tends to follow the same pattern, a higher rate in the north and north-west than in the south and south-east. Several statistical surveys have shown an inverse relationship between CV disease and water hardness. After adjustment for socioeconomic and climatic factors, this relationship is somewhat weakened but remains statistically significant. It can be shown that towns with very soft water ($CaCO_3$ concentration 25 g m^{-3}) have a CV mortality 10–15% higher than in areas with medium-hard water (170 g m^{-3} $CaCO_3$), while any further increase in hardness above these figures does not additionally lower CV mortality. CV disease may be said to be associated with soft water districts; this association may be influenced by either water hardness itself or by some factor closely associated with it. As a consequence, softening of water for domestic use is rarely carried out except for very hard sources. In homes with their own water-softening system, a tap is usually installed allowing hard water to be drawn off for drinking purposes.

2.4.1   Plant nutrients

Block 0: *Biology* mentioned the major and minor plant nutrients, all of which are necessary in varying amounts for the growth, reproduction and well-being of growing plants.

Of the major nutrients of plants, nitrogen and phosphorus are important growth-limiting factors in primary production (i.e. they are likely to run out before any other element needed by the plants). Both nitrogen and phosphorus enter watercourses from natural leaching by water of the soluble nitrates and phosphates found in soils and rocks, as well as from sewage effluent and agricultural sources. Phosphorus is the limiting growth factor for certain types of blue-green algae, and both phosphorus and nitrogen limit the growth of green algae.

2.4.2   Radiological aspects

Environmental radiation comes from a range of naturally occurring and anthropogenic sources, with the former estimated to contribute more than 98% of the radiation dose experienced by people (excluding medical exposure). Any exposure to radiation can lead to cancer, and the greater the exposure, the greater the risk.

The contribution that drinking water makes to radiation intake is very small, and is due largely to naturally occurring radionuclides (isotopes of an element which are unstable and undergo natural radioactive decay) in the uranium and thorium decay series.

Radon, a natural radioactive gas that has no taste, smell or colour, is estimated to contribute some 32% (of the above 98%) of the radiation people are exposed to. It is formed in the ground by the decay of uranium, which is often found in granite (and in phosphate-bearing rocks). Radon dissolved in water is released during handling of the water. Water that has been left to stand will have reduced radon activity, and boiling will remove radon completely. It is thus not seen as a problem.

There are strict guidelines on emissions of radioactive compounds, and the nuclear industry is carefully monitored. Nevertheless, to ensure water quality as regards radiation, limits are imposed.

The maximum dose from one year's consumption of drinking water has been set at 0.1 mSv. This is less than 5% of the average dose attributable annually to natural background radiation. For practical purposes, the maximum recommended guideline activity concentration is 100 Becquerel per litre (Bq l^{-1}) for tritium (a substance coming largely from the nuclear industry). This is based on the consumption of 2 litres of water a day.

2.5   Biological characteristics of natural waters

In addition to the easily visible plants and animals which live in or on a river, there are many small and often microscopic species which play a vital role in maintaining the health of a river. These organisms were introduced in Block 0: *Biology*. Here their relevance to water quality is discussed further.

2.5.1   Algae

Algae are photosynthetic organisms that are generally aquatic; they are primary producers. Many freshwater algae are of microscopic size, but when amassed can be seen as a green, brown or blue-green scum. Blue-green algae are capable of producing toxins and these have caused the death of wild animals, farm livestock and domestic pets which have consumed the contaminated water. The toxins can produce a painful rash on human skin. The extract below shows what happened off the west coast of Scotland in 2000 when algal blooms appeared there.

WWF blames fish farms for poison algae

By Rob Edwards, Environment Correspondent

Dramatic new evidence blames pollution from fish farms for causing the poisonous algae that is devastating Scotland's £50 million shellfish industry.

A report to be published tomorrow by the World Wide Fund for Nature, one of the country's most respected environmental groups, will conclude that the vast amount of waste excreted by the millions of salmon penned in 350 cages along the west coast is linked to toxic algal blooms. Scottish ministers have always denied such a link, and the results of the study will come as a blow to the Executive.

The accusation, made by a leading international marine scientist commissioned by the WWF, could hardly have come at a more embarrassing time. For the last month shellfish farmers have been banned from taking scallops from virtually all of the west coast waters from the Mull of Kintyre in the south to the Orkney Isles in the North. Sampling by Scottish Executive scientists showed that scallops in most western areas now contain dangerous levels of the algal toxin that causes Amnesiac Shellfish Poisoning (ASP) in humans. Symptoms of ASP include vomiting, diarrhoea, memory loss, seizures and comas.

On Tuesday, the Rural Affairs Committee of the Scottish parliament is due to hear a petition from a former shellfish farmer calling for an independent inquiry into the environmental impact of fish farming. Allan Berry, who is also a marine toxicologist, will argue that the discharges from fish farms are implicated in the recent 'epidemic' of toxic blooms.

Tomorrow's WWF report will give Berry powerful new evidence on the enormous amount of waste nutrients that comes from caged fish. Its author, Scottish-based environmental consultant Malcolm MacGarvin, is very critical of the Executive' refusal to acknowledge a connection between waste and the floating algal blooms.

'On the balance of probabilities you cannot rule out nutrients from fish farms as a factor', he told the Sunday Herald. 'If you put in more nutrients, you get more blooms and they last longer and affect a larger geographical area'.

The Executive fails to take account of the complex three-dimensional movement of the coastal waters, which could mean that a lot of fish farm waste remains in the top 10 metres of water where blooms are formed, he argued. It also dismisses laboratory evidence which suggests that nutrients can help the growth of algal toxins.

MacGarvin, who has advised governments, industry and environmental groups around the world on the marine environment, agreed that the absence of absolute proof should not be used as an excuse for inaction. The vast majority of studies in scientific journals were about how emissions of nutrients were linked to toxic blooms, not about whether they were.

'There is a lot of evidence saying that there is relationship between nutrients and blooms', he said. 'This is something we should be worrying about'.

The WWF itself declined to comment on the report until it has been published. The Scottish Executive, however, continues to insist that toxic blooms are naturally occurring and unrelated to the fish farming industry. In a detailed 40-page response to Allan Berry's petition released on the Executive's website last week, it attempted to undermine his arguments.

Executive scientists pointed out that the toxins which cause ASP and other hazardous shellfish diseases occur worldwide in areas where there are no fish farms. 'There is no evidence to support the case that such emissions from fish farms have ever actually been responsible for an algal bloom or shellfish poisoning event in Scotland', they stated.

But Berry claims that 57 of the 60 sites closed due to ASP or other toxins in August are in areas used for fish farming. 'None of these 57 sites had any record of toxicity previous to 1988', he said.

His petition to the Scottish parliament accuses government bodies meant to regulate the fish farming industry of being biased in its favour. 'There are many good reasons to question the propriety and prudence of regulators who have so consistently declined to face up to the damage caused by 'their' industry', it alleges.

'Discharges from the farms are implicated in the epidemic of biotoxin production and contamination of shellfish now regularly occurring in water subject to discharges from sea cage fish farms'.

In February the Sunday Herald disclosed new scientific studies suggesting that waste and pollution from fish farms helped the growth of algal toxins. And in June we reported predictions that there would be widespread bans of shellfishing due to toxic blooms. But whatever the rights and wrongs, it is the shellfishing industry which suffers from the bans. 'It's very tough', said John Holmyard, who farms mussels in Loch Etive, north of Oban. 'It puts you out of business while it carries on and if it goes on for long enough it can put you out of business permanently'.

(Source: The Sunday Herald, *17 September 2000, p.7. Copyright ©2000 Scottish Media Newspapers Limited)*

Algae may be attached to rocks or be floating, in which case they are usually referred to as *phytoplankton*. There are also some macroscopic ones which are branched and attached to stones and rocks. In the seas and oceans, algae are more commonly called seaweeds; they are of various colours, and are large and branching.

In contrast to the large green plants which are rooted in the river bed or banks, algae take their nutrients directly from the surrounding water. For the process of photosynthesis, both carbon dioxide and water are needed. (As mentioned in Section 2.4, blue-green algae have the ability to use bicarbonate as the carbon source.) The carbon dioxide entering the cells of the plants is that dissolved in the water.

Some of the common algae found in waters (illustrated in Figure 14) are:

Diatoms (e.g. *Asterionella* species (spp.))

Blue-green algae (e.g. *Anabaena* spp.)

Green algae (e.g. *Spirogyra* spp.)

In an aquatic environment there are also decomposers and scavengers. These organisms utilize dead plants or animals as sources of food, and in so doing release minerals and nutrients which can then be reassimilated by plant and animal life. The decomposers which are important in the life of aquatic ecosystems are the fungi, bacteria and protozoa.

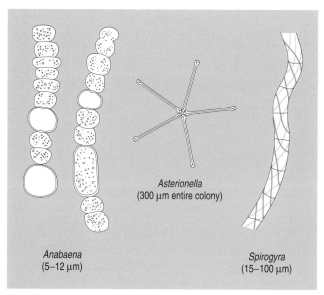

Asterionella
(300 μm entire colony)

Anabaena
(5–12 μm)

Spirogyra
(15–100 μm)

Figure 14   Some common algae

2.5.2   Bacteria

Bacteria are organisms of special significance to the study of clean and polluted waters because they break down organic matter. While most of them are not harmful to humans, some bacteria (e.g. *Clostridium*) are pathogenic. Most bacteria are retained on a filter of pore size 0.45 μm and all bacteria are trapped on a filter of 0.22 μm. They are important in sewage treatment, and in solid waste disposal. They are extremely abundant in almost all parts of the aquatic environment. They occur suspended in the water, on the surface of submerged objects, in river bed debris, and on and in other organisms in the environment. A bacterial cell can be seen with the aid of a microscope; when enough of them are grouped together, they can be seen with the naked eye as a 'colony'.

Most species of bacteria feed on the biodegradable natural wastes produced by other living organisms, as well as on the remains of the dead ones, as these are energy-rich resources. They can also utilize any biodegradable compounds released into the river by soil run-off or waste flows. Many of these bacteria are classified as aerobes: they require dissolved oxygen for aerobic respiration in order to oxidize (burn up) the nutrient compounds so that they can gain energy for their other life processes, such as building new cell material, and for functions such as movement, reproduction and growth. A generalized equation for aerobic bacterial degradation would be:

$$C, H, O, N, P, S ... + O_2 \xrightarrow{\text{aerobes}} CO_2 + H_2O +$$

carbohydrates and   oxygen   carbon   water
proteins   dioxide

$$NO_3^- + PO_4^{3-} + SO_4^{2-} + \text{new cells} + \text{energy}$$
nitrates   phosphates   sulphates

If dissolved oxygen is not available in the water, aerobic bacteria or aerobes cannot thrive; instead, another class of bacteria, anaerobes, make use of the bound oxygen in inorganic salts such as nitrates, sulphates and phosphates. The toxic gas hydrogen sulphide is often produced. In addition, anaerobes convert organic material to *methane* and carbon dioxide. A generalized equation for anaerobic bacterial activity is:

$$C, H, O, N, P, S \ldots + NO_3^- + PO_4^{3-} + SO_4^{2-} \xrightarrow{\text{anaerobes}} CO_2 +$$

carbohydrates and   nitrates   phosphates sulphates   carbon
proteins   dioxide

$$CH_4 + \quad N_2 + \quad PH_3 + \quad H_2S + \text{new cells} + \text{energy}$$

methane   nitrogen phosphine hydrogen
                               sulphide

Certain bacteria use dissolved oxygen if it is available but convert to anaerobic processes when dissolved oxygen is absent. Such bacteria are called facultative anaerobes.

Besides organic compounds, and oxygen in the case of aerobic decomposition, bacteria require a supply of various elements such as iron, magnesium, potassium, calcium and sodium. If any essential nutrient is below the minimum concentration necessary for certain processes, bacterial growth will be prevented. Temperature also has a direct influence, not only on the rate of decomposition, but also on the particular species that accomplish it. Between 10 °C and 20 °C is the optimum range for most river bacteria (mesophiles); while others may flourish at higher temperatures (thermophiles), again within an optimum temperature range. There are also psychrophiles which can live at around 0 °C. An increase in temperature within the appropriate range will tend to speed up the general rate of metabolism of bacteria, thereby increasing the rate of decomposition of organic compounds. You will learn more about these aspects in Block 4: *Wastes management*.

2.5.3   Protozoa

Protozoa are microscopic single cell animals. They utilize solid substances and bacteria as a food source. They can only function aerobically, and in a stream which contains little organic degradable matter they can become a predominant microbial type. They play an important part in sewage treatment where they remove free-swimming bacteria and help to produce a clear effluent.

In an aquatic environment, there are three main types of protozoa:

1   Those which have an amoeboid structure and move by means of an extruded pseudopod or false foot (e.g. *Amoeba*).

2   Those which move by utilizing a flagellum or whip-like tail.

3   Those which move and gather food using hair-like projections (cilia); these can be free-swimming (e.g. *Paramecium*) or held stationary by means of a stalk (e.g. *Vorticella campanula*).

Examples of types 1 and 3 were illustrated in Block 0: *Biology*.

Minute multicellular animals which also feed on debris and bacteria are the rotifers (e.g. *Keratella*), which also play an important part in sewage treatment.

2.5.4   Fungi

Fungi (e.g. species such as *Streptomycin* which are used for manufacture of antibiotics, and yeast) are generally unicellular non-photosynthetic organisms which can tolerate acid conditions. They are capable of degrading highly complex organic compounds. They utilize much the same food sources as bacteria but they require less nitrogen since their protein content is lower. Fungi play an important role in sewage treatment (presented later in Section 9).

In polluted water, particularly near to a sewage works outfall, a material known as 'sewage fungus' is often found. This is not a single organism but a mixture of different species of bacteria, fungi, algae and protozoa. They form a slimy, furry growth (not unlike plumes of cotton wool) (Figure 15) on the river bed and river bank. The organisms most often seen in sewage fungus are the bacterial species *Sphaerotilus natans* and *Zoogloea ramigera*. Other important species are the bacteria *Beggiatoa alba* and the *Flavobacterium* spp., the fungi *Geotrichum candidum*, *Leptomitis lacteus*, *Fusarium aquaductum*, the alga *Stigeoclonium tenue* and the protozoan *Carchesium polypinum*.

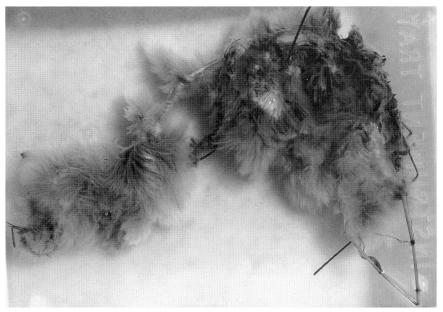

Figure 15   Sewage fungus

2.5.5   Biological indicators

A great many biological species and individuals occur in normal streams. These often differ markedly in their sensitivity to environmental factors, and likewise the tolerances of various species to different types of pollution vary considerably. The major groups of organisms that have been used as indicators of environmental pollution include bacteria, fungi, protozoa, algae, higher plants, macroinvertebrates and fish. The benthic 'bottom living' macroinvertebrates are particularly suitable as ecological indicators because their habitat preference and relatively low mobility cause them to be directly affected by substances that enter their environment.

When a clean river is polluted there are several events which can occur. There can be:

- a decrease in the number of species of organisms;

- a change in the type of species present;

- a change in the number of individuals of each species present.

These changes are due to the death or the moving away of organisms which cannot tolerate the pollution and an increase in number of those organisms which thrive on it.

The ***Biological Monitoring Working Party*** (BMWP) score can be used as a measure of the pollution at a particular site. A visual examination is made of a river sediment sample from the site and a total score is calculated from the organisms found. The more sensitive organisms (e.g.

the stonefly) have high scores while the more tolerant species (e.g. the worm) have low scores. The total score gives an indication of the degree of pollution at that site. Table 3 gives typical scores developed for different organisms. In calculating the total score, each family can only score once no matter how many organisms of that family are present, and only one needs to be present to score. Figure 16 shows examples from the groups of organisms listed in Table 3.

Table 3   Simplified BMWP scores

Groups (families)	Score
Mayfly nymphs (e.g. Ephemeridae, Ecdyonuridae) Stonefly nymphs (all families)	10
Damselfly and dragonfly (all families) Freshwater crayfish (Astacidae)	8
Mayfly nymphs (Caenidae only) Cased caddis larvae (all families) Caseless caddis larvae (e.g. Rhyacophilidae)	7
Freshwater shrimp (Gammaridae) Freshwater limpet (Ancylidae)	6
Water bugs (all families) Water beetles (all families) Caseless caddis larvae (Hydropsychidae only) Fly larvae (Simuliidae, Tipulidae) Flatworm (all families)	5
Mayfly nymphs (Baetidae only) Alderfly larvae (Sialidae)	4
Snails (e.g. Lymnaedae, Planorbidae, Physidae) Freshwater bivalves (Sphaeriidae) Leeches (all families) Water hog louse (Asellidae) Water mites (all families)	3
Fly larvae (Chironomidae only)	2
True worms (all families) Fly larvae (e.g. Culicidae, Tabanidae, Chaoboridae)	1

EXERCISE

A benthic sample taken from a river contained the following:

mayfly nymphs from the Ephemeridae and Baetidae families

3 stonefly nymphs from different families

2 cased caddis larvae from different families

freshwater shrimps (Gammaridae)

freshwater limpet (Ancylidae)

alderfly larvae (Sialidae)

3 snails from different families

What is the BMWP score of the above sample?

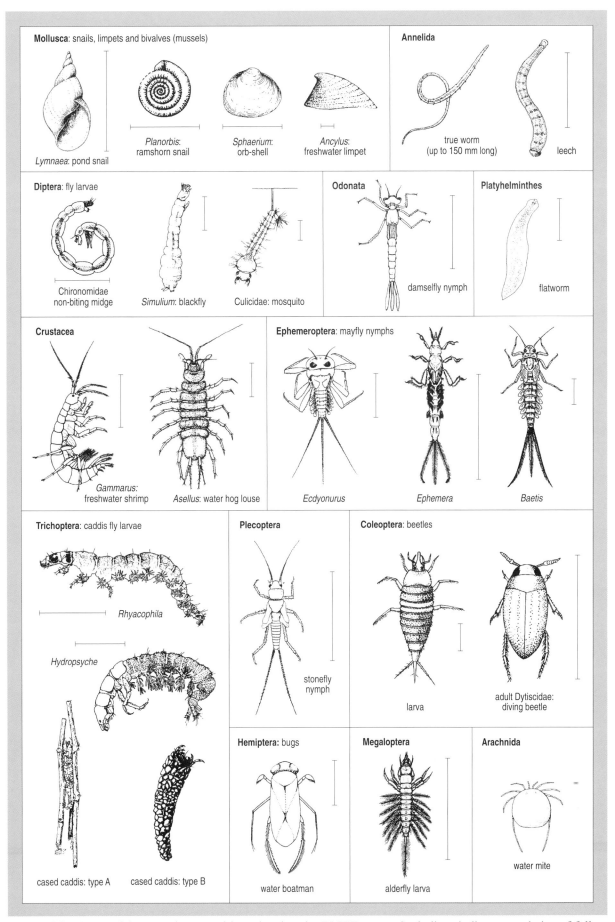

Figure 16 Some of the organisms used in estimating the BMWP score. Scale lines indicate actual size of full-grown individuals

ANSWER

Species		Points scored
Mayfly nymphs	Ephemeridae	10
	Baetidae	4
Stonefly nymphs	3 families	$10 \times 3 = 30$
Cased caddis larvae	2 families	$7 \times 2 = 14$
Freshwater shrimps	Gamaridae	6
Freshwater limpet	Ancylidae	6
Alderfly larvae	Sialidae	4
Snails	3 families	$3 \times 3 = 9$
Total		83

The relatively high score and the presence of clean water indicators (i.e. sensitive species) shows that the river is clean.

The BMWP score can be used both as an instantaneous measure of pollution and as a gauge over a period of time to ascertain how the situation at a particular site is changing. Comparisons can also be made with sites in other parts of the country, providing the same scoring system is used.

The main advantages of biological indicators over chemical methods of assessing water quality are:

1   The organisms show a lasting response to intermittent pollution events which may be missed during sampling for chemical analysis.

2   The biological community of a stretch of river responds to all pollutants both known and unknown, including those which may not have been considered in routine chemical analysis.

One disadvantage in the interpretation of all such scores is the assumption that they reflect changes attributable to pollution and not to other factors. Yet there are various environmental factors other than pollution that can have a considerable effect on the composition of communities of aquatic invertebrates, the chief ones being the nature of the stream bed and the velocity of the water flow.

The invertebrate community present in fast-flowing sections is very different both qualitatively and quantitatively from that present in slow-flowing sections. It is possible to overcome this problem to some extent by sampling in stretches of river that are closely similar in terms of the substratum, flow rate and other variables not connected with pollution.

2.6   Tidal rivers and estuaries

Most of the major cities and harbours in the world are located on estuaries. The estuarine ecosystem is a unique intermediate between the sea, the land and fresh water.

A rather precise definition of an estuary is 'a semi-enclosed coastal body of water, which has a free connection with the open sea, and within which sea water is measurably diluted with fresh water derived from land drainage'. This excludes large bays with little or no freshwater flow, and large brackish seas and inland saline lakes which derive their fresh water from rain only.

This definition is based on salinity; as we have seen in Section 2.4 this is the measure of the total concentration of salts. The salinity of fresh water is less than 0.5 parts per 1000 (0.05%); in the sea it is between 33 and 37 parts per 1000. The salts are composed principally of sodium and chloride ions, but also included are smaller concentrations of K, Mg, Ca and SO_4 and others in minute or trace amounts. Many types of salinity distributions occur in different types of estuaries. They are dependent upon freshwater inflow, evaporation, topography, currents and tides.

The deposition of any sediment is controlled by the speed of the estuarine currents and the particle size. In general, as a tidal current enters an estuary and loses speed it will first deposit gravel, then sand and finally silt which accumulates as mud (Figure 17a). Similarly, a river current will first deposit sand and coarse particles, then silt when its direct flow is finally halted by meeting inflowing salt water.

Stratification also occurs (Figure 17b), but this time it is not necessarily thermal as in lakes but depends on salinity. Fresh water is lighter than sea water and can form a layer on top. Saline stratification can vary between estuaries: for example, the Tees estuary is highly stratified whereas the Thames estuary is not. Figure 17(b) shows that the Tees gives nearly horizontal isohalines (lines which show points of equal salinity), whereas the isohalines of the Thames are nearly vertical.

As in rivers, the oxygen concentration is of prime importance. Several factors influence the quantity present, including mud, salinity and temperature. Mud is rich in food material in the form of organic debris, and it may also be rich in bacteria and other micro-organisms which may put a heavy demand on the oxygen present. The available oxygen may soon be used up and then the nitrates present will be used as an oxygen source, being reduced to nitrogen gas in the process. Finally, sulphate-reducing bacteria may consume oxygen from the sulphates present – this process generates foul-smelling hydrogen sulphide.

We have already learnt that an increase in concentration of dissolved salts lessens the saturation concentration of oxygen in water, therefore sea water (of high salinity) holds less oxygen than fresh water at the same temperature and pressure. There may consequently be an added problem of low oxygen content before any pollution occurs.

As in rivers, temperature also affects the oxygen content. In estuaries, temperature conditions are normally very variable because of the shallowness, and because of the different bodies of water mixing together.

Organisms that naturally inhabit estuaries must be adapted to such changing conditions as salinity, temperature and sediments. Examining Figure 18 we find that the number of such organisms is relatively small, even in a clean estuary such as the Tay. In fact, if we compare the Tay estuary with the less clean Tees estuary, we find that there is little difference in the abundance of species. Although there is a marked dip in dissolved oxygen in the Tees estuary, the distribution of organisms is generally comparable to that of the Tay.

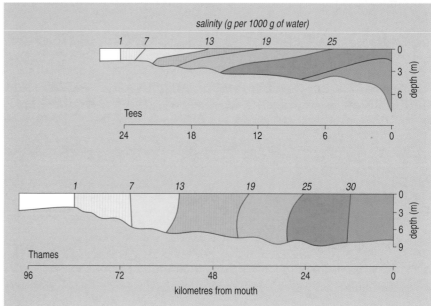

Figure 17 (a) Silt deposits at an estuary. (b) Salinity variation in the estuaries of the River Tees and River Thames

2.7 Summary

Water in its 'natural' state supports a complex, yet fragile, ecosystem. The ability of natural watercourses to sustain aquatic life depends on a variety of physical, chemical and biological conditions. Biodegradable compounds, nutrients and dissolved oxygen must be available for the metabolic activities of the algae, fungi, bacteria and protozoa which are at the lowest level of the food chain. In addition, plant and animal growth cannot occur outside narrow ranges of temperature and pH. Suspended solids can restrict the necessary light penetration for photosynthesis. Stratification, both thermal and saline, can hinder the transport of necessary nutrients. Dissolved carbon dioxide, bicarbonates, carbonates, nitrates, phosphates and hardness salts must all be present in the right amounts for the successful functioning of the life of the river. Biological monitoring, e.g. BMWP scores, can be used as an indication of the state of health of a stretch of river.

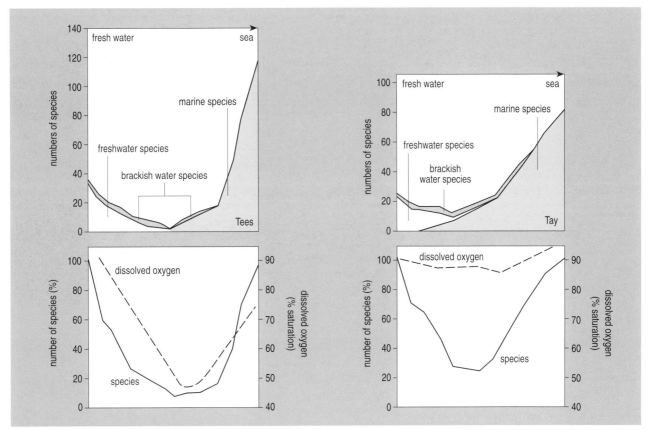

Figure 18   Comparison of the distribution of fauna in the estuaries of the Tees and the Tay (the horizontal axis is the distance along the estuary towards the sea)

SAQ 13

Which of the following statements is true?

A   'Sewage fungus' is a single species of fungus.

B   Carbon dioxide and oxygen both react with water but it is only carbon dioxide which dissociates.

C   *Escherichia coli* is a bacterium which is intestinal in origin and also pathogenic. This makes it suitable as an indicator organism for the presence of domestic sewage.

D   With reference to the bicarbonate–carbonate equilibrium in a water which has a high pH, carbon dioxide present will remain as carbon dioxide.

E   Permanent and temporary hardness both contribute to scaling, but for permanent hardness the scaling is due to decreased solubility, while for temporary hardness the scaling is due to the formation of new insoluble compounds.

SAQ 14

With reference to the bicarbonate–carbonate equilibrium, explain why the pH of water often rises during photosynthesis by aquatic plants.

SAQ 15

A sample of sea water from a sector of the North Sea contains 35 g of salt per 1000 g of water. If the sea water is found to be 30% saturated with oxygen at 8 °C and at 760 mm barometric pressure, what is the oxygen content in grams per m^3?

SAQ 16

A benthic sample taken half a kilometre downstream of an effluent discharge pipe in a river showed the following biological species:

    mayfly nymph (Baetidae)

    snails from two different families

    leeches from two different families

    fly larvae (Chironomidae and Culicidae)

    true worms from three different families.

Calculate the BMWP score and comment on your result.

SAQ 17

Using Figure 17(b), determine:

(a) the salinity for the Tees (in g per 1000 g of water) at 11 km from the mouth of the river at the surface and at a depth of 3 m;

(b) the salinity for the Thames (in g per 1000 g) at 36 km from the mouth of the river at the surface and at a depth of 3 m.

3   WATER TREATMENT

3.1   Introduction

Water for public supply can be obtained from underground sources by wells sunk into aquifers, or from surface sources such as purpose-built reservoirs or lakes (collecting rainwater run-off or water from streams) and rivers. The safety of the water is of utmost concern – several million people die each year after consuming contaminated water. The primary aim in water treatment is the elimination of any pathogenic micro-organisms present. All the above-mentioned sources can be subject to pollution. In the case of underground water, polluted surface water can enter the saturation zone of an aquifer and so lead to its contamination. Pollution can come from waste tip *leachate* containing *heavy metals* and organic compounds, farm run-off containing nitrates and *pesticides,* and industrial wastes which may have been deliberately dumped down old coal mine shafts. River water can be affected by farm drainage, sewage works and industrial effluents, and also the run-off water from roads. Thus there is a need to maintain the quality of the aquatic environment to ensure that the water is suitable for treatment for public supply, and that the cost of treatment is kept as low as possible.

In this chapter we shall be looking at the treatment of water after it has been abstracted from a suitable source.

While the prime function of water treatment is to produce a safe product, several stages are involved:

1   the removal of suspended matter and rendering of the water clean, colourless and free from disagreeable taste and odour;

2   the disinfection of the water so that the numbers of bacteria are reduced to an appropriate level;

3   the removal of chemicals harmful to health and the reduction to low levels of chemicals that might otherwise interfere with normal domestic and industrial requirements;

4   the reduction of the corrosive properties of the water and protection of the pipe supply system;

5   the minimization of the amount of material passing into the supply system which might encourage biological growth.

In Europe, the quality of water for potable supply has to comply with the EU Drinking Water Directive (98/83/EC) passed in 1998 (see Appendix 1).

Raw water is usually abstracted from a river and pumped to a reservoir for storage and settlement. In the reservoir, the number of faecal bacteria is reduced through natural processes such as predation by protozoa and *ultraviolet radiation* from sunlight. Also, a large portion of the suspended solids settles out. The water is then conveyed from the reservoir to a treatment works.

In some situations, particularly in hilly areas, rainwater is abstracted from a storage reservoir made by damming a valley in an upland catchment area, instead of from a river. In other instances, water may be drawn from aquifers. (These waters usually require little treatment due to their often unpolluted nature.)

The basic treatment for river water is shown in Figure 19. It should be noted that not all the processes shown will be required for water from every source. The treatment used will depend on the quality of the abstracted water. For water that has little pollution, it may only be necessary to use preliminary settlement, rapid sand filtration and chlorination, whereas poor quality water may require even more treatment than that shown.

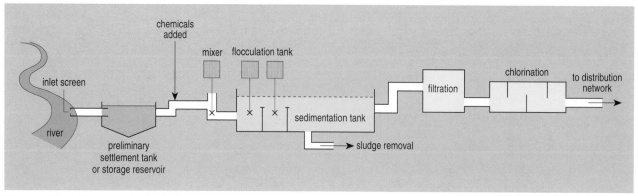

Figure 19   Diagram of a typical water treatment process

3.2   Preliminary treatment

The abstracted water is first screened to remove suspended and floating debris, such as leaves or branches, which could interfere with the operation of machinery in the treatment works. The water may then enter a preliminary settlement tank or storage reservoir. It then passes through *screens* again and goes to the treatment works. Screens may be classified by the size of their openings as coarse or fine, and may be in the forms of bars or continuous belts. Coarse screens are used primarily to protect the treatment works from physical damage, while the fine screens serve to remove material which might eventually block pipework in the system. Coarse screens usually consist of a series of metal bars spaced 5–15 cm apart. Fine screens, which follow the coarse screens, have a bar spacing of 5–20 mm. Screens are positioned in the inlet channel of the treatment plant at an angle of 60° to facilitate removal of the collected material or *screenings* by raking. The cleaning of the screens is important to prevent them choking. *Bar screens* can be raked by hand but are more usually cleaned by a mechanical raking operation, either on a time basis or by pressure-sensing probes which are activated by an excessive head loss (pressure drop) across the screen. A continuous chain scraper can also be used to clean bar screens (Figure 20). There are also fine mesh screens which are cleaned by water jets. These meshes can be on frames or, more commonly, in the form of a drum.

A variation of the fine screen is the microstrainer (Figure 21). This consists of a rotating drum with a stainless steel micromesh fabric. The mesh size can range from 15 μm to 64 μm so that very fine suspended matter such as algae and plankton can be trapped. The trapped solids are dislodged from the fabric by high-pressure water jets using clean water, and carried away for disposal.

Storage of the screened water in a preliminary settlement tank or reservoir smoothes out fluctuations in the water quality and helps to reduce the suspended solids content. It also reduces the number of pathogenic bacteria present, and the oxidation which can occur will allow the degradation of organic matter and the precipitation of soluble iron and manganese as oxides and hydroxides. It is generally recommended that

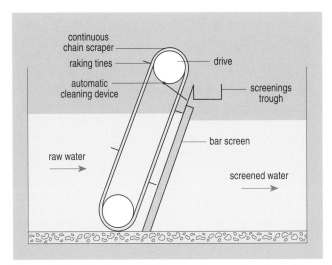

Figure 20   Continuous chain scraping system for a bar screen

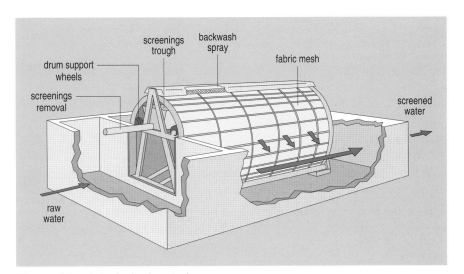

Figure 21   A typical microstrainer

storage should be for at least seven days in the case of river-derived supplies. The storage of water is particularly valuable when abstraction is not possible, e.g. during droughts, or when the water source is badly contaminated or in flood condition.

After preliminary settlement, it may be necessary to aerate the water in the case of poor quality water with a low dissolved oxygen content. There are several ways in which this can be done but the simplest is to allow the water to fall over a series of steps so that it is able to entrain oxygen from the air. This is known as cascade aeration. In addition to increasing the oxygen content, aeration also helps to liberate soluble gases, such as carbon dioxide and hydrogen sulphide, and volatile organic compounds which could give an undesirable taste to the water.

Aeration can reduce the corrosiveness of raw waters which are acidic due to their carbonic acid content. When the water is aerated, some of the dissolved carbon dioxide is displaced by the oxygen dissolving in the water. This causes some of the carbonic acid that has been formed in the water by the carbon dioxide to be converted back to carbon dioxide and water in order to maintain chemical equilibrium, as we discussed in Section 2.4.

Aeration is also used to remove iron and manganese from solution. Iron and manganese can cause peculiar tastes and can stain clothing. Iron is soluble in water only in the absence of dissolved oxygen and at pH values below 6.5, when it is in the ferrous (Fe^{2+}) state. Aeration converts soluble iron into its insoluble hydroxide [$Fe(OH)_3$] which can then be removed by filtration. Manganese can be removed in the same way.

After aeration, the water may be passed through a further fine screen before entering the treatment works proper.

3.3   Coagulation and flocculation

Coagulation is always considered along with *flocculation* and is used to remove particles which cannot be removed by sedimentation or filtration alone. These particles are usually less than 1 μm in size and are termed colloids. They have poor settling characteristics and are responsible for the colour and turbidity of water. They include clays, metal oxides, proteins, micro-organisms and organic substances such as those that give the brown coloration to water from 'peaty' catchment areas. The important property which they all have is that they carry a negative charge and this, along with the interaction between the colloidal particles and the water, prevents them from aggregating and settling in still water. The particles can be aggregated by adding either multivalent ions or colloids having an opposite (positive) charge. These are added as chemical coagulants.

Chemicals commonly used as coagulants in water treatment are aluminium and ferric salts which are present as the ions Al^{3+} and Fe^{3+}. These positively charged multivalent ions neutralize the naturally occurring negatively charged particles, thus allowing the particles to aggregate. At high concentrations of aluminium or ferric salts, and in the presence of sufficient alkalinity, insoluble hydroxides of aluminium or iron are formed (see below). In the precipitation reaction the colloidal particles are enmeshed within the precipitate and thus removed. The use of aluminium salts is not popular because of the (unproven) scare about Alzheimer's disease. The move away from aluminium salts was accelerated when *aluminium sulphate* was accidentally put into the treated water tank for the town of *Camelford* in 1988. Most plants now use ferric salts.

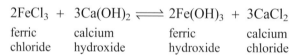

$$2FeCl_3 \; + \; 3Ca(OH)_2 \; \rightleftharpoons \; 2Fe(OH)_3 \; + \; 3CaCl_2$$

| ferric chloride | calcium hydroxide | ferric hydroxide | calcium chloride |

If there is inadequate alkalinity in the water, it can be added in the form of lime (calcium hydroxide $Ca(OH)_2$) or soda ash (sodium carbonate Na_2CO_3).

In some waters, even with the optimum dose of coagulant, coagulation is poor and so it is necessary to add extra substances known as coagulant aids. These aids can be clay, silica or *polyelectrolytes*. Polyelectrolytes (Figure 22) are long-chain organic molecules with chemical groups attached along the length of the chain, which becomes charged when the molecule is dissolved in water. The negative colloidal particles are attracted to positively charged chemical groups on the polyelectrolyte.

As the coagulants are added, the water is mixed rapidly in a mixing chamber using a high-speed turbine. In small plants, coagulants are often added upstream of a weir in order to use the consequent turbulent motion to aid in mixing. Once coagulation has taken place, a very fine precipitate or floc will form. To aid this floc to coalesce with neighbouring particles and grow into larger flocs with more settleable masses, the water is gently stirred. The process of coalescence is known as flocculation. The gentle stirring can be achieved using paddles or baffles to induce a rolling motion in the water, and this continues for some 20–45 minutes. After this treatment, the water is passed for sedimentation.

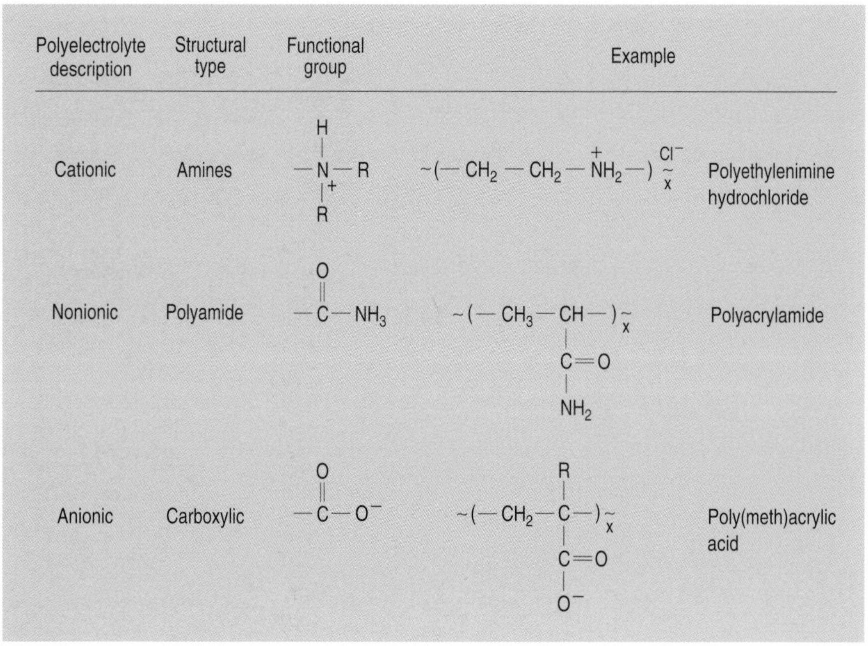

Polyelectrolyte description	Structural type	Functional group	Example	
Cationic	Amines	$\begin{array}{c} H \\ | \\ -N-R \\ |+ \\ R \end{array}$	$\sim(-CH_2-CH_2-\overset{+}{N}H_2-)\underset{x}{\sim}\ Cl^-$	Polyethylenimine hydrochloride
Nonionic	Polyamide	$\begin{array}{c} O \\ || \\ -C-NH_3 \end{array}$	$\sim(-CH_3-CH-)\underset{x}{\sim}$ $\begin{array}{c} | \\ C=O \\ | \\ NH_2 \end{array}$	Polyacrylamide
Anionic	Carboxylic	$\begin{array}{c} O \\ || \\ -C-O^- \end{array}$	$\sim(-CH_2-\overset{R}{\underset{|}{C}}-)\underset{x}{\sim}$ $\begin{array}{c} | \\ C=O \\ | \\ O^- \end{array}$	Poly(meth)acrylic acid

Figure 22 Structure of typical polyelectrolytes

3.4 Sedimentation

When water has little or no movement, suspended solids sink to the bottom under the force of gravity and form a sediment. You will recall that we discussed a similar process in estuaries, with solids separating from the water. This process is called *sedimentation*. In water treatment it is used to remove solids from waters which are high in sediment content, and also to remove particles rendered settleable by coagulation and flocculation.

The theory of sedimentation would seem to be quite simple. Earlier we had a widening river flowing more slowly, so if we make the settling tank large enough and the flow slow enough, this will enhance the rate of fall of the sediment towards the bottom of the tank.

What other factors do you think need to be known?

It will be necessary to know the density and the size of the particles to calculate their rate of fall. There should be no turbulence in the tank as it will tend to reduce settlement, and there must be an even flow through the tank to prevent a narrow stream flowing through quickly from one end to the other (i.e. channelling).

Because of these factors we shall now look at settlement in greater detail. Sedimentation tanks can be of various types: rectangular with horizontal flow, circular with *radial flow*, or hopper-bottomed with upward flow (Figure 23).

The circular and rectangular tanks are equipped with mechanical sludge-scraping devices to remove the wet sludge that has settled. In hopper-bottomed tanks, the sludge concentrates at the bottom of the hopper from where it can be drawn off. In radial and horizontal flow tanks any floating material is skimmed from the surface by a blade carried by the scraping mechanism, and is discharged to be combined with the settled sludge. In upward flow tanks, the main sludge removal is from the top of the sludge blanket (see Figure 23(c)).

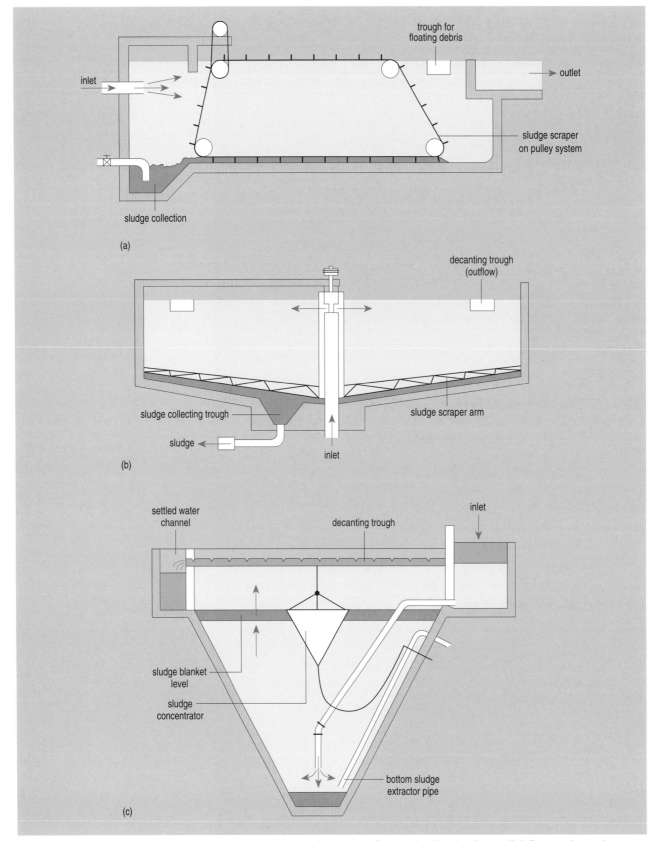

Figure 23   Typical sedimentation tanks: (a) rectangular horizontal flow tank; (b) circular, radial-flow tank; (c) hopper-bottomed, upward flow tank

An idealized representation of a circular radial-flow tank is shown in Figure 24. There are four important zones in the tank:

(a) Inlet zone – at the central well, which has a round baffle plate, the flow is established in a uniform radial direction so that short-circuiting does not take place.

(b) Settling zone – where settling is assumed to occur as the water flows towards the outlet.

(c) Outlet zone – in which the flow converges up and over the decanting weirs.

(d) Sludge zone – where settled material collects and is pumped out.

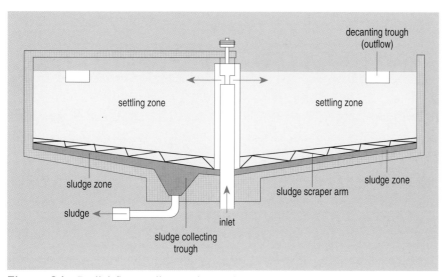

Figure 24   Radial-flow sedimentation tank

The performance of a settling tank is related to the settling velocity of the fine particles in suspension. The settling velocity is the speed at which the particles move downwards under gravity through the suspension, and for discrete particles this is dependent on the particle density and size. The retention time required by the particles to settle to the bottom of a settling tank is related to the settling velocity by the simple relationship

$$\text{retention time} = \frac{\text{depth of settling zone}}{\text{settling velocity}}$$

The time available for particles to settle out in the settling tank also depends on the flow rate of the suspension through the tank

$$\text{retention time} = \frac{\text{volume of settling zone}}{\text{flow rate through tank}} \qquad (2)$$

This expression assumes that no short-circuiting takes place in the tank, i.e. that the water doesn't flow straight from inlet to outlet.

Table 4 shows settling velocities for various types of suspended solids and the required retention times for sedimentation in a 3 m deep tank.

Table 4   Settling velocities for different types of suspended solids and the retention time required in a 3 m deep tank for sedimentation to occur

Nature of solids	Settling velocity (mm s^{-1})	Retention time for settling to occur in 3 m deep tank (hours)
Clay, silt	0.07	11.9
Primary organic waste	0.42	1.98
Aluminium and iron flocs	0.83	1.00
Activated sludge	2.00	0.42
Grit	20.00	0.042

Notice that to achieve a separation of materials with low settling velocities, the retention time in the settling tank must be increased. In practice, this can be achieved by increasing the settling tank volume or decreasing the flow rate of suspension through the tank.

EXERCISE

100 m^3 d^{-1} of a suspension of silt is passed through a settling tank with a 3 m deep settling zone. What is the effective settling zone area?

ANSWER

From Table 4,

retention time for 3 m depth = 11.9 hours

$$= \frac{11.9}{24} \text{ day}$$

Volume of settling zone = settling area × depth

$$= \text{flow rate} \times \text{retention time (from Equation 2)}$$

So, settling area $= \dfrac{\text{flow rate} \times \text{retention time}}{\text{depth}}$

$$= \frac{(100) \times (11.9/24)}{3} \text{ m}^2$$

$$= 16.5 \text{ m}^2$$

SAQ 18

A circular radial-flow tank has a settling zone depth of 4 m and a settling zone area of 700 m^2. What is the retention time necessary to remove organic detritus with settling velocities of 0.4 mm s^{-1} and greater? What flow rate is required through the tank?

In order to achieve the required retention time in SAQ 18 the throughput of suspension must not be greater than 0.28 m^3 s^{-1}. But what if the same suspension was passed through a 2 m deep tank – half the depth? One might expect that in a shallow tank the same particles would reach the sludge zone at the bottom more quickly. Would this allow a larger throughput? Halving the tank depth would halve the retention time of particles in the tank; but would also halve the tank volume. So the flow rate through the shallower tank would be the same as for the deep tank. This independence of settling behaviour with depth has led to the development of shallow depth sedimentation tanks in which the flow is passed in parallel through a number of closely spaced inclined channels arranged in a device called a parallel plate separator (Figure 25). The slope of the settling channels is steep so that the tank is continuously self-cleaning (the solids slide off and go to the bottom of the tank). The advantage of such an arrangement is clear. For the same tank area, with *n* channels, throughput can be *n*-fold whilst retaining the same settling velocity in each channel.

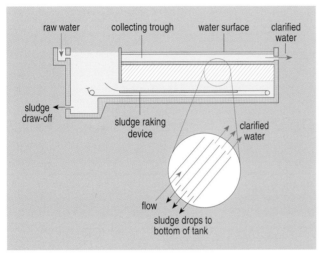

Figure 25   A parallel plate separator within a sedimentation tank

The discussion so far has dealt with 'ideal' conditions in which particles settle under gravity without hindrance from other particles in the vicinity. An example of such a situation would be the settling of heavy grit particles or sand. There are, however, types of particles called flocculent particles which interact with other particles in their vicinity. An example would be organic suspended solids or the floc particles produced by chemical coagulation and flocculation of water, with a broad spectrum of sizes and surface characteristics.

Different-sized particles settle at different rates so that larger particles will overtake or collide with smaller particles. These collisions may result in coalescence into larger aggregates with an increasing settling velocity so that the typical path of a flocculent particle is curved (Figure 26), indicating the increasing velocity with depth. One important requirement of settling tanks for treating flocculent suspensions is, therefore, that the depth should be great enough to provide the opportunity for particle agglomeration to occur. This is in contrast to the behaviour of discrete particles whose settling behaviour is independent of depth. The effect of tank depth on removal efficiency is shown in Figure 26. If the tank depth is reduced by half, the retention time is halved and the depth reached by each type of particle during that time is reduced. Nevertheless the discrete particle will again just reach the bottom of the reduced depth tank, whereas the flocculent particle will not have reached the tank floor and will be drawn off in the tank outflow. This is a simplification of what actually happens inside a sedimentation tank; however, it is generally considered that the overall effect of reducing settling tank depth is to reduce removal efficiency when treating flocculent particles.

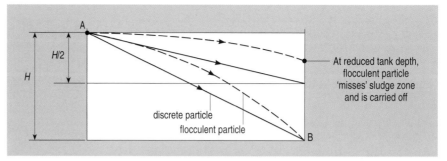

Figure 26 Effect of tank depth on removal of discrete and flocculent particles

Settlement tanks must therefore be designed deep enough to allow all particles to settle, and also to have flow such that settled solids are not disturbed and carried over the weir at the outlet of the settlement tank.

A parameter known as the surface overflow rate or surface loading rate is used in the design of sedimentation tanks.

This is defined as

$$\frac{\text{maximum flow per day}}{\text{tank surface area}} = \text{m}^3 \text{ m}^{-2} \text{ d}^{-1}$$

Typical values for the surface loading rate range from 30 to 45 $\text{m}^3 \text{ m}^{-2} \text{ d}^{-1}$.

EXERCISE

What would the surface loading rate be for a rectangular sedimentation tank of surface area 10×30 m^2 with a maximum flow through rate of 8000 m^3 per day?

ANSWER

$$\text{Surface loading rate} = \frac{\text{maximum flow per day}}{\text{tank surface area}}$$

$$= \frac{8000 \text{ m}^3 \text{ d}^{-1}}{10 \times 30 \text{ m}^2}$$

$$= 26.7 \text{ m}^3 \text{ m}^{-2} \text{ d}^{-1}$$

Another important parameter in settlement tanks is the rate at which water flows over the weir, known as the weir overflow rate, expressed as

$$\frac{\text{maximum flow per day}}{\text{total length of weir}} = \text{m}^3 \text{ m}^{-1} \text{ d}^{-1}$$

Typical values for the weir overflow rate range from 300 to 450 $\text{m}^3 \text{ m}^{-1} \text{ d}^{-1}$.

EXERCISE

What is the weir overflow rate for the tank in the previous exercise, the weir being on the shorter side of the tank?

ANSWER

$$\text{The weir overflow rate} = \frac{\text{maximum flow per day}}{\text{total length of weir}}$$

$$= \frac{8000 \text{ m}^3 \text{ d}^{-1}}{10 \text{ m}}$$

$$= 800 \text{ m}^3 \text{ m}^{-1} \text{ d}^{-1}$$

This overflow rate exceeds the typical range of 300–450 m^3 m^{-1} d^{-1} and if used would tend to disturb the settled sludge. An acceptable value can be obtained by increasing the effective weir length. This can be achieved by increasing the breadth of the tank, but this would take up more land and be costly. An alternative and less costly solution would be to insert V-notches in the weir and so effectively increase the weir length, or have a suspended collection trough at the end of the tank so that the effluent could flow into the trough from either side, thus doubling the weir length. In our example the effective weir length could be doubled by using a trough and the overflow rate would be reduced to a more acceptable 400 m^3 m^{-1} d^{-1}.

SAQ 19

What length of effective weir would be required for a rectangular sedimentation tank with a maximum flow of 0.25 m^3 per second if the weir overflow rate is to be 350 m^3 m^{-1} d^{-1}?

In the UK, upward-flow or hopper-bottomed sludge-blanket clarifiers (Figure 23c) are extremely popular. This type of tank is an inverted cone, with the flocculated water entering from the bottom of the cone. Because the cross-sectional area of the tank increases rapidly from the apex (at the bottom) to the base of the cone (at the top) the upward velocity of the water is reduced as it rises. In the tank there will, therefore, be a horizontal plane where the upward water velocity equals the average downward rate of fall of the floc. This results in the formation of a horizontal 'blanket' of floc suspended in the water. This blanket of floc acts as a filter through which the upward flowing water must pass. Maximum use of the tank is made when the top of the floc blanket is as high as possible in the tank. When the blanket becomes too dense, it is removed by bleeding off the excess floc. These days, due to cost reasons, upward flow tanks are often flat-bottomed with internal pipe work to distribute the flow across the full area of the tank base.

SAQ 20

Which of the following characteristics of raw water are greatly improved by coagulation, flocculation and sedimentation?

A Colour.

B Taste.

C Clarity.

D Chloride concentration.

E Nitrate concentration.

3.5   Flotation

An alternative technique to that of sedimentation is flotation. This uses gas bubbles to increase the buoyancy of suspended solids. The gas bubbles attach to the particles and make their effective density lower than that of the water. This causes the particles to rise through the water to float to the top. Flotation may be achieved by several methods but the most effective form is dissolved air flotation. In this process (Figure 27) air is dissolved in water at elevated pressures and then released as tiny bubbles (30–120 µm) by reducing the pressure to atmospheric level.

The principal advantages of flotation over sedimentation are that very small or light particles that settle slowly can be removed more completely and in a shorter time. Once the particles have reached the surface, they can be collected by a skimmer. Flotation does, however, require careful control to achieve high quality output.

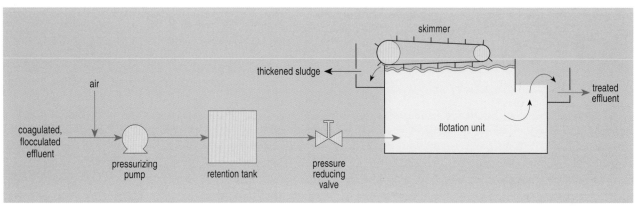

Figure 27   Diagram of a dissolved air flotation system

3.6   Filtration

In filtration, the partially treated water is passed through a medium such as sand or anthracite, which acts as a 'strainer', retaining the fine organic and inorganic material and allowing clean water through. The action of filters is complex and in some types of filter biological action also takes place. Sand filters are used in water treatment to remove the fine particles which cannot be economically removed by sedimentation. They have been effective in removing *Cryptosporidium*, a protozoan parasite (see Section 7.5.6).

Mechanical straining of the water is only a minor part of the filtration process, as the main process by which particles are retained is adsorption. In adsorption, the particles adhere to the filter material or previously adsorbed particles. If a particle passes close to a solid surface, there may be either electrical attraction or repulsion, depending on the surface charges of both the particle and the solid surface.

Filtration in water treatment can be carried out using simple slow sand filters or, as is more usual for flocculated water, rapid gravity sand filters.

A slow sand filter consists of a shallow basin in which about a metre of sand rests on a gravel base, underneath which there is a system of collection pipes and channels for the filtered water (Figure 28). The water to be treated flows down through the filter bed and, as it does so, a layer a few millimetres thick of algae, plankton and other microscopic plant life forms on the top. This layer is known as the *Schmutzdecke*, which is

German for film or deck of dirt. In this layer, fine filtration takes place. In order to preserve this layer, the temperature and velocity of the inflow must be carefully controlled. Some biodegradation also takes place on the *Schmutzdecke,* resulting in a reduction of the organic matter, nitrate and phosphate which may be present in the water. The flow rate is normally in the range 0.1–0.2 m^3 m^{-2} h^{-1}. This means that a filter of, say, 21 m^2 would produce a maximum of $0.2 \times 21 = 4.2$ m^3 of water per hour.

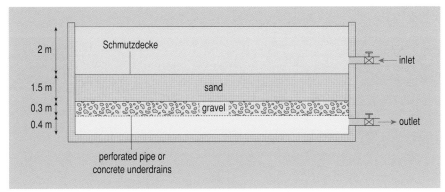

Figure 28 Section through a slow sand filter

When the rate of filtration begins to tail off after a month or two, the filter is drained and the top 2 cm of sand is removed to be replaced by fresh sand. Slow sand filters are expensive to build and operate, and require a large amount of space. They cannot be used for coagulated waters because of rapid clogging.

Slow sand filters have been largely replaced by rapid gravity sand filters, which are particularly effective for water treated with coagulants and are less expensive than slow sand filters (Figure 29). The flow is much greater than in slow sand filters, being 4–8 m^3 m^{-2} h^{-1}; hence a smaller filter (requiring a smaller space) will be adequate. Because of the high rate of flow, no *Schmutzdecke* is formed and hence little or no biodegradation takes place in these filters. The filter is cleaned at intervals of 24–48 hours by pumping water and air (to assist in scouring) under pressure backwards through the filter to wash out the trapped impurities. This process is called *backwashing.* Unlike slow sand filters which tend to produce water with a particularly low bacterial count, rapid filters produce water with high bacterial counts, increasing the necessity to follow them with disinfection before supplying the water to the public.

In many treatment plants where slow sand filtration is the key processing stage, rapid gravity filtration is employed prior to the slow sand filter in a process called double sand filtration. In this arrangement, the rapid gravity filters reduce the load of solid matter in the water before it goes to the slow sand filters. This allows a greater overall rate of treatment and the slow sand filters do not then need to be cleaned so often.

A variation of the filtering process is the use of a layer of large anthracite grains (1.2–2.5 mm) on top of a layer of smaller (0.5–1.0 mm) sand grains, which are denser and have a smaller 'intergrain' pore size. Anthracite–sand filters tend to clog less rapidly because some of the floc adheres to the larger anthracite grains before the water filters through the sand. This means that increased filtration rates are possible without deterioration in filtrate quality.

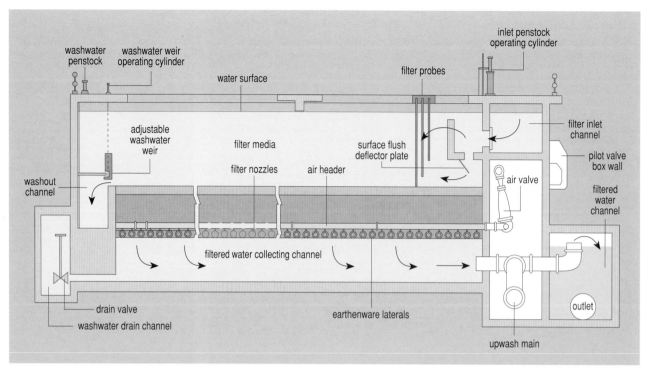

Figure 29   Section through a rapid gravity sand filter

SAQ 21

List the advantages and disadvantages of slow sand filters and rapid gravity filters.

3.7   Disinfection

Before water can be passed into the public supply, it is necessary to remove all potentially pathogenic micro-organisms. Since these micro-organisms are extremely small, it is not possible to guarantee their complete removal by sedimentation and filtration, so the water must be disinfected to ensure its quality. Disinfection is the inactivation of pathogenic organisms and is not to be confused with sterilization, which is the destruction of all organisms.

Worldwide, chlorine is the most popular disinfecting agent for drinking water, although the use of ozone has recently become more widespread. The use of chlorine in water treatment, while not being acceptable to all, does save lives. In Peru, the reduction of the chlorine dose led to a cholera outbreak in which thousands died. Chlorine acts as a strong oxidizing agent which can penetrate microbial cells, killing the micro-organisms. It kills most bacteria but not all viruses. It is relatively cheap and extremely soluble in water (up to 7000 g m^{-3}). It has some disadvantages. If organics are present in the water being disinfected, it can lead to the formation of potentially carcinogenic disinfection by-products (e.g. trihalomethanes; see below). The World Health Organization has given health-based guidelines for a variety of disinfection by-products, such as chloroform. If the water has been previously treated by coagulation and flocculation, the chances of organic pollutants being present to form trihalomethanes are remote. Slow sand filters are effective in removing trace organics.

Chlorine is a dangerous chemical and so requires careful handling. It can also give rise to taste and odour problems: for example, in the presence of phenols it forms *chlorophenols* which have a strong medicinal odour and taste.

$$Cl_2 + H_2O \rightleftharpoons HCl + HOCl$$

HOCl, hypochlorous acid, is the disinfecting agent and is referred to as free available chlorine. Since chlorine is an oxidizing agent, it reacts with all compounds in water which can be oxidized, e.g. converting nitrites to nitrates, and sulphides to sulphates. As mentioned above, it also reacts with any organics present and can form trihalomethanes (THMs). These are single carbon compounds with the general formula CHX_3 where X may be any halogen atom (e.g. chlorine, bromine, fluorine, iodine, or a combination of these). Some THMs are known to be carcinogenic. There is evidence to link long-term low-level exposure and rectal, intestinal and bladder cancers. There is therefore a limit of 100 μg l^{-1} for total THMs in water supplied for potable use. Chlorine also reacts with ammonia to form chloramines. Thus when chlorine is added to water there is an immediate chlorine demand which must be satisfied before a residual of chlorine exists for disinfection.

The formation of chloramines is as shown below:

$$NH_3 + HOCl \rightleftharpoons H_2O + NH_2Cl \quad \text{(monochloramine)}$$

$$NH_2Cl + HOCl \rightleftharpoons H_2O + NHCl_2 \quad \text{(dichloramine)}$$

$$NHCl_2 + HOCl \rightleftharpoons H_2O + NCl_3 \quad \text{(trichloramine)}$$

The chloramines are disinfectants but not nearly as effective as free chlorine (they may have to be 25 times more concentrated to have the same effect).

Chlorine in compounds such as chloramines is referred to as combined residual chlorine. Although not as effective as free chlorine in disinfection, combined chlorine is less likely to produce objectionable tastes and smells. One reason for this is that combined chlorine does not react with phenols, which may be present, to form chlorophenols. In fact, ammonia is sometimes added to water for this reason. Combined residuals also last longer than free chlorine.

For disinfection with chlorine, the World Health Organization (WHO) guidelines recommend a minimum free chlorine concentration of 0.5 mg l^{-1} after a contact time of 30 minutes at a pH less than 8, provided that the turbidity is less than 1 NTU. The water leaving the chlorine contact tank is usually discharged with a chlorine concentration of 0.5–1.0 g m^{-3} to ensure that the water is kept safe throughout the supply and distribution system.

Concern with hazards of chlorine storage has led to the adoption of electrolytic generation of chlorine on large water treatment plants. In this process, sodium hypochlorite solution with a chlorine content of 6–9% is generated through the electrolysis of a solution of sodium chloride.

Recently, *ozone* (O_3, a blue gas and a very strong oxidizing agent) has become popular as a disinfectant, particularly as it is effective against viruses and spores. In the UK, it is often used to oxidize any pesticide residuals present. Also, ozonation does not produce toxic by-products such as trihalomethanes which can occur with chlorine. It can, however, form toxic bromates if bromine is present in the water. In France, there are about 600 water treatment plants using ozone as a disinfectant. The drawback with ozone, however, is that it is not possible to have a residual level, as there is for chlorine, to confer protection in the supply and distribution system (O_3 rapidly breaks down to oxygen when any particles are present). In ultra-clean water, however, it will remain as O_3). Hence, after ozonation, the water is chlorinated before it goes into the supply system. The ozone used in water treatment plants is usually generated by passing dry air or oxygen between plates, across which a high voltage is imposed. It is expensive to produce, and the necessary equipment is complex.

Ultraviolet radiation can also be used to disinfect water, but care must be taken to ensure that no suspended solids are present which could shield the micro-organisms and prevent them from being destroyed. UV systems are generally only used in small-scale water treatment units. They do not give a residual for protection in the distribution system.

3.7.1   Mixed oxidant gases system

This is a relatively new system of disinfection. It involves electrolysis of high-purity NaCl brine to produce a mixture of chlorine dioxide, ozone and hypochlorite. This mixture is separated within the electrochemical cell by a membrane, or by exploiting density difference, and is then metered into the water requiring disinfection. The mixed oxidant gases are generated on demand and this is a great safety advantage, compared with having storage tanks of chlorine on site. The source for the disinfectant (high-purity NaC1) is relatively inexpensive and the mixed oxidants are more effective than chlorine alone in disinfection. Importantly, the mixed oxidant gases yield substantially lower levels of disinfection by-products than chlorine gas or hypochlorites.

The disadvantage of the mixed oxidant gases system (sometimes called MOGGOD – mixed oxidant gases generated on demand) is that it requires extensive skilled maintenance of the electrochemical and dosing systems.

3.7.2   Elimination of pathogens through solar disinfection

The lack of safe drinking water in many developing countries has prompted research into simple methods of disinfecting small quantities of water. One such investigation at the University of Beirut in the Lebanon revealed that 99.9% of total bacteria in a water sample could be destroyed by 300 minutes exposure to direct sunlight. In effect this means that if you left a sample of water in a translucent container, a lot of the bacteria in it would be killed.

Research to date has concentrated on transparent *PET (polyethylene terephthalate)* bottles, these being more robust than glass bottles and hence more practical for use in rural areas. It is important to first remove any particles in the water which may harbour or shield pathogens from the sunlight. Removal is effected by allowing any solids to settle out by sedimentation. It has been found that inactivation of pathogens is more effective if the water is fully oxygenated (see step 3 below).

The following is a procedure which works well:

1   Collect the raw water in a large jar and leave for about 12 hours, till the water appears clear. (Ideally, the turbidity should be reduced to below 30 NTU.) Pour the liquid above the residue (supernatant) through a piece of cotton cloth into a clean bucket.

2   Obtain a clear plastic bottle and clean it and its lid with some safe (boiled) water. Paint half of it black. (An alternative is to have a black surface, e.g. a black bin bag or a piece of tyre, on which to lay the bottle.)

3   Half fill the bottle with the clear water from (1) and put the lid on it. Shake the bottle vigorously for 30 seconds. This will ensure that oxygen from the headspace (the air space above the water) dissolves in the water.

4   Fill the remaining half of the bottle with the clear water from (1).

5   Lay the bottle on its side, and in such a position as to allow maximum sunlight to fall onto it. UV radiation from the sun reacts with the oxygen molecules in the water and, together with the heat from the sunlight, inactivates the pathogens. These pathogens in contaminated water sources are commonly viruses and bacteria, including *Vibrio cholera*.

6   Leave the bottle in the sun for at least five hours. If the weather is cloudy, leave outside for two days.

7   At the end of this period, the water should be safe for drinking.

The graph below (Figure 30) shows the decay rate of faecal coliforms with exposure to sunlight. The UV-A band (320–400 nm) of solar radiation is primarily responsible for the inactivation of the micro-organisms.

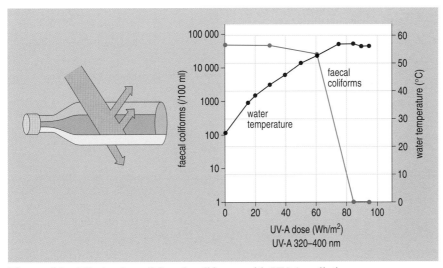

Figure 30   Elimination of faecal coliforms with UV-A radiation

UV-A radiation intensity on a sunny day in the tropics is generally 10–20 W m^{-2}, while total solar radiation might be 500–800 W m^{-2}.

SAQ 22

Why is it necessary to have a black surface in step (2) above?

SAQ 23

List the advantages and disadvantages of chlorine and ozone as disinfecting agents.

SAQ 24

Which of the following would be applicable to MOGGOD systems?

A They are cheap and simple.

B They use gases produced off-site.

C The raw material is inexpensive.

D Since chlorine is produced, the same problems arise with disinfection by-products as can happen with conventional water treatment.

E None of the above.

3.8   Additional treatment

As a result of strict standards set by the EU Directive on the Quality of Drinking Water (see Appendix 1), it is now often necessary for drinking water to have further treatment to remove components such as nitrates and trace of organics.

3.8.1   Nitrate removal

Nitrate in water has become a significant problem and the EU Directive sets a maximum admissible concentration of 50 g m^{-3} measured as NO_3^-. This is equivalent to 11.3 g m^{-3} as N. High nitrate levels can cause cyanosis or methaemoglobinaemia in babies (see Block 0: *Chemistry*). Legislation allows the designation of nitrate-vulnerable zones and these help to prevent nitrate levels in natural waters increasing in affected areas.

Ion exchange is used in some treatment plants to remove nitrates from drinking water. In this process the water is passed through an ion exchange resin which removes the undesired ions and replaces them with ions which do not affect the water quality. This technology for nitrate removal was developed from water softening systems, which were used to remove the hardness-conferring ions Ca^{2+} and Mg^{2+}. At first, ion exchange was carried out with zeolites, which are naturally occurring insoluble sodium aluminosilicates. Zeolites were able to exchange sodium ions for other ions such as Ca^{2+} and Mg^{2+}. Artificial zeolites such as permutit are now produced. If the cation exchange sodium resin is represented by Na_2R, where R is the complex resin base, then the reaction for water softening is

$$Mg^{2+} + Na_2R \longrightarrow MgR + 2Na^+$$

$$Ca^{2+} + Na_2R \longrightarrow CaR + 2Na^+$$

The treated water then becomes richer in sodium and, unless the water was particularly hard, this is less of a problem.

When all the sodium ions in the exchange resin have been replaced, the resin can be regenerated by passing a strong solution of sodium chloride through it:

$$MgR + 2NaCl \longrightarrow Na_2R + MgCl_2$$

For removal of nitrate ions, the exchange is with R*Cl where R* is another complex resin base:

$$R^*Cl + NaNO_3 \longrightarrow NaCl + R^*NO_3$$

The ion exchange vessels are taken out of service sequentially for regeneration using a brine solution which displaces the captured nitrate ions. The nitrate-rich brine product has to be disposed of. Recently, a process has been developed whereby this brine is electrolysed to convert the NO_3 to N_2 gas, allowing reuse of the brine.

As mentioned earlier, ion exchange is also used to reduce the hardness of a water (for example, the small units available for the home) by removing calcium and magnesium ions from water. It can also be used as a *desalination* system to reduce the salt content of a water. Small-scale ion-exchange units are commonly used in laboratories to produce pure water called deionized water, an alternative to distilled water. Deionized water requires the use of both cationic and anionic exchangers.

Reverse osmosis (explained in the next paragraph) has become popular in removing pollutants such as trace organics and salts and it is worth considering for nitrate removal.

When a solution of a salt is separated from pure water by a semi-permeable membrane that permits the passage of pure water but prevents that of the salt, water will tend to diffuse through the membrane into the salt solution, continuously diluting it. This phenomenon is called osmosis. If the salt solution is in an enclosed vessel, a pressure will be developed. This pressure in a particular solution is known as the osmotic pressure of that solution. Reverse osmosis is a process in which water is separated from dissolved salts in a solution by filtering through a semi-permeable membrane at a pressure greater than the osmotic pressure caused by the dissolved salts in the water. The pressure required increases in direct proportion to the concentration of salts. The salts could be in any form including nitrates. Removal rates in excess of 93% for nitrate have been reported for reverse osmosis systems. Operating costs and space requirements are said to be less than for equivalent ion exchange plants.

The basic components of a reverse osmosis unit are the membrane, a membrane support structure, a containing vessel, and a high pressure pump. Cellulose acetate and nylon are the most commonly used membrane materials.

The water to be treated is pumped at high pressure through the membrane module, and clean water is collected as permeate (Figure 31), with the unwanted material remaining in the retained liquid (retentate).

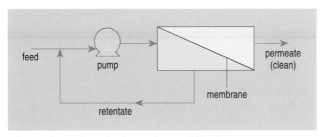

Figure 31   A typical membrane filtration process

The concentration of retained material in the feed builds up with time, and the membrane can get clogged. To prevent this, periodic backwashing with either water or gas under pressure is undertaken.

Continuous filtration with the feed flowing over the membrane surface is preferred over a batch process, as the flow promotes self-cleaning and enables longer runs between backwashing or replacement.

To prevent clogging of the membrane, prior filtration of the feed water is necessary. To decrease scaling potential, iron and manganese removal may also be necessary. The pH of the feed should be adjusted to a range of 4.5–7.5 to inhibit scale formation. Figure 32 shows a schematic of a reverse osmosis system.

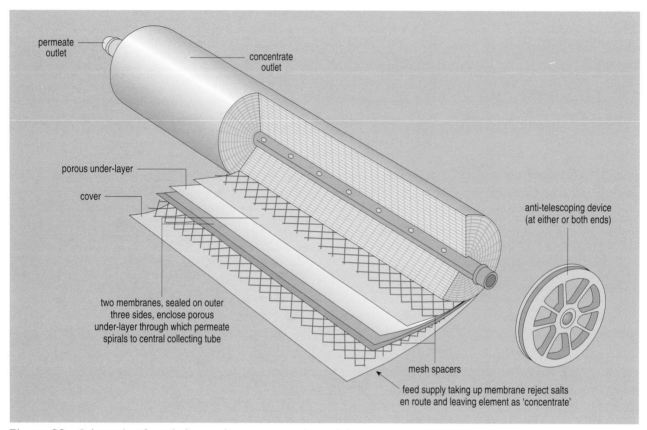

Figure 32   Schematic of a spiral-wound reverse osmosis module

Other options for nitrate removal include electrodialysis (Section 3.14.3) and biological denitrification (Section 9.10.2).

3.8.2 Removal of trace organic compounds

After conventional treatment, water may still contain trace concentrations of synthetic organic compounds, which, if left in the water, can lead to taste and odour problems. The problem is most likely to arise where the raw water source has been badly polluted. The problem can be solved by including the process of granular *activated carbon* adsorption after the filtration process. Activated carbon is carbon which has been activated by heating in the absence of oxygen. This results in the formation of many pores within each carbon particle. Charcoal is a form of activated carbon but with fewer pores. Granular activated carbon (GAC) can be obtained from roasting vegetable or animal matter at 800–900 °C in a vacuum furnace. It can have a surface area of up to 1000 m^2 g^{-1}. GAC is therefore an effective adsorbent of organic compounds. Its effectiveness can be measured by the reduction in the *chemical oxygen demand* (the oxygen needed to chemically oxidize all carbonaceous material present, COD) and the total organic carbon of the water. GAC can be used for the removal of soluble phenols which would produce strongly smelling and tasting *chlorophenols* upon reaction with chlorine in the disinfection stage. In the event that trihalomethanes are formed after disinfection by chlorine, GAC can be used to eliminate these toxic compounds. GAC, once exhausted, can be regenerated by heat treatment.

Another method of removing trace organics is to oxidize them to harmless products such as CO_2 by using ozone. Ozone and activated carbon are capable of removing trace quantities of organics present in water. These substances are used for the reduction of pesticide levels in water supplies to comply with the limit specified by the European Union.

Powdered activated carbon is also an option. It can be added to water for the adsorption of trace organics. It has been used to eliminate tastes and odours in drinking water brought about by algae, actinomycetes and fungi. It is usually added in the coagulation stage prior to sand filtration. Unlike GAC, the regeneration of powdered activated carbon is not practicable, so it is only used when intermittent water quality problems occur.

Membrane filtration is becoming popular in water treatment and nanofiltration (see next section) has been employed for trace organics (pesticides) removal. Nanofiltration is similar to reverse osmosis, which you have already come across. Pesticides, which are often carcinogenic, are not at all desirable in potable water. The limit of each individual pesticide is $0.1 \, \mu g \, l^{-1}$, and for the sum of all the individual species, the limit is $0.5 \, \mu g \, l^{-1}$. The latter is still a very low concentration. It's the sort of concentration of sugar you'd get if you dissolved 1250 sugar cubes in Loch Ness!

3.9 Membrane filtration

Membrane filtration is a process whereby particles smaller than about 10^{-2} mm (which can pass through sand filters) are removed using synthetic polymeric membranes and a high pressure. The membrane effectively acts as a sieve.

It is increasingly becoming popular as an advanced treatment process for water (especially for removal of *Cryptosporidium*) and wastewater (where water reuse takes place), and various possibilities are:

> microfiltration
>
> ultrafiltration
>
> reverse osmosis
>
> nanofiltration

3.9.1 Microfiltration

This process removes particles between 0.05 and 5 μm in size. The water is pumped at a pressure of 100–400 kPa through the membrane module.

Microfiltration has been adopted by water companies as a means of removing some stages in the life cycle of the chlorine-resistant pathogens *Cryptosporidium* and *Giardia*. It is widely used to produce pure water for the electronics, pharmaceutical, chemical and food industries, by removing microbial cells and small particles.

3.9.2 Ultrafiltration (UF)

This employs membranes with smaller pores (0.001–0.02 μm) than those for microfiltration and utilizes much greater pressure (up to 3000 kPa).

An atomic mass unit is 1/12 of the mass of a neutral atom of the most abundant isotope of carbon, i.e. 1.66×10^{-27} kg.

Commonly, the membranes are made of polysulphone, polyacrylonitrile, polyamide and cellulose acetate. Inorganic ceramic membranes are also used. Owing to its ability to remove very small particles, UF is mainly used for the separation of macromolecules, allowing molecules with a mass of 1000 atomic mass units (amu) to pass through the membrane. UF is used as protection against *Cryptosporidium* by one water company in the south-east of England.

It is also used in the removal of bacteria and viruses for food processing waters and for the removal of colour and humic substances from drinking water in small upland supplies.

3.9.3   Nanofiltration

Nano is a prefix that means 10^{-9}, i.e. very, very small. You may have come across nanotechnology. Nanofiltration is similar to reverse osmosis and employs membranes that are capable of physical sieving and diffusion-controlled transport. Nanofiltration systems operate at much lower pressures than reverse osmosis systems, but yield higher flow rates of permeate. The quality of the permeate is not as good as with reverse osmosis, with particles in the size range 0.0005–0.005 μm being removed. It is used for the removal of colour, humic acids, and trace organics such as pesticide residues, from drinking water.

SAQ 25

Which of the following is true?

A There are three important zones in a sedimentation tank, namely, the inlet zone, the settling zone and the outlet zone.

B Flocculent particles in general will reach the base of a settlement tank ahead of discrete grit particles.

C For a surface loading of $30 \text{ m}^3 \text{ m}^{-2} \text{ d}^{-1}$, in a sedimentation tank with floor dimensions $14 \text{ m} \times 50 \text{ m}$, the maximum flow rate allowed is $2.4 \text{ m}^3 \text{ s}^{-1}$.

D It is the positive charge carried by colloidal particles and micro-organisms that prevents them from aggregating and settling.

E An ion exchange resin to remove nitrate from water can be represented as NaR where R is the complex resin base.

F Free available chlorine is a disinfection agent and is present in water as HOCl, hypochlorous acid.

G Both granular and powdered activated carbon can be regenerated.

3.10   Fluoridation

The addition of fluoride to water has caused much controversy and public debate. The problem seems to be that some see it as the addition of a poison, and others see it as the use of mass medication whether the individual wishes it or not.

Many waters do, however, have a natural fluoride content (Figure 33) and it has been suggested that the presence of fluoride in a concentration of 1.0 mg l^{-1} is beneficial in preventing dental decay. Above this concentration there is the likelihood of 'mottled teeth' occurring. The EU Drinking Water Directive specifies a maximum value of 1.5 mg l^{-1}.

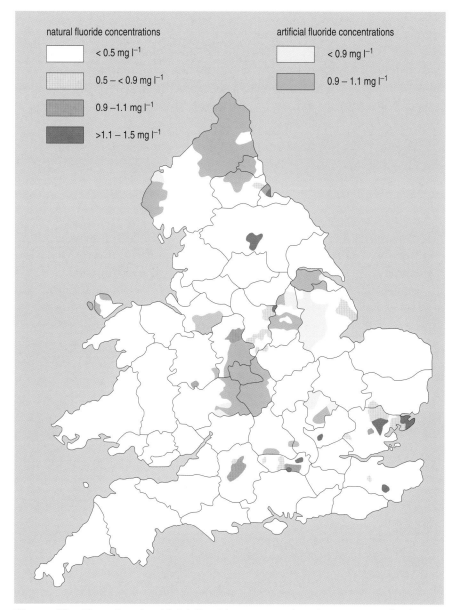

natural fluoride concentrations

< 0.5 mg l⁻¹

0.5 – < 0.9 mg l⁻¹

0.9 – 1.1 mg l⁻¹

>1.1 – 1.5 mg l⁻¹

artificial fluoride concentrations

< 0.9 mg l⁻¹

0.9 – 1.1 mg l⁻¹

Figure 33   Natural and artificial fluoride concentrations in water supplies in England and Wales

Fluoride is added to the water as the last process in water treatment. There are three commonly used chemicals:

- disodium hexafluorosilicate (Na_2SiF_6);
- sodium fluoride (NaF);
- hexafluorosilicic acid (H_2SiF_6).

In water, all these chemicals dissociate to give fluoride ions, e.g.

$$SiF_6{}^{2-} + 2H_2O \longrightarrow 4H^+ + 6F^- + SiO_2$$

The three chemicals must be handled carefully during their addition to the water as they are harmful if they are inhaled, ingested or come into contact with the skin. It must, however, be remembered that the addition of chlorine to water is readily accepted and chlorine is a poisonous gas!

EXERCISE

A natural water contains 0.55 mg l^{-1} of fluoride ion and is to be treated with sodium fluoride so that the final concentration will be 1.0 mg l^{-1} of fluoride ion. The flow of water to be treated is 1000 litres per second. Calculate the daily weight of sodium fluoride that will be required.

ANSWER

The fluoride ion to be added is the difference between the required concentration and the natural concentration, i.e.

$$1.0 - 0.55 = 0.45 \text{ mg } l^{-1} \text{ F}^-$$

The molecular mass of sodium fluoride $= 23 + 19 = 42$.

Therefore, to add 0.45 mg of F^- will require

$$0.45 \times \frac{42}{19} = 0.9947 \text{ mg of NaF}$$

This amount is required for 1 litre of water.

$$\text{Daily water flow} = 1000 \times 60 \times 60 \times 24 \text{ litres}$$

$$= 86.4 \times 10^6 \text{ litres}$$

$$\text{Therefore, amount of NaF required} = \frac{0.9947 \times 86.4 \times 10^6}{10^6} \text{ kg}$$

$$= 85.94 \text{ kg}$$

SAQ 26

1000 kg of hexafluorosilicic acid (H_2SiF_6) is added per day to a flow of 15 000 l s^{-1} to achieve a concentration in the water of 1.0 mg l^{-1} fluoride ion. What was the original concentration of fluoride in the water?

As mentioned in Section 3.7, fluoride belongs to a group of chemicals called halogens. If compounds of bromine (another halogen) – called bromides – are present, and the water is treated with ozone (as might happen if pesticide residues are present), then there is a danger of bromates being formed. Bromates have been found to induce a high incidence of kidney tumours in male and female rats, and peritoneal mesotheliomas in male rats. Bromate is mutagenic *in vitro* and *in vivo*. There is therefore a limit of 10 mg l^{-1} imposed on levels of bromate in drinking water.

3.11 Plumbo-solvency

Many *water supplies* in the UK are naturally acidic, and when this type of water is supplied through lead pipes the lead dissolves into the water. Lead pipes are dominant in many older established areas. The Drinking Water Directive has set a maximum admissible concentration of 10 µg l^{-1} lead in water, to be achieved by the year 2013. The obvious solution to this problem is to remove all lead piping but this is a costly exercise. As an interim measure, the water leaving the treatment works can be dosed with lime or phosphate to increase the pH to 8.0–8.5 (making the water less acidic), thus reducing the extent to which the lead dissolves in the water. The solubility of lead is much reduced in hard water where the lead is precipitated as insoluble lead carbonate. Another practical measure (in the home) is to let the water run for a minute or two before using it. This is especially advisable in the morning when the lead concentration in the water may be high because the water has stood in the pipes overnight.

3.12   Sludge treatment and disposal

The sludge collected in any sedimentation tank in the water treatment process has to be disposed of. In some instances the wet sludge is transported to the nearest sewage works where it is discharged into the raw sewage inlet channel. The presence of the added chemicals can help in the primary sedimentation of the crude sewage. Alternatively, the sludge can be sent to a landfill site after it has been concentrated into a cake by dewatering.

The dewatering is carried out by pressure filtration, vacuum filtration or centrifugation. In pressure filtration, the sludge is pressed at high pressure between filter cloths. Vacuum filters are popular in the USA but few treatment works in the UK employ them. A slowly revolving drum, partly immersed in the sludge, carries a filter cloth through which water is sucked from the sludge under vacuum. In centrifuging, chemically or biologically conditioned sludge falls onto the centre of a rapidly rotating bowl. The solids are thrown to the outer edge of the bowl where they are removed by a scraper. With chemical-conditioned sludge, 80–98% of the solids can be separated this way. These solids would contain typically 10–35% water.

3.13   Groundwater treatment

The treatment of groundwater frequently does not extend beyond disinfection. However, groundwater may contain dissolved substances such as carbon dioxide and iron for which additional treatment (aeration, biological treatment, etc.) may be required. In some instances groundwater may be hard, and where the concentration of dissolved solids is greater than about 300 g m^{-3} it may be desirable to soften the water to reduce scale formation and soap wastage. The methods usually adopted for softening are precipitation or ion exchange.

3.14   Desalination

In many parts of the world, surface water or non-saline groundwater stocks are not adequate to satisfy the water demand. While one may immediately think of the Middle East as being one such area, it is less obvious that many islands (e.g. the Canary Isles, Madeira, the Channel Islands) also suffer the same problem. In such circumstances, people have been forced to consider the sea and brackish underground aquifers as water sources. To make these saline waters potable, the salt has first to be removed by *desalination*. Desalination systems are also used on ships and on offshore oil and gas production platforms as a means of producing potable water. The two major desalination processes used worldwide are multistage flash distillation and *reverse osmosis*. Other techniques commonly used are electrodialysis and solar distillation, often for small communities.

3.14.1 Multistage flash distillation

In this process (Figure 34) saline water (screened first, if it is sea water) is distilled under reduced pressure in a series of sealed tanks. Due to the reduced pressure, the water evaporates suddenly or 'flashes' at a temperature lower than 100 °C, typically 80 °C. Pure water condenses on cooling coils in the tanks and is collected. As the temperature of the feed water falls in each succeeding tank (as the latent heat of evaporation is extracted from it) a correspondingly lower pressure has to be maintained for flashing off to occur.

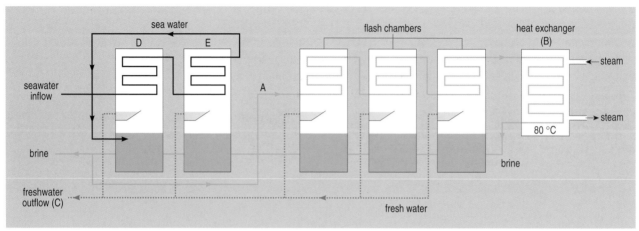

Figure 34 The multistage flash-distillation process. Brine at (A) passes under pressure in the condenser coils of the flash chambers to heat exchanger (B), and as it flows in the reverse direction, water vapour flashes off and is condensed on the cooler brine-filled coils above. The condensate forms part of the freshwater outflow at (C). The brine, now at 60 °C, passes into flash chambers D and E, which contain condenser coils fed with raw sea water. This is recycled into the concentrated brine of the last flash chamber, and the resultant liquid is partly run off as waste and partly recycled to A.

Multistage flash (MSF) units are often located alongside power generation plants in order to utilize the waste heat generated in them. MSF plants can suffer from scale deposition and corrosion. Scale deposits of, for example, $CaCO_3$ and $Mg(OH)_2$ can interfere with the transfer of heat between different parts of the process, and can increase the resistance to fluid flow due to an increase of surface friction. Scale deposition is usually prevented by the addition of scale inhibitors to the feed. These modify the crystal structure of the scale and prevent it building upon surfaces.

Sulphate-reducing bacteria, often present in sea water, can contribute to corrosion. Under anaerobic conditions these bacteria reduce sulphate ions to hydrogen sulphide, which in turn dissolves away iron, forming iron sulphide. This results in 'pitting' corrosion. Other bacterial species can oxidize the H_2S to sulphuric acid, which is very corrosive. Control of all forms of bacterially induced corrosion consists essentially of either eliminating conditions suitable for their growth, or, if this is not practicable, using biocides to prevent them colonizing the parts at risk.

3.14.2 Reverse osmosis

This technique, explained in Section 3.8.1, is rapidly becoming a major means of desalination, with research producing membranes with lower operating pressures (and hence lower operating costs). Originally a pressure of 14×10^6 Pa was needed to separate pure water from sea water but with newer membranes only half this pressure is required. Reverse osmosis membranes operate at ambient temperature, in contrast to multistage flash distillation, and this lower temperature minimizes scaling and corrosion problems. To prevent problems with organic fouling of the membrane, pretreatment of the feed water is required.

3.14.3   Electrodialysis

Electrodialysis is an electrochemical process in which ion transfer separates salt from water. It is effective only for substances that can be ionized: for example, salt (NaCl) becomes, in solution, a mixture of Na^+ and Cl^- ions. (Silica, on the other hand, does not ionize and hence is not removed by electrodialysis. It could, however, be removed by reverse osmosis.) When electrodes, connected to a suitable direct current supply, are immersed in a salt solution, current will flow, carried by the ions. The ions with a positive charge are attracted towards the negative cathode and are called cations. Negatively charged anions flow towards the positive anode. In electrodialysis, filters or membranes selectively impervious to cations or anions are placed alternately between the electrodes (Figure 35). Cation filters permit the flow of anions but act as a barrier to positively charged cations. Conversely, anions are held back by the anion filter while cations pass through. In certain compartments of the tank, ions will collect as their flow is checked by an appropriate filter. Cells of increasing salt concentration thus alternate with cells of salt depletion. Water that is sufficiently desalinated is extracted from the appropriate compartments. Electrodialysis is only generally used with brackish waters as it is uneconomic for sea water desalination. It is used together with ion exchange and activated carbon to produce ultra-pure water for the electronics and pharmaceutical industries.

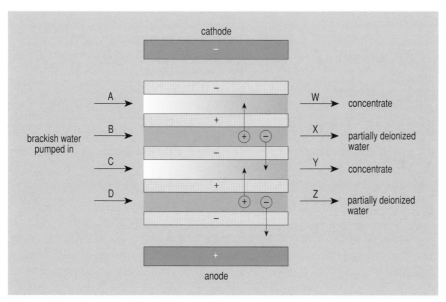

Figure 35   The principle of electrodialysis

3.14.4   Solar distillation

The energy available in solar radiation can be harnessed to distil sea water. In a simple and inexpensive solar still system designed by the Technical University of Athens, for the island of Patmos, sea water is first pumped to a feed reservoir from which it flows by gravity, when required, into a large shallow basin divided into long narrow sections (Figure 36). Separating these channels are concrete strips, which provide access for maintenance. The interior surface of the entire basin is lined with butyl rubber sheet. Above each water-filled section is a double sloping glass roof supported by a light aluminium structure. Heat from the sun passes through the glass, causing evaporation from the sea water surface. The vapour condenses on the inside of the glass and runs down to channels at the edges of the sealed unit along which it travels to the freshwater storage reservoir. The salt concentration in the basin sections grows steadily stronger, and once every two days the resulting brine is run off to the sea, being then replaced by more sea water. Experience has shown that the 48-hour cycle avoids the formation of scale. As the sun does not shine every day, the designers have incorporated a second water channel in the concrete strips. These are fed from the upper surface of the glass panels, and from the concrete itself, when it rains.

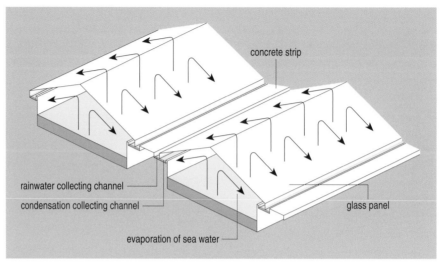

Figure 36   Principle of a solar still

The output of distilled water from the Patmos solar still averages three litres per square metre of water surface per day. The only running costs of the system are those for pumping sea water to the feed reservoir, and for general maintenance, which includes cleaning the glass panels.

If you have tried to drink distilled water you will know that water without any salts is insipid. It is also corrosive, due to the deficiency of ions which would be present if the water were in its natural state. Lime ($Ca(OH)_2$), phosphates and bicarbonates are added to raise the alkalinity and make the water less corrosive. These chemicals also raise the level of total dissolved solids (TDS) to about 300 mg l^{-1}, to give the water taste. If unpolluted brackish groundwater is available, this can be used instead to raise the TDS level. Often a combination of the two – addition of chemical salts and blending with underground water – is economic. Such a procedure is used in the water supply of Muscat in the Sultanate of Oman. After adjustment of TDS content, the pH is corrected if necessary. Finally, the water is disinfected and passed into transmission mains to feed service reservoirs (see Section 4).

3.15   Summary

The basic water treatment process for surface waters consists of preliminary screening and storage, followed by coagulation and flocculation to allow the aggregation of colloidal particles. Sedimentation of the aggregated particles produces sludge and partially purified water. The purification process is completed by filtering and disinfecting the water before distribution. Some waters may require additional treatment: for example, nitrate removal, or fluoridation, or further removal of organic material by granular or powdered activated carbon. The pH may have to be adjusted to minimize plumbo-solvency in areas served with lead distribution pipes. The sludge produced in water treatment can be sent to a sewage works where it can aid primary sedimentation, or it can be dewatered and buried at a landfill site. Small quantities of water can be disinfected by solar radiation and this is useful in remote locations.

In areas of the world lacking adequate quantities of surface water or non-saline groundwater, desalination is practised, with the major processes being multistage flash distillation and reverse osmosis.

SAQ 27

List the four commonly used desalination processes for the production of potable water.

4   WATER SUPPLY

4.1   Introduction

This section is concerned with the plant used in carrying water from the treatment works to houses, farms, blocks of flats and other buildings of a community. The major components of this distribution network are shown in Figure 37 and comprise:

1   the service reservoir, which must balance the fluctuating demands of the users against the steady output from the source of supply, as well as provide a back-up supply should there be a breakdown at the source;

2   the pipelines or 'mains', which, together with their associated valves and fittings, must carry the required quantities of water between the different parts of the system. The pipes taking water from the service reservoir to the supply points are called distribution mains.

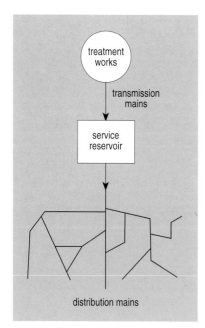

Figure 37   A water distribution network

4.2   Service reservoirs

Transmission mains convey treated water from the water treatment works to the service reservoir throughout all, or most of, the day. However, as with the demand for electricity or gas, the demand for water varies with the time of day. The variations are greater in small networks. Typically, the water demand at night is about 20% less than the average daily demand, whereas the peak demand, occurring around midday, is about 40% greater than the average daily demand.

Figure 38(a) shows the cumulative volume of water entering and leaving a service reservoir during the day. The straight line of constant slope represents the constant rate of inflow (supply) to the reservoir, and the variable line running at first below and then above the supply line represents the changing demand from the reservoir. Figure 38(a) is an example of a mass diagram for a reservoir. The effect of variations between supply and demand on the level of water in the reservoir is shown in Figure 38(b).

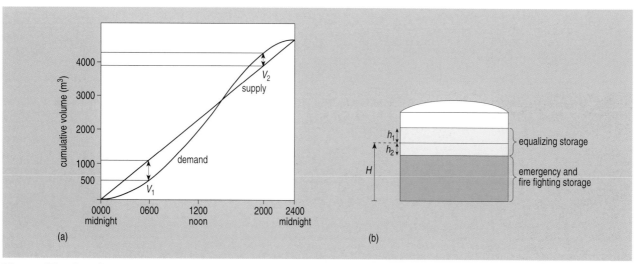

Figure 38   Supply and demand in service reservoirs: (a) mass diagram; (b) reservoir levels

For example, starting at midnight, the water level in the reservoir is H. During the early hours of the morning, supply exceeds demand and the water level in the reservoir increases. By 0600 hours the level has reached a maximum value $H + h_1$. This corresponds to the situation shown on the mass diagram where 1100 m^3 has been supplied to the reservoir, whereas only 500 m^3 has been withdrawn. This represents a surplus V_1 of 600 m^3.

After 0600 hours the rate of demand increases (as the nation awakes) and by 1500 hours the level in the reservoir has returned to its initial level H with supply matching demand exactly.

By early evening the situation has reversed. At 2000 hours, the mass diagram shows that the deficit V_2 between the amount of water supplied and that withdrawn is 400 m^3, at which time the water in the reservoir has reached its lowest level, $H - h_2$.

Thereafter, water demand 'eases off' again with the water level in the reservoir rising back to its initial level at midnight.

The volume $V_1 + V_2$ is called the equalizing storage, because it performs the function of equalizing supply and demand. Without equalizing storage the transmission mains would need to be large enough to cope with peak demand and would be underutilized most of the time. With a service reservoir the transmission mains need only carry the average daily demand (together with an extra 15–25% to account for leakage). Extra capacity may be incorporated in a service reservoir, in addition to equalizing storage, for emergency and fire-fighting use. Such an extra capacity is shown in Figure 38(b).

Usually, service reservoirs (Figure 39) are constructed of concrete and frequently, for reasons of both economy and appearance, they are sunk wholly or partly below ground level. The reservoir needs to be positioned with sufficient elevation to provide an adequate flow to the distribution area and to raise the water to the top of buildings. In flat areas, where elevated sights for ground level tanks are not available, or where it is necessary to supply tall buildings, water towers (Figure 40) may be used. In exceptional cases, tall buildings may require their own system of pumps to raise water to the top.

The elevation of the water surface in a reservoir above a given baseline is a measure of the static *head* of water available (Figure 41). For example, the elevation of the reservoir level above Point A in Figure 41 is 50 m. So the static head at A is 50 m. In other words, the water pressure available to the house at A is equivalent to the pressure at the base of a 50 m high column of water. At point B in Figure 41 near the top of the high-rise building, the static head is only 10 m.

Figure 39 Prestressed concrete service reservoirs

Figure 40   A water tower

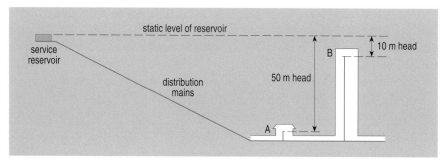

Figure 41   Static head in distribution mains

The water pressure in the distribution mains should usually be such as to be able to fill a storage tank at second-floor roof level, and enable the cold-water tap in a ground-floor kitchen to fill a 4.5-litre container in 30 seconds. This will be achieved if the static head at the boundary of the property is 10 m.

SAQ 28

What should the flow rate at the kitchen tap be to satisfy the requirement that a 4.5-litre container be filled in 30 seconds?

In a distribution main, the head should not normally be lower than 30 m for fire-fighting purposes and should not exceed 70 m. Many domestic fittings, including taps, ball valves, stopcocks and domestic washing machines are designed to operate at pressures between 30 m and 70 m (appropriate pressures). At higher pressures, wear of fittings becomes excessive, seals need frequent replacement and the system is noisy and more liable to 'knocking' and vibration. Furthermore, at high pressures the system is likely to leak at a greater rate than at low pressures.

Pressure-reducing valves are sometimes used if the water pressure is too high. These valves are designed to limit the pressure downstream of the valve to a predetermined value, irrespective of the pressure upstream.

Figure 42 shows a possible arrangement of service reservoirs, water towers, mains and buildings. We can see how this arrangement is used to create appropriate pressure zones.

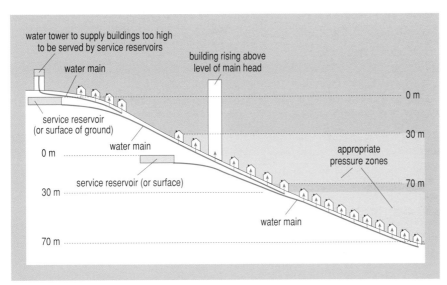

Figure 42   Distribution of water from service reservoirs

It is not always possible to take advantage of flow under gravity in transmission systems. The necessary head for flow then has to be raised by pumping through part or all of the pipeline. Where pumping occurs, the pipeline is called a rising main.

In England and Wales, water companies are legally required to provide fire hydrants as requested by the fire service, but there is no guidance on the quantity of water to be made available or its pressure. Nevertheless, fire-fighting requirements govern the size of main that is considered to be desirable. When a pipe is fed from both ends (e.g. in a loop), a diameter of 75 mm is usually considered to be satisfactory. A 100-mm diameter pipe is preferred where only one end is fed. If the fire service considers that there would be insufficient water available for quenching a fire, it will ask for a larger main. Under these circumstances the extra cost is borne by the fire service, both for the larger main and for the provision and maintenance of the hydrant.

SAQ 29

Figure 43 shows the hourly variation of demand from a service reservoir. Plot a mass diagram for the service reservoir and estimate the volume of equalizing storage required.

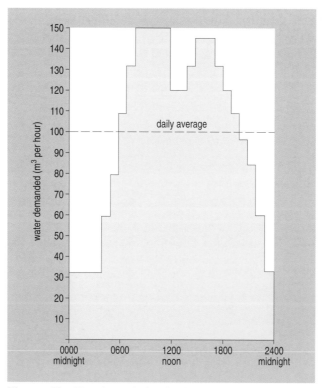

Figure 43   Hourly variation in demand from service reservoir

SAQ 30

Select the appropriate option(s) 1–4, for each of the components A, B and C.

A Storage tower

B Spur water main of diameter 100 mm

C Pressure-reducing valve

1 To meet fire-fighting requirements

2 To give a reasonable water pressure at the top of a tall building on flat land

3 To avoid a water head of less than 30 m

4 To avoid a water head of greater than 70 m

4.3   Distribution systems

The water from service reservoirs is distributed by a network of pipes (see *pipe flow* in the Set Book) of various sizes, laid beneath the streets, pavements and verges of our towns and cities. Any part of a distribution system can be isolated by valves at appropriate points. Figure 44 shows both a loop (as at A) and a spur or dead end (as at B) within a typical distribution layout. Looped or ring mains are always preferred to spurs or dead ends because when the rate of flow is restricted in a long spur, the water will remain there for a long time, and its quality may deteriorate. Bacteria can proliferate in stagnant water at dead ends.

In the event of repair work, the whole length may need to be isolated. In a ring system, water can flow through a lightly loaded section to meet demands elsewhere. There is also the advantage that one section of a ring main may be isolated without cutting off the sections on either side. For example, the section *ab* of the ring main shown in Figure 44 may be isolated. However, water could still flow in sections *ac* and *cb*. The distribution grid is arranged so that any pipe can be taken out of service without cutting off the output to the others.

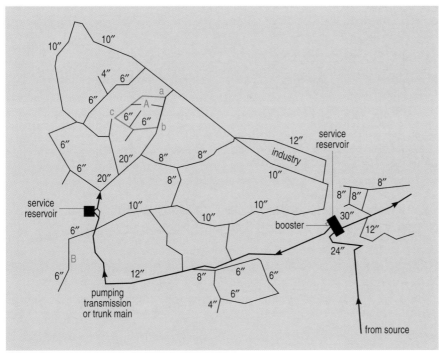

Figure 44   Part of a typical distribution system

A mains pipeline can be subject to a variety of loading conditions. There is the static loading due to the internal water pressure in the pipe. Also, pipelines are often subject to water hammer. Changes in flow direction and velocity at bends, contractions, expansions and partly closed valves lead to additional loading on the pipe, as does the thermal expansion or contraction of the pipe material.

The choice of pipe material clearly depends on the magnitude and nature of these stresses. However, other factors have to be considered:

1 the ground conditions, in so far as these affect the possibilities of ground movement and corrosion;

2 the corrosive nature of the water;

3 the size of pipe;

4 the ease of jointing;

5 the cost.

The joints between adjacent lengths of pipe must be watertight. Occasionally, joints are welded, but it is more usual to find some form of sealing ring contained in a socket at the end of one pipe or at each end of a separate collar.

Cost, as the last factor, is by no means the least important. It is usual to aim for the minimum overall cost. The materials used for transmission mains and their respective merits are listed in Table 5. Asbestos cement pipes are no longer laid in the UK. The existing asbestos cement pipes are replaced by more modern substitutes, e.g. MDPE, whenever they develop cracks, etc. All MDPE underground pipes are colour-coded to prevent accidents – water is blue, gas is yellow, electricity is black, and telephone is grey.

Table 5   Materials used for transmission mains

Material	Merits	Disadvantages
Steel	High strength and ductility resulting in light weight. Jointing easy with mechanical or (in large sizes) welded joints.	Requires careful protection against external and internal corrosion.
Cast iron	Modern ductile iron pipes have strength and ductility approaching those of steel. Push-fit joints are easy to make. The pipes are cast in an automatic machine to obtain light but strong walls free from imperfections.	Requires special protection against external corrosion in some types of ground. Often subject to growth of incrustations or tuberculations internally unless lined with concrete.
Asbestos cement	Economical and resistant to decay under most soil conditions. Light and easy to handle and lay.	Vulnerable to damage during handling.
UPVC (unplasticized polyvinyl chloride) and MDPE (medium density polyethylene)	Light and flexible, easy to handle and install. Low cost compared with metal pipes.	Deformation and stretching due to stress over a period of time. Susceptible to aromatic hydrocarbons (e.g. petrol) penetrating the pipe wall and contaminating the water supply.
Prestressed concrete	Sometimes economic in large sizes.	Heavy and somewhat inflexible in use. Cannot be cut on site and joints allow only limited angular deflection.

4.4   Summary

After passing through a treatment works, water flows via transmission mains to service reservoirs which act to even out variations in consumption during a 24-hour demand period. It is then taken by distribution mains from the service reservoirs to the consumers. The head of water necessary for flow is provided by positioning the service reservoir at the correct level or by pumping. A pumped pipeline is called a rising main. The size of mains pipelines depends on the quantity and flow rate of water carried. The construction material depends on stresses imposed during use and other factors (size, ground conditions, etc.).

5   WATER DEMAND

5.1   Introduction

Water is a basic necessity of life. Figure 45 illustrates some of the more common uses of water in a community.

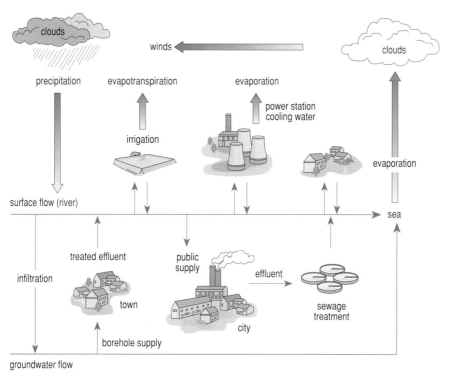

Figure 45   Simplified diagram to illustrate how water is abstracted from the natural cycle and returned to it after use and reuse

People take water from lakes, reservoirs, rivers or underground sources, and use and reuse it for a variety of purposes before returning it to watercourses, or to the atmosphere. Most of the water used for irrigating crops is returned through drainage and evaporation.

The returned water, although still in the liquid state, may be polluted, sometimes grossly. Some of the water used for cooling purposes in power stations or in industry is evaporated, but most of it is returned relatively near to the point at which it was withdrawn. For instance, of the cooling water used in electricity generation, about 2% is lost by evaporation and 98% is discharged at a temperature some 5–6 °C higher than ambient. By the time it reaches the sea, some of the water in a river may have been used again and again, as illustrated in Figure 45.

5.2   Principal uses of water in the UK

In the UK, usage of water can be classified into five main groups:

1   *Public water supplies.* Of the total water supplied by water companies and public authorities some two-thirds is for domestic use and the remaining one-third is for industry. However, a proportion of the water used by industry is for domestic purposes in the factory, such as lavatory flushing, washing, cleaning and canteen use, the remainder being used for manufacturing processes and as boiler feed water.

2   *Industry.* For certain processes, industry uses large amounts of water both as a coolant and as a medium for conveying substances, such as cellulose fibres in paper making, crushed rock in ore preparation and so on. This is obtained by direct abstraction. Occasionally, when a high standard of water is needed, direct abstraction is followed by special treatment, but usually such water is obtained from public supplies. As indicated in (1), industry takes about a third of public supplies.

3   *Electricity.* The electricity generating companies use large quantities of water, mainly for cooling. Quality requirements are minimal and supplies are always obtained by direct abstraction either from rivers, lakes, estuaries or the sea.

4   *Agriculture.* In the UK, water used by agriculture forms only a minor proportion of the total consumption. Part is used for irrigation, especially in the eastern counties, and the remainder for cattle watering, dairy cleaning and other general purposes. (Worldwide, however, some 65% of water is used in agriculture. The figure for Europe is 26%.)

5   *Fish farming, watercress growing and amenity ponds.* The cultivation of fish for food has become an important industry due to health concerns about other protein sources. Fish need flowing water to provide an adequate supply of oxygen, as well as to carry away faecal waste products. Watercress growing is also gaining in popularity. The provision of adequate water space for water-based sports and other activities is of growing importance, and we already see reservoirs being built and canals and rivers being improved for recreational and amenity purposes alone.

The amount of water abstracted for various uses in England and Wales in 2003 is shown in Table 6.

Table 6   Water abstracted in England and Wales in 2003 for various uses

Use	Ml d^{-1}
Public water supply	16 920
Private water supply	61
Electricity generating companies	31 378
Other industry (excluding water power, saline and tidal abstractions)	6 623
Fish farming, watercress growing, amenity ponds	3 077
Agriculture (cattle watering, dairy cleaning, etc.)	132
Spray irrigation	315
Other (frost protection use, etc.)	86
Total	58 592

Source: www.defra.gov.uk/environment/statistics/inlwater/iwabstraction.htm#iwb22
Accessed 29 January 2007.

A word has to be said about spray irrigation. While it is a minor use, it may have a significant impact on available resources as it tends to be used mostly during periods of hot dry weather when water resources may already be stretched. Almost all the water used in this way is lost to the atmosphere or ground, unlike water abstracted for other uses which is usually treated and returned to rivers, thus becoming available for use again. The proportions of water supply devoted to these domestic and industrial uses vary appreciably throughout the UK. For instance, in many rural or coastal communities, the industrial element is very small. Elsewhere it may form the major part, for example in the heavily industrialized Teesside region in the north-east of England.

5.3   Per capita consumption

The per capita consumption is the amount of water supplied to a household divided by the number of residents. The average per capita consumption generally decreases with increasing household size (Table 7).

Table 7   Household size and water consumption in the UK

Household size	1	2	3	4	5	6	7	8
Consumption (litres per head per day)	211	154	130	122	103	103	108	54

SAQ 31

Much of the Government-projected growth in the number of households in the UK in the coming decades is expected to be from an increase in single-person households.

If, in a town of 50 000 households with an average of three persons per household, 10 000 children left home to live in their own flats, work out the increase in water demand that can be expected.

As regards the actual use of the water, Anglian Water measured water consumption in 3000 homes with detailed analysis of usage in 100 of these. The data revealed the pattern shown in Figure 46. Consumption was found to rise by about 10% in the warmer months (May to October).

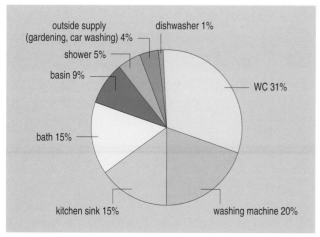

Figure 46   Domestic water consumption averaged over a year, based on data from 1993 to 1998

In one of the home experiments, you will be measuring the rainfall that your home receives, and you will use these data to calculate the proportion of your daily needs that rainfall could satisfy. If you have a metered water supply, calculation of your average daily usage will be easy (since your average water consumption can be ascertained from the figures in your water bill). If your water supply is not metered you will have to make an estimate along the lines of Table 7.

5.3.1   Water consumption in different countries

Table 8 shows the water consumption in different countries, with the usage ranging from 102 to 326 litres per head per day.

Table 8   Per capita domestic consumption in various countries

Country	Per capita consumption (l/head/day)
Australia	268
Austria	135
Belgium	122
Canada	326
Czech Republic	113
Denmark	139
Finland	145
France	137
Germany	116
Hungary	102
Ireland	142
Italy	213
Japan	278
Korea	183
Netherlands	130
New Zealand	165
Norway	140
Poland	158
Portugal	119
Spain	210
Sweden	191
Switzerland	158
Turkey	195
England and Wales	136
United States of America	305

The consumption rates for some industrial countries stand out. One possible reason for this might be their external use of water. Recent figures suggest that about 50% of total household water consumption in the USA and Australia takes place outside the home. Possible explanations include swimming pools, larger gardens needing watering, and the tendency to recreate 'cool temperate' gardens in unsuitable environments.

SAQ 32

Using the information in Table 7, what is the average occupancy rate of the houses in England and Wales which gives rise to a per capita consumption of 136 litres per head per day?

SAQ 33

From Table 8, identify those countries where the per capita consumption of water is high. Suggest reasons, other than those given, why the consumption might be as it is.

Is your household a high water user? You can find out from your water bill, if you're on a metered supply.

One way of reducing demand (in non-emergency situations, that is) is by metering and charging on the basis of volume of water consumed. This is discussed later.

In some countries, such as Spain, savings in water bills are encouraged through a system of rising block tariffs. For example, in Barcelona in 2000, charges were as shown in Table 9.

Table 9   Water charges in Barcelona, 2000

Water consumption (m^3 per quarter per household)	Charge (Spanish pesetas per m^3)
0–18	44.10
18–48	89.30
>48	121.80

There can also be different tariffs based on water demand, such as those offered by Anglian Water. The company offers a 'Normal' tariff, a 'SoLow' for people who are very low consumers, and 'Plus 4' available to high consumers receiving social security.

5.3.2   Minimization of water use in the home

The consumption of potable water in the home has been generally observed to rise (Table 10) in England and Wales over the years. (There was, however, a drop in 2000–2001. Possible reasons could be less water use in gardening due to greater rainfall, a greater extent of metering, and the greater awareness of water conservation.)

The increased usage has been variously attributed to the greater use of washing machines, more frequent showering and more use of water in gardening.

Table 10   The measured average consumption of water in the home in England and Wales

Year	Per capita usage (litres per person per day)
2005–2006	136
2004–2005	139
2003–2004	141
2002–2003	137
2001–2002	136
2000–2001	132
1999–2000	137
1998–9	136
1997–8	138
1996–7	134
1995–6	134
1994–5	129

Data from Office of Water Services, the water industry regulator for England and Wales

If the rate of water consumption picks up again, greater abstraction is likely to lead to stress on the environment as river flows are diminished. The construction of water reservoirs is also not without detrimental effects on the environment, in addition to costs to the water companies concerned. Global climate change also plays a part – the two years from April 1995 to April 1997 constituted the driest period in the UK since records began, more than 230 years ago. In the summer of 1996, London had less rainfall than Istanbul or Rome! Then in autumn 2000 the UK had a massive amount of rain, leading to floods in several areas. It is difficult to predict if water resources will be adequate but to be on the cautious side one should try not to waste water.

Tables 11 and 12 list possible ways in which the use of potable water may be reduced within the home and in the garden. Technology in this area has been encouraged by the *Eco-label* scheme, which seeks to promote products with lower environmental impact. Also, see what xeriscaping can do for you in Table 12!

A most effective measure towards conservation has been found to be the installation of water meters and the introduction of charges for the amount of water used. In trials carried out over 1989–93, in 12 locations (mostly in southern and central England) metering was found to reduce consumption by an average of 11%. By 2002, some 22% of households in England and Wales were metered for water supply. The Water Industry Act (1999) obliges water supply companies to fit meters free of charge to households which request them, provided the installation is practical and not unreasonably expensive. The take-up in some areas has been dramatic – the percentage of households serviced by Anglian Water which have meters is 43%! In fact all new homes in England and Wales now come fitted with a water meter. Water companies can require households which use large quantities of water for non-essential purposes, such as for swimming pools and garden sprinklers, to have water meters.

Table 11 Ways to conserve potable water within the home

Advice	Notes
Fix leaking taps.	A dripping tap wastes about 13 litres of water a day.
Never let the water run while brushing teeth, etc.	Leaving the tap running can waste up to 9 litres a minute.
Install spray nozzles on taps.	These reduce consumption by 10–20%.
Use a pressure cooker instead of a normal saucepan.	Needs less water.
Use water-economical washing machines and dishwashers, and use them only with a full load.	Typically, washing machines consume 65 litres per wash. Requirements under the 1999 Water By-laws limit the water use per cycle in new machines to 35 litres. Some washing machines can 'sense' the size of the washing load, and adjust their water consumption accordingly. Such machines get a well-deserved *Eco-label*!
Have a shower instead of a bath.	On average, a 6-minute shower will use up to 30 litres of water, while a bath will consume 80 litres. (Power showers, however, will consume more water than a bath if used for more than five minutes.)
Use a cistern device such as a bottle or a 'Hippo' (a plastic bag to hold water) to displace a given volume of water.	Reduces the amount of water used in each flush. The volume displaced by the various devices range from 1 litre to 3 litres.
Use new-model WCs which use less water.	Regulations introduced in 1999 for new installations from 2001 reduced the amount of water used to no more than 6 litres per flush. Dual-flush WCs can also reduce consumption, if used correctly.
Use rainwater for toilet flushing and for outside use.	(See Section 5.6).
Reuse greywater (the non-faecally contaminated used water from baths, showers and hand basins) for toilet flushing, after appropriate treatment.	(See Section 5.3.3). Water from kitchen sinks, washing machines and dishwashers usually contains food particles, grease and oil that are difficult to filter.
Use supply restrictor valves (plumbing fittings that reduce water flows into domestic appliances, taps and showers).	Essentially, the valve works by reducing the diameter of the supply pipe when there is a change in mains pressure, thus giving a constant flow. The result is that even when the tap is fully open the same flow rate of water is maintained. A valve is also available that can detect leaks and shut off supplies automatically.

Table 12   Ways to use less water in gardening

Advice	Notes
Collect rainwater by connecting a water butt to the downflow pipe from the roof.	The water is free, and good for plants.
Water the garden in the evening.	The rate of evaporation is lower at this time.
Use mulch (e.g. chopped bark, grass cuttings, polythene mulching mats)	Reduces the extent of evaporation from the soil around plants.
Use drip-feed irrigation.	Ensures water reaches only the required parts of the garden.
Water the lawn only once a week (twice a week in the hottest weather) with a sprinkler moved around the garden.	Watering more frequently encourages the roots of the grass to seek the surface, and overwatering encourages moss. Spiking the lawn will help the water soak down.
Don't cut the grass too short.	Longer grass shades the soil so that it retains moisture longer, and stays green longer, too.
Use a watering can instead of a sprinkler.	On average, in just one hour, a sprinkler will use as much water as a family of four uses in two days.
If a hose is used, equip it with a trigger.	The water supply can be cut off when it is not needed.
Add compost or other organic matter to soil.	Improves its water retention.
Build paths of gravel instead of paving slabs.	All the rainwater seeps into the garden.
Grow drought-resistant plants which require less water.	For example, climbing roses, vines, red hot poker, poppies, cornflowers, lavender, thyme, rosemary, mint and sage. This is known as 'xeriscaping' or landscaping for water conservation.
Don't water trees and shrubs once they are established.	Watering brings the roots to the surface. Established roots will seek out groundwater so don't need watering.
Only water frequently those fruits and vegetables that have edible leaves, and water root crops and tomatoes only when their roots or fruits are swelling.	Watering at other times is not necessary.
Insert sections of downpipe into the soil beside plants.	The water for irrigating them reaches the roots directly.
Reuse dirty water from fish tanks for the garden or houseplants.	It's rich in nitrogen and phosphorus.

Water companies in England and Wales have a duty to promote the efficient use of water by their customers (both household and non-household). This is an interesting situation, isn't it? The companies are there to make a profit by selling water but yet they have to inform people on how to use less! All is not lost, however. Compensation is made by the Office of Water Services (OFWAT), which adjusts the selling price of the water to account for the loss in earnings.

Typically, water companies have to ensure that all customers have access to cistern water-saving devices, and the advice necessary to promote their effective use. For instance, the larger 'Hippos' (see Table 11) are only effective for the older, large 13-litre cisterns: when installed in new cisterns, they impede the flushing operation and customers find that they have to double flush to get rid of the waste. This only wastes water. Companies now tend to promote small devices displacing only one litre of water. The companies also have to promote advice on self-audits (on water use) for schools, hospitals and other community premises.

Composting toilets which do not use water at all are available but these tend to be used in areas without mains sewerage. They look like normal WCs but the solid and liquid wastes are collected in a tank beneath the commode. The solid waste composts and is removed every few months to be used as a fertilizer. The liquid waste can also be put to the same use.

The water companies are encouraged to make their water-saving literature practical, eye catching (with plenty of pictures and charts) and customer-friendly (easy to read). Have you seen the ones from your water supplier?

Household audits

Household audits to reduce water use have been conducted by Essex and Suffolk Water (operating in a very dry part of England). Leaking taps have been fixed, and cistern devices and more efficient shower heads installed. Water savings of approximately 10% have been achieved. But, interestingly, after one year, the savings were found to have fallen. The causes of this unexpected finding were manifold: people moving house, the removal of cistern devices and showerheads due to operational problems, and the recurrence of leaks and drips from taps fixed during the original audit.

The application of rising block tariffs (mentioned earlier) also encourages savings in water consumption.

The whole subject of water efficiency is of interest to water companies and several of them are involved in sponsoring the building of water-efficient homes.

5.3.3 Saving water in public buildings

The potential for saving water is especially high in institutions such as schools, colleges and universities, and in offices.

Commonly installed are cistern devices, spray taps, shower and tap controls (allowing the water to flow for a predetermined period at the push of a knob), infrared controls at urinals (activating flushing of the urinals only when they are used), and waterless urinals. Waterless urinals are coated with a urine-repellent gel coat which ensures the immediate draining of urine into a cartridge where a biodegradable fluid (lighter than urine) prevents odours emerging. The urine flows through the cartridge and out. The cartridge is changed 2–4 times a year. The cost of installing water-saving measures in 13 schools in Yorkshire was monitored and shown to be recoupable in 2–5 years. Many water companies offer water audit services to institutions and industries to help identify water-saving opportunities.

The *water conservation* entry in the Set Book contains some interesting information which you might like to read.

5.3.4 Greywater recycling

Greywater, the wastewater from baths, sinks and showers, is a significant output of our daily water usage. Greywater can, with appropriate treatment, be used for low-grade water uses such as toilet flushing.

Hollow-fibre ultrafiltration membranes operating at about 200 kPa have been used in trials to treat greywater for reuse as flush water. Another option is to use a mini hydrocyclone (Figure 47) to remove pollutants present in the greywater.

The treated water is disinfected and stored for reuse. Greywater recycling has considerable potential for multi-use buildings such as halls of residence, blocks of flats, offices and hotels. Not only are savings made in the amount paid for water consumed but sewerage charges are also reduced, since these are based on the amount of water used.

SAQ 34

What are the potential pollutants in greywater?

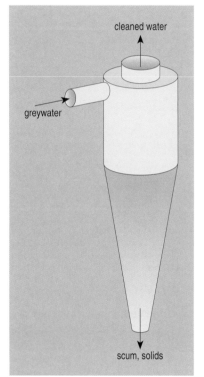

Figure 47 Schematic of a hydrocyclone

5.4 Water losses

In every distribution system there is some loss of water due mainly to individual joints leaking quantities that are not easily detectable. Large leaks are noticed more quickly, especially if surveys for the detection of leaks are made at regular intervals. In addition, there is usually some apparent loss at meters due to inaccurate registering, but it is not easy to tell exactly what these losses are. Losses can be reduced by using a pressure in the mains which is just enough for efficient supply. Excess water pressure is likely to exacerbate leakage. The use of automatic pressure control valves has significantly reduced losses in many distribution networks. Pressure from the water regulator OFWAT and the Environment Agency has led to much less wastage through leakage in England and Wales.

In the UK, most industrial supplies and some household supplies are metered and the consumers are charged on the basis of the quantity of water used. In areas where metering is total, the leakage can be estimated by deducting the amount used by the consumers from the total supplied to the distribution system. In areas where only industrial usage is metered, the probable loss is estimated by measuring demand at night when domestic consumption is at its lowest. Leakage occurs mainly due to pipes fracturing with age or vibration from heavy traffic overhead. One quarter of all leakage is estimated to occur within the household.

Metering the individual consumer's supply and billing at established meter rates prevents wastage of water by users and tends to reduce actual water usage. The waste and unaccounted-for water in metered systems ranges from 10% to 15% of the total water entering the distribution system. The corresponding rate in unmetered systems is much higher (25–30%). Leakage detection and elimination is seen as an effective means of increasing the available water supply, but not at any cost. There comes a point where it is uneconomic to spend further on leakage reduction. The level of leakage at which it would cost more to make further reductions than to produce the water from another source is known as the economic level of leakage. Operating at the economic level of leakage means that the total cost of supply water is minimized.

Water conservation and related matters are discussed in the DVD related to this block.

5.5 Minimization of water use in industry and commerce

Industry, faced with rising water costs, is minimizing water usage in process operations wherever possible. Savings in water usage also translate into lower costs for treatment because of the lower volume of effluent generated. In many plants the effluent is treated on-site and reused.

Agriculture, though not a major user of water in the UK, can also play its part in water conservation. For instance, drip-feed systems can be used in place of spray irrigation units.

Not all uses of water require a high-quality potable-grade supply. For instance, cooling processes in industry often use river water which has been given minimal treatment (e.g. screening to remove gross solids and chlorination to inhibit microbiological growth in pipelines). A further example is on ships and offshore oil and gas platforms where sea water is used for toilet flushing. In such instances, two water distribution networks are required – one carrying potable water for drinking, washing, bathing and cooking, and the other carrying lower quality water for non-potable uses. Such networks have to be well designed to prevent cross-contamination of the potable supply by the non-potable line. In Hong Kong, some 75% of the population have seawater pipelines for use in toilet flushing. Using such dual distribution systems means that potable water can be conserved. In Kuwait City, a dual distribution system takes potable water and *brackish water* to homes, where the latter is used for watering plants in gardens.

5.6 Rainwater harvesting

In many regions of the world where piped water supplies are not available, rainwater harvesting has been adopted. At its simplest, this could be through using a container to collect rainwater falling on the roof of a house, saving the occupants from walking many kilometres to collect clean water. In Uganda, rainwater is also collected from trees, using banana leaves (which are broad) or stems as temporary gutters; up to 200 litres of water may be collected from a large tree in a single storm.

Rainwater harvesting can also be used as part of an integrated water supply system, where the piped supply is unreliable, or where local water sources dry up for part of the year.

It can also happen that rainwater is used only for drinking and cooking purposes (the higher water quality demands) with a poorer quality local water source used for other activities. In the Canadian province of Nova Scotia, approximately 320 000 people are served by private well supplies. In some areas, the groundwater is unacceptable for domestic use because of gypsum deposits, saltwater intrusion, or the presence of iron and manganese. Houses in such areas have adopted rainwater harvesting as a solution. The roofs of the houses act as collection surfaces, and gutters and downspouts direct the rainwater to a storage tank in the basement or underground. The rainwater is filtered and disinfected and then reused. In the UK, rainwater-use schemes have been implemented in several locations. Twenty-two houses in Surrey have each been built with a concrete tank buried under the front garden to collect rainwater run-off from the roof. A filter removes debris before the water goes into the tank. The water is used for toilets and outside taps. There is a mains back-up, should the rainfall be inadequate.

5.6.1   Contaminants in rainwater

The danger of atmospheric pollution of rainwater is negligible (unless one is immediately downwind of an industrial complex!) and the probability of collecting airborne pathogens is low.

Contamination of the rainwater might arise, however, from the roofing material itself, or from substances that have accumulated on the roof, or in the gutter. Corrugated iron roofs protected by galvanizing (coating with zinc) are common in rural areas of developing countries, but fortunately zinc has a low toxicity so the roof run-off does not exceed WHO-permitted zinc levels. Roof paints, including bitumen, may entail some risk to health and may impart an unpleasant taste to rainwater, and should be avoided. Asbestos-reinforced cement mortar roofs are also common but the chances of developing cancer from ingested asbestos are very low.

Dust, leaves, bird-droppings and other debris are likely to collect on roofs and gutters. Thus the initial run-off from the roof can be highly polluted. It is common practice to divert to waste the first five litres or so of the run-off at the beginning of a rainstorm. This can be done automatically using proprietary devices, or manually. If this first flush is excluded, a water source with modest levels of turbidity and moderate levels of bacterial contamination (<10 faecal coliforms per 100 ml) can be obtained.

The storage tank should be sealed so as not to allow access to insects, lizards (in tropical countries) and rodents. Light should also not enter the tank.

SAQ 35

Why is it important to exclude light from the storage tank?

5.6.2   Rainwater harvesting on a larger scale

It can be disastrous if rainwater is led into already-overloaded sewers. A housing development in Edinburgh overcame this problem by laying infiltratable concrete block paving in its car parking areas. It is also used in commercial areas (Figure 48). Rainwater drains into the aggregate-filled voids and percolates into the ground, instead of contributing to surface run-off entering the sewer. This method of dealing with surface run-off is becoming widespread. The Environment Agency is promoting this technique in its efforts towards sustainable drainage.

However, just as households can make savings in potable water use by collecting rainwater run-off from their roofs, the potential for collecting vast quantities exists in large industrial buildings, and from car parks. Rainwater can be collected from car parks by appropriate grading of the surface. In new constructions, the car park is constructed so that it is porous, and atop a gravel bed with a geotextile membrane base and adequate porosity to store water, which can later be drawn out.

Figure 48   Infiltratable concrete blocks

Vortex filters (Figure 49) can be fitted to downflow pipes carrying rainwater from roofs. The rainwater passes through a 170 µm mesh and flows to an underground collection tank. Leaves and other debris are kept out, and flow away with some 10% of the rainwater to the drains.

Filtered rainwater can be used for washing vehicles, or for irrigation around a factory site. In Gullivers Land (a theme park in Milton Keynes), for instance, rainwater is collected in the extra large water flume for use in irrigation of the plants around the site.

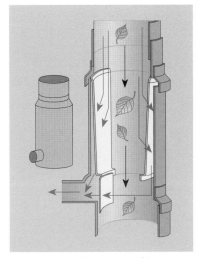

Figure 49 The WISY filter collector

CASE STUDY: THE MILLENNIUM DOME

A good example of water conservation, greywater recycling and rainwater harvesting was at the Millennium Dome (Figure 50). Some 500 m^3 of water was required daily at peak flow to service more than 600 toilets and 200 urinals. The supply was a mixture of three different types of water:

- greywater collected from handwash basins;
- rainwater collected from the 100 000 m^2 roof area of the Dome;
- rising groundwater extracted from a borehole at the site.

The water collected had to be treated before being used as flush water.

Figure 50 The Millennium Dome in London

5.7 Education

Education in the subject of water conservation is seen as paramount by water supply companies, if money is not to be spent in developing new sources. Southern Water used a theatre company to present *Drips in School*, a 30-minute play showing how the Drip family wastes water, to children in over 100 schools in its region. Most water companies now include information on water saving in literature sent to customers. Customers can request further details, and often are offered water-saving devices such as water butts at competitive prices.

Many water companies have established educational centres to promote the message. Teaching packs are often sent to schools for dissemination. Thames Water has a mobile 'Water Wise Home' (Figure 51) which incorporates innovative and imaginative interactive displays to promote water efficiency. The mobile home visits events such as the annual Ideal Home Exhibition in London, and also visits schools.

Figure 51   Thames Water's 'Water Wise Home'

5.8   Summary

The main consumers of water are the public, the electricity generating companies, industry and agriculture. The per capita consumption of water in the home decreases with increasing household size. The largest use of water internationally occurs in the appliance-rich countries. There are several ways in which the consumption of potable water can be reduced, both inside the home and in the garden. Metering and billing of water supplies tends to reduce water usage and wastage. Water savings are possible also in industry and in agriculture. Education is the way forward in water conservation.

6 POLLUTION OF THE AQUATIC ENVIRONMENT

6.1 Sources of pollution

After studying Chapter 2 we now realize that there are important physical, chemical and biological properties characteristic of unpolluted water, but that these can vary enormously from one watercourse to another. In addition, all waters are subject to a degree of 'natural' pollution. This can happen through too much decaying vegetable matter and other materials being washed out of the soil and into the water. However, a greater part of the pollution of rivers has its beginnings in the daily life of the community and the operations of industry within the catchment areas.

To some extent a river is a self-renewing resource. If polluting discharges to a river are intermittent then the river is often able to return to a clean and unpolluted condition as the pollutants are flushed out and carried down to the sea. In addition, because of the organisms present, river water has some capacity for self-purification, unless too many of these organisms are killed off too quickly.

Some pollutants are objectionable because they overload the self-purification processes of the river. As rivers are often the raw water sources for potable supplies, this can have dire consequences. An example of such pollution is the discharge of domestic sewage effluent to rivers. In small quantities it does no serious harm and may indeed be beneficial by providing a source of organic carbon that provides nutrients to the creatures in the river. But, if inadequately treated and in excessive quantities, sewage effluent can seriously damage the plant and animal life of a river by reducing the oxygen content of the water. In extreme cases, where the oxygen content is reduced to zero, or nearly so, the river will support very little life, and will become foul smelling and grossly offensive. A river in such a state is obviously not desirable as a water source for potable supply.

Some industrial effluents discharged in large quantities can be similarly harmful. For example, effluents from the food industry are not particularly toxic, but by reason of their organic content and large volume, they can exert a considerable oxygen demand on the environment in the region of the discharges.

The two pollution sources described above are classified as point sources, as the pollutants are generally collected by a network of pipes or channels, and conveyed to a single point of discharge. Non-point, or diffuse, sources are characterized by multiple discharge points. Examples of diffuse sources are run-off from fields and roads. Point sources are easily controlled, whilst diffuse sources are virtually impossible to collect and control. The latter pose great challenges in efforts to upgrade the quality of rivers.

Lakes are much more vulnerable to pollution. Once a pollutant enters a lake it will stay there for a long time. The flushing effect which characterizes rivers is much less evident in lakes, and the dilution factor is much less than is available in the sea. Only the self-purifying ability of the water will abate the pollution in the short term.

Lakes are particularly prone to eutrophication (discussed in detail in Section 7.2). This occurs when nutrients contained in discharges to lakes encourage the growth of algae to the point where, at certain times of the year, they constitute a serious nuisance. Later, as the algae die and decompose, the oxygen content of the lake is seriously depleted, as decomposition is an oxygen-consuming process.

When considering the effects and problems of pollution of estuarine environments, various factors affect the probability and extent of the pollution. These are:

dissolved oxygen

nutrients   as in rivers and lakes

indigenous flora and fauna

salinity (stratification)

tides

waves

currents

sediments and mud

Estuaries suffer from four main sources of pollution: domestic sewage, industrial waste, other extraneous matter brought down by the rivers, and the sea. The last source may be surprising but research has shown that in north European estuaries a lot of the sediments deposited have come in from the sea, brought in by incoming seawater currents along the estuary bottom. The extension of the Control of Pollution Act 1974 to the three-mile limit at sea is a reflection of the importance of protecting estuaries and the shore. This section of the Act is tied to the EU Directives concerning bathing beaches and water quality required for shellfish growth (EU Directives 76/160/EEC and 79/923/EEC respectively).

In a normal inland stream one would look for the effect of a polluting discharge below the point of discharge, but in a tidal river the effect may be apparent for quite long distances upstream and downstream of the discharge point; this is because a 'packet' of polluted water will not move steadily downstream but instead will oscillate around the discharge point. For example, the time necessary for polluted water to clear the mouth of the River Thames is said to be about 6 weeks at minimum river flows, and 2 or 3 days during periods of high flows.

It is useful to know where river pollutants originate since they can be controlled more easily at source. A list of specific sources would be very long but the following categories can be identified:

1   Discharges from sewage works, which often contain some industrial wastes.

2   Wastes from manufacturing and industrial plants, including mines.

3   Discharges from animal rearing, fish farming and agricultural activities.

4   Seepage from domestic and industrial waste landfill sites.

Each of these will be discussed below.

6.1.1   Discharges from sewage works

Inadequately treated sewage and trade wastes are the major sources of river pollution. They can contribute to high levels of oxygen demand and also introduce toxic substances into the aquatic environment. Dissolved organic matter (such as sugars, organic acids and detergents), suspended organic matter (such as fats, proteins, carbohydrates, organic acids, soaps and detergents) and inorganic matter (such as compounds containing sodium, calcium, potassium, magnesium, chlorine, sulphur, phosphorus, bicarbonates and ammonia) may all be present in the sewage effluent. Detergents discharged with sewage are a major source of phosphates, contributing some 50% of the total phosphate present in the effluent. The remaining 50% comes from human body wastes and from food discharged to sewers from kitchen sinks and waste-disposal units.

Micro-organisms such as bacteria, viruses and protozoa will also be present. Trade wastes may contribute toxic substances such as heavy metals and *PCBs*.

There are plants where combined sewer overflows (mixtures of storm water and raw sewage which exceed the capacity of sewage treatment works) can be a major source of pollution.

The treatment of sewage to minimize pollution will be discussed in Chapter 9.

6.1.2 Discharges from manufacturing and industrial plants, including mines

Wastewater from manufacturing plants may contain organic and inorganic material. This material may be in suspension or in solution.

Manufacturing and industrial plants utilize water in three ways: as a process material, as a heat exchange medium, and as a means of transport. Examples of where water is used as a process material are the fabrication of steel products and soft-drinks manufacture. Water may be used primarily to remove dirt or impurities from a product (as in the textile industry) or it may be exploited for transporting the product in industries such as sugarbeet refining and potato processing. Much of the water used is recycled, but there is almost always an effluent discharge which requires treatment. Plants processing food generate large volumes of effluent containing natural organic compounds such as carbohydrates, proteins and fats, while plants producing chemicals often generate low-volume but highly toxic waste streams. Toxic effluents can also be produced in the paper, leather and electroplating industries: for instance, cyanides and heavy metals may be present in wastewaters from electroplating.

Manufacturing and industrial effluents may be treated at their points of origin and discharged into a river, or may be discharged into a sewer to be treated at the nearest sewage treatment works. In either case, the discharges are subject to stringent standards as regards quantity and quality.

Wastewaters from industrial processes differ in their 'strengths' or potential for polluting rivers. The strengths of effluents from various trades and industrial processes are compared in Table 13. The values in column 2 are those of the standard five-day biochemical oxygen demand (BOD) test for each waste. As you can see, typical BOD values for domestic sewage are 250–300 g m^{-3} at the inlet to sewage treatment works. By comparison, clean river water normally has a BOD value of 2 g m^{-3} or less.

Table 13   Comparative strengths of different liquid wastes

Type or source of waste	5-day BOD $(g\ m^{-3})$	pH value	Suspended solids $(g\ m^{-3})$
Domestic sewage	250–300	6–8	250
Cotton	200–1000	8–12	200
Wool scouring	2000–5000	9–11	3000–30 000
Tannery	1000–2500	11–12	2000–3000
Laundry	1600	8–9	250–500
Brewery	1340	4–6	90
Dairy	600–1000	<7	200–400
Cannery: citrus	2000	<7	7000
Cannery: pea	570	<7	130
Slaughterhouse	1500–2500	7	800
Potato processing	2000	11–13	2500
Sugar beet	450–2000	7–8	800–1500
Farm	1000–2000	7.5–8.5	1500–3000
Poultry	500–800	6.5–9	450–800
Grass silage	50 000	<7	low
Coke oven	780	7–11	70
Oil refinery	100–500	2–6	130–600

Another major use for water is in transferring heat. The condensate or cooling water from indirect heat exchangers (where the coolant does not come into direct contact with the substance to be cooled) may be non-polluting so that no treatment other than cooling and, possibly, aeration is needed. However, leakage can occur in heat exchangers resulting in process substances being added to the cooling water. Thermal power stations require vast quantities of cooling water in order to absorb the waste heat from steam turbine exhausts.

Mining activities can generate wastewaters – the washing of coal produces an effluent containing coarse and fine particles. Streams receiving such colliery effluents may be opaque, grossly distorting the types and numbers of aquatic inhabitants present. Other types of mines, e.g. copper, use water in the extraction process. The effluent from this process contains heavy metals, chemicals and particulates, and is sent to tailings dams for sedimentation and evaporation rather than being discharged into a river.

Disused mines can also generate effluents on account of mine drainage water seeping out. In early 1982, millions of gallons of effluent from the Wheal Jane tin mine, containing arsenic, mercury, cadmium, iron, zinc and copper, entered the Fal estuary in Cornwall when the pumping usually used to remove the water was stopped. The estuary turned orange due to the formation of coloured compounds when the effluent met the sea water.

6.1.3 Discharges from animal rearing, fish farming and agricultural activities

The intensive rearing of animals results in large volumes of organically polluted washwater being generated on farms through the cleaning of animal houses. This slurry is often stored in lagoons or tanks prior to spreading on land. Problems, however, occur when such lagoons or tanks leak or overflow, allowing the slurry to flow into watercourses, causing contamination. Storage of *silage* for winter feed also produces heavily polluting silage liquors. If these wastewaters are not carefully disposed of, serious pollution of watercourses can result. As seen from Table 13, grass silage effluent can have a BOD as high as 50 000 g m^{-3}.

SAQ 36

Accidents with something as innocuous as milk can also be devastating if the amount concerned is large. Consider a 10 m^3 tank (common on dairy farms) which ruptures and empties its entire contents into a river.

Why might this event be devastating?

Hint: Dairy wastes (from Table 13) have a BOD of 600–1000 g m^{-3} but what will pure milk be like?

In recent years fish farming has expanded considerably. These farms use large quantities of water in flow-through systems. The effluent discharged often contains unconsumed food and faecal matter from the fish. The effluent can also contain chemicals such as *antibiotics* used in the rearing of the fish and these may cause problems due to their potential mutagenicity (see *mutagen* in the Set Book), their ability to produce allergic responses and the possible development of resistant strains of micro-organisms. These aspects are particularly important where the river is used as a source for public water supply.

Wastewaters from animal rearing and fish farming can contribute to the suspended solids, BOD and the ammonia loading of a watercourse. A further source of pollution related to farming is from agricultural land which has been excessively fertilized using inorganic chemicals. The run-off may then contain nitrates and phosphates which contribute to eutrophication. Leaching of nitrates affects groundwater in particular. Excessive use of *pesticides* can result in some finding its way to watercourses too, through being washed out by rain. The subject of agricultural pollution is considered in more detail in Chapter 11.

6.1.4 Seepage from domestic and industrial landfill sites

Many landfill sites, particularly those which are older and less well-designed, generate *leachate*, which is highly polluting in terms of BOD. Where industrial waste has been dumped, a toxic chemical stream may also be produced. These leachates have to be collected and treated so that pollution of groundwater and rivers does not arise. More on leachates and leachate treatment is given in Block 4: *Wastes management*.

6.2 Summary

A variety of pollutant discharges are generated by the day-to-day activities of communities. Principally, these waste streams originate from sewage works, manufacturing and industrial plants, the farming sector and landfill sites. Of the various effluents, potentially the most highly polluting and/or toxic discharges usually come from farming and industry.

SAQ 37

Select the true statements from the following:

A Any input of pollutants into a river is undesirable.

B Seawater currents only bring pollutants to the beach.

C The phosphate content in sewage can be largely attributed to detergents, food wastes and excretion from the human body.

D The BOD of silage effluent is more than 150 times that of domestic sewage.

E The only concern with antibiotics being discharged with effluents into rivers is the fact that antibiotic-resistant bacteria will emerge.

7 THE EFFECTS OF POLLUTANTS ON THE AQUATIC ENVIRONMENT

Problems occur when the natural characteristics of a river are altered by pollutant discharges. Pollutants can be divided into the following categories:

1 organic materials

2 plant nutrients

3 toxic pollutants

4 physical pollutants

5 biological pollutants.

7.1 Organic materials

Organic substances constitute the major freshwater pollutants, coming from domestic sewage discharges (even after treatment) and from certain industries such as food processing. This section will deal with the biodegradable forms, but there are also inert (non-biodegradable), toxic, and biodegradable forms which will be discussed later.

The major polluting effect of biodegradable organic materials is the reduction in oxygen concentration in the water. Bacteria and other organisms (decomposers) break these materials down into simpler organic or inorganic substances. They use up oxygen in the process, and as their population increases there is an extra demand for dissolved oxygen.

When a potentially polluting effluent is released into a stream, there follows a sequence of events in time and distance. This sequence leads to different environmental consequences and different aquatic communities compared with those immediately upstream and the successive reaches downstream. After a certain distance, natural processes will often return the river to something like its original condition.

Three stages of organic pollution may be defined. When the load is small, there will be little change in the species of plants and animals present in the water and little variation in the natural cycles. Initially, the dissolved oxygen will be near to saturation level. Any organic pollution apparent at the point of discharge will disappear within a short distance downstream as it is removed by the natural processes of self-purification. It may be said that, in some instances, mild organic pollution is beneficial to the river, since it increases the nutrient supply for micro-organisms present in the natural state. This minimal pollution can benefit the whole aquatic ecosystem.

However, if the load increases, the dissolved oxygen level will drop significantly and the river will appear to be polluted for a considerable distance from the point of discharge. Some species of animals and plants will flourish at the expense of others. In the absence of further pollution, the river will probably recover downstream, but if the area around the discharge remains polluted, this can act as a barrier to the passage of migratory fish.

If the polluting load is increased still further, the natural ecosystem will be grossly distorted and its effectiveness in coping with the pollutant load greatly reduced.

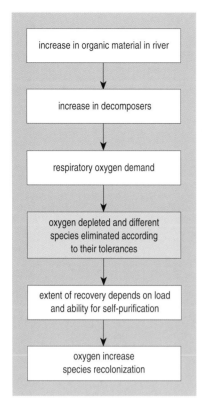

Figure 52   Events following organic pollution

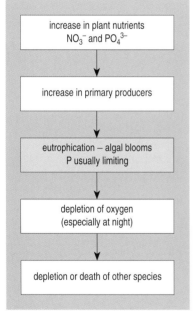

Figure 53   Events following eutrophication

The level of dissolved oxygen will be very low, or fall to zero (you may like to refer back to Figure 9, the dissolved oxygen sag curve, to refresh). Often the only organisms to flourish will be sewage fungus, certain worms and larvae. (These organisms give a low BMWP score, indicating the polluted nature of the river.) Also, anaerobic bacteria may thrive and give a foul smell to the water by utilizing organic substances and producing methane, hydrogen sulphide and ammonia. Few algae are able to thrive under severe organic pollution, so reoxygenation by photosynthesis will be hindered. The river will now remain polluted for a much greater distance downstream. The sequence of events is shown in Figure 52.

Deoxygenation can also occur from inorganic materials, e.g. when ferrous iron enters a river. In the reduced ferrous (Fe(II)) state the iron is in solution, but on meeting the oxygen in the river, it is oxidized to red insoluble ferric (Fe(III)) iron, a process which reduces the dissolved oxygen in the river water. The oxidized iron is now in suspension so that in addition to reducing the oxygen content it reduces light penetration. It finally settles out slowly downstream of the discharge point, giving rise to all the problems associated with suspended solids (Section 2.3). This type of problem is usually associated with coal-mining effluents.

7.2   Plant nutrients

Certain inorganic substances are essential for normal plant metabolism but they can reach such levels as to be considered pollutants.

The possibility of naturally occurring eutrophic water bodies has already been described in Chapter 2. Pollutants can greatly accelerate these events by increasing the inputs of nutrients so that algae grow rapidly and algal blooms form (Figure 53). The rapid removal of carbon dioxide by photosynthesis can upset the bicarbonate–carbonate equilibrium and cause a pH rise, which in itself is damaging to the ecosystem. In addition, at night the excess respiration (without the replacement of oxygen by photosynthesis) can deplete oxygen reserves, causing the death of higher organisms, such as invertebrates and fish. This process can be compounded when algal blooms, through their decay, further reduce the oxygen content of water. The formation of benthic (bottom-dwelling) mats of macro-algae can also lead to the deoxygenation of sediments. This can hinder the supply of oxygenated water to eggs and impede the emergence of fry from salmon-rich spawning grounds.

Of the plant nutrients, the total inflow of phosphorus and nitrogen (especially at the productive time of year, spring and summer) is the most important. There are two types of algae associated with algal blooms, and different conditions are needed for their continued growth. Blue-green algae are able to fix atmospheric nitrogen and therefore are not limited by nitrate levels in the water. Neither are they dependent on dissolved carbon dioxide because they can use the bicarbonate ions present. In addition, they are tolerant of relatively high pH. Their growth is limited by the phosphorus content. In contrast, green algae require nitrate as they cannot fix nitrogen from the atmosphere. They also require fairly high levels of carbon dioxide as they cannot use bicarbonate ions, and they are not tolerant of elevated pH values. Their growth is limited by both phosphorus and nitrogen.

Contact with blue-green algae, or ingestion of it, can cause skin rashes, eye irritation, vomiting, fever and pain in the muscles and joints, due to toxins produced by the algae. The build-up of aquatic vegetation and associated silt deposition affects the carrying capacity of channels and can enhance the risk of flooding.

Generally, increases in both phosphate and nitrate concentrations seem to be the most important in governing the rate of eutrophication in most waters. However, whether this is the only factor which limits the rate of eutrophication is still a matter of controversy. Any eutrophication is contingent on other aspects of the particular ecosystem such as the hardness, pH value and the original distribution of algal species.

Levels of 0.3 g m^{-3} for nitrate and 0.01 g m^{-3} for phosphate have been suggested as limiting values for significant algal populations. These levels are still speculative as 'blooms' can occur when concentrations are lower, and, conversely, many aquatic ecosystems seem stable in the presence of higher concentrations.

Nitrates can have a more significant effect on human health than phosphates if they are present in drinking water supplies. When nitrates are absorbed into the human body they can be converted to nitrite by bacteria in the digestive system. Nitrites combine with haemoglobin and prevent it from combining with oxygen and from carrying out its normal function. If this happens extensively then a serious condition called **_methaemoglobinaemia_** results, which in young babies can be fatal. There is also concern about the possible effects of nitrate on the incidence of stomach cancer. To date in the UK, even in high nitrate areas (e.g. the agricultural areas of East Anglia) methaemoglobinaemia is extremely rare, and epidemiological evidence suggests little effect, if any, on gastric cancer in the UK. Evidence is accumulating that nitrate in water can only affect these diseases when there is also malnutrition, particularly deficiency of vitamin C.

Water quality standards exist to control pollution of domestic water supplies. The maximum limit set for nitrates in drinking water (as mentioned in Section 3.8.1) by the EU is 50 g m^{-3} (as NO_3^-). The EU has also passed a directive to protect groundwater from pollution where the limits for nitrates are the same. With the passing of the 1989 Water Act (and later the 1991 Water Resources Act) the Secretary of State is able to designate water protection zones where farmers can be restricted in the use of nitrate fertilizer (see the T210 Legislation Supplement). Water with a high nitrate content can be treated for drinking using ion exchange or reverse osmosis (as detailed in Section 3.8.1).

The biota differences between organic pollution and artificial eutrophication may be summarized as in Figure 54. When organic pollution occurs, the main types of organisms present are the decomposers. In the case of eutrophication, the producers are dominant, and in larger quantities than in 'clean' waters.

7.3 Toxic pollutants

The term 'toxic' is a rather misused one. It is misleading to refer to one material as a toxic substance and to another as non-toxic without qualification. The toxicity of all materials depends on the concentration. Further complications may be introduced by the fact that some materials are essential components of an animal's diet, but that in anything other than very low concentrations they may have a toxic effect. Other environmental factors to be taken into account include the extent of biodegradation, the rate of accumulation within the biota and so within the food chain, and the retention time of a substance within an organism. The most important mechanism for toxicity in the body is the poisoning of **_enzymes_**, which are the catalysts of all the bodily functions.

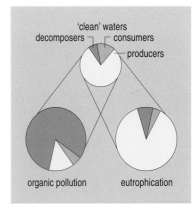

Figure 54 Ecological imbalances caused by inorganic and organic pollutants

The terms used when explaining the effects of a toxic substance on an organism are:

lethal	death by direct poisoning;
sublethal	death caused indirectly by affecting growth, reproduction or activity leading to a reduction in number of species and/or individuals;
acute	causing an effect (often death) within a short period;
chronic	causing an effect (lethal or sublethal) over a prolonged period of time;
accumulative	effect increased by successive doses.

To test the effects of toxicity the LD_{50} (*lethal dose*) test is commonly used. Some examples of LD_{50} values for different chemicals are given in Table 14.

Table 14   Oral toxicities of some chemicals in small mammals

LD_{50}	Examples	Classification
1–10 mg per kg body weight	arsenic	highly toxic
10–100 mg per kg body weight	cadmium copper lead mercury	moderately toxic
100–1000 mg per kg body weight	aluminium molybdenum zinc	slightly toxic
>1000 mg per kg body weight	sodium iodine calcium potassium	relatively harmless

The final effects of a toxic substance in water depend on environmental factors such as temperature, pH and hardness. For example, heavy metals are generally less toxic in calcium-rich water; a nickel–cyanide complex is 500 times more toxic to fish at pH 7.0 than at 8.0; and ammonia is 10 times more toxic at pH 8.0 than at 7.0.

An additive effect, *synergism*, may occur. For example, an equal parts solution of cadmium and zinc is more than twice as toxic as the same amounts of either metal on its own.

The main toxic pollutants are the heavy metals and synthetic organic substances such as some of the pesticides. Salts of heavy metals such as copper, silver, lead, gold, nickel, chromium, zinc, cadmium and mercury are toxic and will generally kill most aquatic organisms at very low concentrations. Also, certain inorganics, such as cyanides, fluorides, sulphides, sulphites and nitrates, may be classified as toxic. Compounds of cyanide and sulphide interfere with the utilization of oxygen in the respiratory reactions in cells. Excess fluoride can lead to mottling of teeth and bones in humans. Nitrates, as discussed previously, can cause methaemoglobinaemia in babies.

The main problem with manufactured substances is that they are unknown in nature and organisms have not evolved to deal with many of them. If they are biodegradable they may be split into harmless substances, but in most cases this does not happen and the pollutants remain in the organism exposed to them. This organism in turn may fall prey to another organism, and so the toxic substances accumulate as they move up the food chain. This is known as bioaccumulation.

The European Union (then the European Economic Community) in 1976 (in List 1 of Framework Directive 76/464/EEC) drew up a '*black list*' of 129 substances which it considered to be sufficiently toxic, persistent or bioaccumulative for steps to be taken to eliminate pollution by them. A supplementary list (List 2 in the same Framework Directive) of less harmful but nevertheless polluting substances was also drawn up, and this became known as the '*grey list*'.

> The EU Directive 75/440/EEC, concerning the quality required of surface water intended for the abstraction of drinking water in the EU Member States, proposes standards for surface water to be used for public supply and classifies the sources and treatment needed into A1, A2 and A3. Whereas A1 waters require only simple physical treatment (e.g. filtration) and disinfection, A2 and A3 waters require more complex treatment, such as pre-chlorination, coagulation, flocculation, filtration, adsorption and disinfection.

As an example of limits on toxic substances, Figure 55 shows the maximum concentrations of certain toxic substances that can be permitted in surface waters used as an A1 grade of supply.

Highly acidic waters can dissolve heavy metals, especially if the pH is below 3.0. This occurs in the case of mine wastewaters and also in some naturally occurring springs. The metals present tend to be brought into solution, especially iron, zinc, lead and molybdenum. An increase in the pH is related to a decrease in zinc uptake by fish and a decrease in the numbers of deaths. Conversely, the increase in deaths of many fish species at pH below 5.0 is due to a combination of the direct effects of acidity and the toxicity of metals present, especially aluminium. Table 15 shows a summary of damage to the aquatic environment with decreasing pH.

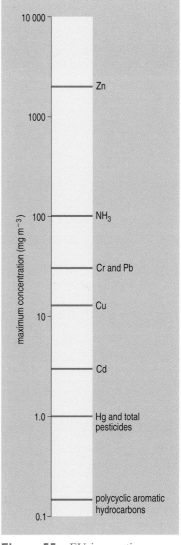

Figure 55 EU imperative criteria for A1 standard of surface

Table 15 Damage to the aquatic environment which occurs with decreasing pH

pH	Effect
8.0–6.0	A decrease of <0.5 units results in a very slight change in biotic environment.
8.0–6.0	A decrease of 0.5–1.0 units results in detectable alterations in community composition. Some species eliminated.
6.0–5.5	Reduction in species numbers, and among remaining species considerable alteration in ability to withstand stress.
5.5–5.0	Many species eliminated and a few pH-tolerant invertebrates become abundant.
5.0–4.5	Decomposition of organic detritus is severely impaired. Most fish species eliminated.
<4.5	All above changes greatly exacerbated; fish cannot survive.

The information that is available on metal pollutants tends to refer to the total concentration of the metals; unfortunately this provides little information on a metal's bioavailability (i.e. the ability of an organism to take up the metal) or how long the metal will stay in solution before it is removed into sediment.

To be able to predict the adverse effects of metal pollutants in water it is necessary to determine the physical form or chemical form (speciation) of the metal present. Metals can exist in a wide range of forms.

The subject is very complicated, too complicated to be covered fully in this block. It is possible, however, to look at two extreme cases of metal pollution to show the range of events that can occur.

The effluent from a lead-acid battery factory is discharged into a river after treatment to remove most of the lead. The lead concentration in the effluent is still about 4 g m^{-3} and is found to consist mainly of soluble ions and ion pairs, along with a trace of particulate lead in the form of lead sulphate. In the river the lead sulphate settles out quickly. The soluble lead becomes attached to particles greater than 12 μm in size and settles out in the river. The discharge therefore causes a relatively small increase in the lead content of the river. The opposite effect is shown by metals in a sewage effluent discharge. Here the sewage effluent is contaminated with *cadmium* from industrial sources. The cadmium is in the form of organic complexes formed in the sewage treatment process from the organic-rich sewage. In the river this form of cadmium does not settle out and is carried downstream over a long distance, remaining available to biological life throughout.

The uptake of metals in solution by organisms such as phytoplankton is by diffusion across the external membrane. Fish can take in metals by diffusion across the membrane of their gills. Fish can also ingest metals but metals taken in this way are not as readily bioavailable. Filter feeders such as oysters and cockles inhabit the surface of sediments and consume considerable amounts of particulate matter from the water which passes through them; they accumulate metals in solution by ingestion in the process. These examples show how metals in water can enter the food chain.

7.3.1   Toxicity-based conditions on consents to discharge

In late 1996/early 1997, the Environment Agency proposed the introduction of toxicity-based conditions to supplement the existing conditions on consents to discharge (permission to discharge an effluent into a water body or sewer – see Appendix 2 for an example). The reason was that, in cases where a complex mixture of chemicals is discharged, it is very difficult to specify limits for each component chemical. Also, the interaction between the different chemicals is unknown. To overcome these problems, it was proposed that a technique called direct toxicity assessment (DTA) be used to control and monitor discharges that contain a mixture of chemicals.

DTA involves testing the effect of an effluent on organisms from different levels of the food chain, for example, algae, macroinvertebrates and fish. The results of these tests help to specify the level of treatment required for the effluent before dilution by the receiving waters to ensure that aquatic life is protected.

DTA has been trialled at three sites where there was evidence that effluent discharges were causing ecotoxicity – at the River Aire, near Bradford, the

River Esk (south-east of Middlesbrough), and the lower Tees Estuary (near Redcar). A suite of test methods was used to screen complex sewage and industrial discharges to characterize toxicity. Of the 17 effluents screened, 12 were found to be toxic to aquatic organisms. The measured ecotoxicity could not be predicted from the characteristics of the effluents of the individual constituents. The trials provided evidence for support of the DTA approach.

It is the intention that initially toxicity-based conditions will be incorporated into new and existing discharge consents to complement current forms of control. In the future, such conditions may entirely replace concentration limits for certain substances.

It's not all good news, however. DTA costs a lot more than chemical analysis at the moment. With time, as DTA becomes more routine, and employs high throughput procedures, the costs are likely to come down.

7.3.2 Assessing toxicity

The effect of the effluent on algae, macroinvertebrates and fish are assessed using established toxicity tests, and the organisms most sensitive to the effluent should be used as the test species. By testing the effluent at different dilutions, the dilution required to achieve no observed toxic effect using the most sensitive of the species is determined. This is the predicted no-effect concentration (PNEC) for the effluent.

Owing to the fact that DTA will take at least 96 hours to carry out, the Environment Agency is considering rapid methods of toxicity assessment. Some of these are detailed in Chapter 8.

7.4 Physical pollutants

7.4.1 Suspended solids

Various industries produce suspended material in their effluents and this has several consequences. All solids tend to reduce light penetration, so the growth of plant life in watercourses is inhibited. This will have secondary effects on food chains. The bottom-living animals and plants may be smothered as particles settle. If the particles settle on gravels, fish spawning can be seriously disrupted. Predators which hunt by day may be restricted in their activities: for instance, in turbid water there may be an abundance of leeches as fish are no longer able to see and consume them as food.

One of the most important effects on animals is the damage to fish gills. The gills tend to thicken, which reduces oxygen intake and therefore restricts the population. In laboratory tests, at a concentration of 30 g m^{-3} *suspended solids* (SS) the death rate of fish was negligible, at 90 g m^{-3} SS some deaths from thickened gills occurred, and at greater than 270 g m^{-3} SS a high proportion of the fish died. The absence of fish in certain streams in Cornwall has been attributed to the SS discharged by the china clay industry there.

The European Inland Fisheries Advisory Commission (EIFAC) has produced criteria for chemically inert suspended solids in respect of freshwater fisheries (Table 16).

Table 16   Effects of increasing concentration of suspended solids on fisheries

Suspended solids $(g\ m^{-3})$	Effect
<25	No harmful effects.
25–80	Good to moderate fisheries possible, but yield may be somewhat reduced.
80–400	Unlikely to support good fisheries, but some in lower range.
>400	At best, only poor fisheries.

Some effluents pollute because substances in them enter into chemical reaction with salts already dissolved in the water. For example, iron hydroxide may be precipitated if water containing this metal is discharged into a naturally alkaline river. This phenomenon typically arises from the abandonment of mines where the *clear* water pumped out and discharged into a *clear* stream can produce a bright orange coloration which prevents penetration of light and hence inhibits plant life.

Some suspended solids can cause harmful effects when soluble toxic components present in them are dissolved into the water by biological or chemical action.

7.4.2   Immiscible liquids

Immiscible liquids may be present as oils, greases or tarry substances, often in the form of emulsions. (An emulsion is a colloidal suspension of one liquid in another, as in mayonnaise.) They may affect turbidity in the same way as suspended solids. However, emulsions are not likely to settle to the bed of the river. Frequently they float on the surface and adhere to vegetation at the water line. Some immiscible liquids are decomposed slowly by aquatic micro-oganisms.

Oil is generally lighter than water and will spread over the surface to form an extremely thin film; a small quantity is therefore likely to pollute a large area. Even when the oxygen demand in the water is low and oil imposes little additional biological load, the presence of an oil film with a thickness of only one thousandth of a millimetre ($1\ \mu m$) may reduce the rate at which oxygen is transferred from air to water. It can also affect the life cycle of insects, since larvae float on the surface.

Oil is one of the more serious pollution problems. Many oils and tars are slightly soluble in water and thereby impart tastes and odours to it.

7.4.3   Discharges contributing to a temperature change

Industrial effluents are frequently discharged at temperatures different from those of the receiving river. Almost invariably the effluent is warmer than the river, since water is widely used for carrying away heat.

Some of the effects of an increase in temperature have already been described. Within limits a raised temperature increases the metabolic rates of all aquatic organisms. It also decreases the concentration of dissolved oxygen needed for saturation. The overall effect on the oxygen balance of a particular heated effluent therefore depends to a certain extent on the oxygen balance in the river at the point of discharge. A small increase in the temperature of a clean fast-flowing stream may not affect the ecosystem adversely. Provided oxygen is plentiful, plants and animal populations may be altered slightly but remain in a balanced state. Species indigenous to warmer climates may become established in a heated portion of a river. It has been said that some aquatic ecosystems benefit from a slightly warmer environment.

However, heated effluents are usually discharged to watercourses already polluted to some degree, so the polluting effects are compounded. A heightened BOD on the river water due to a sewage discharge upstream may be exacerbated by raising the temperature. Any animals or plants that die as a result of the heat or greater oxygen deficit (e.g. the saturation concentration of oxygen in water at 5 °C is 12.79 mg l^{-1} while at 15 °C it is 10.01 mg l^{-1}) are decomposed by bacteria, which decreases the oxygen level even more.

If unacclimatized fish have to pass upstream through a mass of warm water, they may not survive, even though the higher temperature does not exceed the limit which such fish are accustomed to elsewhere. Thus a 'plug' of warm water may prevent fish moving upstream and result in a reduction of the fish population in the upper reaches of a river. Although fish may survive at temperatures just below the lethal limit in the short term, they are not likely to flourish and are even less likely to breed. Also, the resistance of fish to disease is reduced at the higher temperature.

7.4.4 Discharges causing variations in flow rate

Variations in flow of a river can result from excessive abstraction or from intermittent discharges of relatively large volumes of effluent, as when settling ponds (used to remove particulates from otherwise clean water) are emptied. There are, however, maximum limits which must be adhered to.

Since the organisms that become established in a river will be those which are best suited to its conditions, sudden and repeated fluctuations in the rate of flow will mean that only those organisms that can withstand the changes will survive. Plants growing in silt deposits on the bed of a stream will be destroyed when the silt is washed away by a sudden increase in flow. When the flow falls, organisms which are dependent on a high dissolved oxygen concentration will die if the river reverts to a series of near-stagnant pools.

7.4.5 Substances causing taste, odour and colouration

Very low concentrations of some chemical compounds will produce unpleasant tastes and *odours*, or will taint the flesh of fish living in water contaminated by them. Interaction between substances may produce tastes which are apparent at concentrations well below those at which either substance is individually detectable. An 'antiseptic' taste of chlorinated tap water is obvious if the raw water supply contains phenols, since this results in the formation of chlorophenols. (Phenolic compounds can occur naturally in lowland rivers.) Unpleasant tastes and smells, usually earthy or sulphurous in nature, can also occur naturally from decaying vegetation.

The ecological effect of colour will depend theoretically on its light-absorptive properties in relation to the spectral requirements of algae and plants. Many rivers are naturally coloured (e.g. those draining peat are light brown) and yet are able to support biota, including trout. The ecological effects of colour are usually minimal compared with other factors.

7.5   Biological pollutants

These are organisms which may be harmful to other forms of life. The rest of this section considers the main types of organisms that are regarded as water-borne pollutants.

7.5.1   Pathogenic bacteria

Besides the bacteria found naturally in river water and essential for the natural cycle of nutrients, there may be other bacteria which are less desirable. They are the pathogenic bacteria which can cause disease in a variety of organisms, including humans. Since the presence of pathogenic bacteria is generally due to the activities of humans, it constitutes a form of pollution. Non-pathogenic bacteria, by definition, are harmless and, indeed, can be beneficial and form an essential part of the aquatic ecosystem.

A possible source of pathogenic bacteria is raw sewage. Effluents from sewage treatment works contain some pathogenic bacteria, but in far smaller numbers than in incoming sewage since the sewage treatment processes will generally eliminate more than 99% of them. Since pathogenic bacteria are accustomed to human body temperature (i.e. about 37 °C) they do not flourish in river water and die off relatively quickly. For example, 99% of *typhoid* bacteria (Figure 56a) present in contaminated river water are said to be destroyed if the river water is simply stored for seven days. Part of the removal process is due to the activities of predators (hence pathogenic bacteria can survive for longer periods in clean water).

7.5.2   The coliform organisms

Coliforms are non-pathogenic bacteria, often of intestinal origin. The coliform *Escherichia coli* (*E. coli*; Figure 56b) is present in the intestines of humans and other mammals. Its presence in water implies that human pathogens from faeces may also be present. *Escherichia coli* is a rod-shaped faecal coliform about 0.5 µm × 2–3 µm in size. The species usually present in humans is harmless and occurs consistently in faeces in far greater numbers than pathogenic bacteria. There are other strains, such as *E. coli* 0157H, which are pathogenic. These have been found in partially cooked meat and have led to deaths (as happened in Scotland in 1997). The presence of *E. coli* in water in concentrations as low as 10 cells per litre can readily be demonstrated within 18 to 48 hours of taking a sample. At such a low concentration of coliform organisms, the possibility of sufficient numbers of associated pathogenic bacteria being present to cause disease is negligible, even supposing that any are present at all, which need not be the case.

If *E. coli* is present in a water sample, this indicates faecal pollution and the possible presence of pathogenic types that often occur in the intestines as well; the absence of *E. coli* from a sample shows that the chances of faecal contamination of the water, and therefore of pathogens being present, are negligible. Thus the presence or absence of *E. coli* in a water sample provides an important indicator of pollution and public health.

7.5.3   Faecal streptococci

The faecal streptococci consist of the species *Streptococcus faecalis* (Figure 56c) *Str. faecium, Str. durans, Str. equinus* and *Str. bovis.* They are approximately 1 µm in diameter and occur in chains of varying length. They die fairly quickly outside their host and so their presence is indicative of recent pollution.

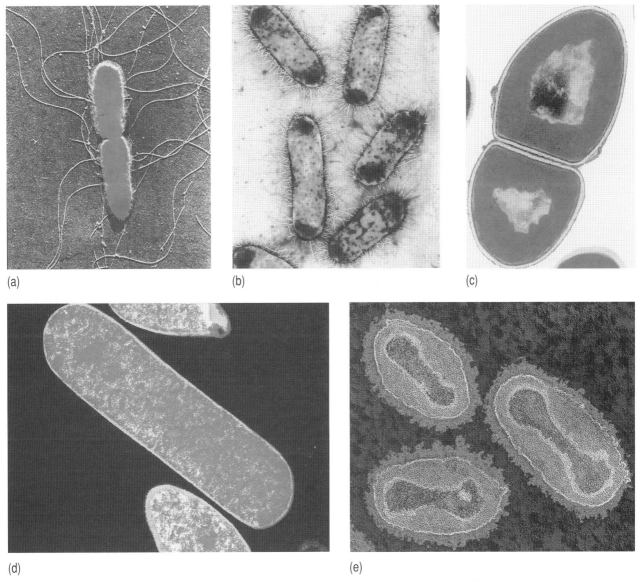

Figure 56 A range of micro-organisms: (a) *Salmonella typhi*; (b) *Escherichia coli*; (c) *Streptococcus faecalis*; (d) *Clostridium perfringens*; (e) smallpox viruses (*Variola*)

7.5.4 *Clostridium perfringens*

This is an anaerobic organism (Figure 56d) present in the intestines of humans and animals. While harmless in the intestine, it is a human pathogen, causing gas gangrene. The cells are rod-shaped (about 5 μm × 1 μm) and can form endospores.

Endospores, or spores, as they are commonly referred to, are hardy structures that certain bacteria can form into when their environment becomes unfavourable for growth. The purpose of the endospore is survival. A spore is very resistant to heat and desiccation and can survive for many years at ordinary temperatures. When the environmental conditions are favourable for growth, it germinates to form a normal single vegetative cell.

This ability leads to *Cl. perfringens* being present in unchanged numbers long after other faecal indicators have died out. Its presence in the absence of *E. coli* indicates intermittent faecal contamination.

7.5.5 Viruses

These are other forms of life which may be harmful to humans and animals. Viruses can grow only in living cells. A smallpox virus is illustrated in Figure 56(e). There are over 120 distinct known types of human pathogenic viruses.

Most viruses are able to remain viable in water at low temperatures, provided there is some organic matter present. Once excreted, the number of viruses cannot increase since they only multiply within living susceptible cells.

The main threat comes from human enteric viruses which are produced by infected persons and excreted faecally, consequently contaminating sewage effluent which may be discharged into a river. If the river water is abstracted and treated for drinking purposes the viruses will often not be removed. (It is possible for a person to be susceptible to only one viral particle.) Some enteric viruses are more resistant than coliforms to chlorination.

The four water-borne viruses which have caused illness in western Europe are polio virus, hepatitis virus A, norwalk virus and rota virus. The presence of any enteric virus can be taken as an indication of the possible presence of other harmful viruses. In temperate climates, enteric viruses occur at peak levels in sewage during late summer and early autumn. The exception is the hepatitis virus which increases in the colder months.

7.5.6   Protozoa

There have been several outbreaks of protozoal infections from water in the UK in past years. An outbreak of giardiasis occurred in Bristol in 1985 and cryptosporidiosis occurred in Ayrshire in 1988, and in Oxford and Swindon in 1989. In 1989 *Cryptosporidium* affected 7904 people in England and Wales and 1243 in Scotland. The sources have been traced to farm run-off and sewage from infected populations entering rivers and groundwaters. There was a major incident in Perthshire, Scotland, with up to 200 people affected in April 2005, and in November that year 231 people were taken ill with cryptosporidiosis in North Wales.

Cryptosporidium causes an influenza-like illness lasting about two weeks. The main symptoms are diarrhoea, abdominal pains, fever and nausea. Some people can act as carriers of *Cryptosporidium*.

The seriousness of the *Cryptosporidium* outbreaks in the UK led to the setting up of a committee to investigate the sources of *Cryptosporidium*, its effects and methods for its removal. The findings were published as the Badenoch Reports in 1990 and in 1995. Then in 1995 there was another major outbreak, in Torbay. This led to new regulations being brought into force in 1999 concerning the quality of treated water. A legal limit of less than one oocyst (type of egg cell) in 10 litres of water was set.

Cryptosporidium and *Giardia* can be trapped by membrane filtration or slow sand filters in drinking water treatment. Other types of filters such as wound fibre filters are also employed. Chlorination and UV radiation at normal doses are ineffective against these organisms.

7.5.7   Helminths

Helminths or parasitic worms can also cause ill health to humans. Infection occurs through ingestion of the helminth eggs which may be present in food; for example, helminth eggs may be present in the meat of cattle grazing on land contaminated by poorly treated sewage effluent or sludge.

7.5.8   Other biological pollutants

Many of the forms of pollution previously mentioned may also be considered as biological pollutants, e.g. algal blooms and the growth of sewage fungus. Examples that are more clearly of this type of pollution are the many species of blue-green algae which produce substances toxic to terrestrial organisms and which can impart tastes and odours to water.

Another concern which has arisen in recent years is the problem of endocrine disrupters. These are chemicals that cause genital abnormalities in fish. Natural chemicals such as oestrogens concentrated in sewage treatment are thought to be responsible. The situation is exacerbated by the use of contraceptive pills which raise the concentration of oestrogen in a woman's body 1000-fold. Synthetic chemicals such as alkyl phenol ethoxylates (used in the wool scouring industry) are also known to cause oestrogenic effects. Oestrogens cause male fish to produce a female egg protein called vitellogenin and to develop abnormal sex organs containing egg cells. The oestrogenic effects in fish can be measured by estimating the levels of vitellogenin in the specimens. Researchers have found that the effects of natural oestrogens are quickly dissipated while those of the synthetic chemicals are persistent due to their poor biodegradability and their accumulation in sediments.

In March 2000, the Environment Agency published a strategy on these substances. It produced a list with two categories of substances (Table 17). The first category comprises substances already subject to statutory control but which will be subject to further reduction when authorizations for discharge come up for renewal.

Discharges of substances in the second group are to be 'reduced'. Environmental quality standards for total steroids (covering the natural oestrogens 17ß-oestradiol and oestrone, and the synthetic ethinyl oestradiol) and the alkyl phenols will be developed.

Table 17   Endocrine disrupters being considered by the Environment Agency

Category 1: Substances already under statutory control	
DDT	Endosulfan
Drins	Simazine
Lindane	Trifluralin
PCBs	Demeton-S-methyl
Dioxins and furans	Dimethoate
Tributyl tin	Linuron
Atrazine	Permethrin
Dichlorvos	

Category 2: Substances not under statutory control	
Nonylphenol	Ethinyl oestradiol
Nonylphenol ethoxylates	17ß-oestradiol
Octylphenol	Oestrone
Octylphenol ethoxylates	

Source: Environment Agency (2000) *Endocrine-disrupting Substances in the Environment: The Environment Agency's Strategy,* available online: http://environment-agency.gov.uk/news/

7.5.9   Typical pathogens

Table 18 lists some of the major pathogens that cause disease to humans and which are likely to be found in polluted water. See also *infections, water-borne* in the Set Book.

7.6   Summary

Different pollutants affect the aquatic environment in different ways. While at low concentrations many pollutants (e.g. organic materials, N and P) may be beneficial, at high levels they can adversely affect the ecology of the system. Excess nitrate can be particularly harmful to babies. Many of the toxic pollutants in effluents are synthetic in kind and therefore difficult to biodegrade naturally. The effects of physical pollution on the ecology of a river system can be complex, affecting the feeding and breeding habits of the different species. Biological pollutants can spread disease through water, and also disrupt the ecology. The measurement and control of water quality is therefore of crucial importance in the interests of public health and the maintenance of the environment.

Table 19 gives a summary of the effects of the different pollutants discussed in this chapter.

Table 18 Some of the major pathogens likely to be present in sewage and in faecally polluted streams

Organism	Example	Disease	Remarks
Bacteria	*Vibrio cholerae*	Cholera	Transmitted by sewage and polluted waters in cholera-endemic areas.
	Salmonella typhi	Typhoid fever	Common in sewage and effluents in times of epidemics.
	Salmonella paratyphi	Paratyphoid fever	Common in sewage and effluents in times of epidemics.
	Salmonella spp.	Food poisoning	
	Shigella spp.	Bacillary dysentery	Polluted waters are main source of infection.
	Bacillus anthracis	Anthrax	Found in sewage. Spores resistant to treatment.
	Brucella spp.	Brucellosis – Malta fever in humans. Contagious abortion in sheep, goats and cattle	Normally transmitted by infected milk or by contact. Sewage also suspected.
	Mycobacterium tuberculosis	Tuberculosis	Isolated from sewage and polluted streams. Care needed with sewage and sludge from sanatoria.
	Leptrospira icterohaemorrhagiae	Leptospirosis (Weil's disease)	Carried by sewer rats. Also present in water contaminated by urine from infected animals and humans.
Virus	Polio virus	Poliomyelitis	Exact mode of transmission not yet known. Found in effluents from sewage treatment plants.
Protozoa	*Entamoeba histolytica*	Dysentery	Spread by contaminated waters and sludge used as fertilizer. Common in warm countries.
	Giardia lamblia	Giardiasis	Found in inadequately treated water. Resistant to chlorine and ozone. Can be reduced significantly in number by carefully operated slow sand filters.
	Cryptosporidium spp.	Cryptosporidiosis	Carried by agricultural livestock and infected persons. Unaffected by UV or chlorination but killed by ozone. Can be reduced significantly in number by carefully operated slow sand filters or membrane filters.
Helminths	*Taenia saginata*	Tapeworms	Eggs very resistant, present in sewage sludge and sewage effluents. Danger to cattle on sewage-irrigated land or land manured with sludge.
	Ascaris lumbricoides	Nematode worms	Danger to humans from sewage effluents and dried sludge used as fertilizer.
	Schistosoma haematobium, Schistosoma mansoni	Bilharzia	Carried by water snails in rivers and irrigation ditches in specific regions of the world. Enter humans by direct penetration of skin, or via aquatic plants (e.g. watercress) or fish eaten raw.

Table 19 Classification of pollutants

Pollutant	General effect	Effect on biota	Effect on water supplies	Sources: natural	Sources: result of human activity
Organic (biodegradable wastes)	Increased oxygen demand. Food provided for organisms lower down in food chain	Tolerated if release not too quick, serious if dissolved oxygen (DO) drops too quickly	Increased need of treatment	Run-off and seepage through soil	Domestic sewage; food processing; animal wastes
Endocrine disrupters	Alteration of ecology	Feminization of fish	None ascertained to date	Sewage	Chemical manufacture; intensive farming
Plant nutrients	Excessive plant growth	Secondary demand on DO	Increased need of treatment	Nitrogen cycle	Animal wastes; fertilizers; detergents; industrial wastes
Toxic chemicals (e.g. heavy metals, phenols, PCBs)	Toxic to humans/ animals/plants	Could be lethal	Increased need of treatment or control	Rare	Detergents; pesticides; tanneries; pharmaceuticals; wool scouring; refineries
Acids/alkalis	Lowering/raising of pH. Acids can dissolve heavy metals	Only narrow range of pH tolerable for most plants and animals. Heavy metals toxic	Corrosion	Naturally acid or alkaline rock	Battery, steel, chemical, and textile manufacturing; coal mining
Suspended solids	Reduction in light penetration (turbidity). Blanketing. Introduction of colour	Photosynthesis reduced. Blanketing of benthic plants and animals. Obstruction of gills	Obstruction of filters. Increased need of treatment	Soil erosion; storms; floods	Pulp mills; quarrying
Immiscible liquids	Formation of a layer which could prevent O_2/CO_2 interchange	Reduced DO. Insect breeding affected	Interference with treatment processes	Unlikely	Oil-related activity
Heat	Decrease in DO. Increase in metabolic rate	Possible reduced breeding/growth	None	Unlikely	Power plants; steel mills
Taste, odour and colour-forming compounds	Taste, malodour, colour	Tainting of fish	Increased need of treatment	Peat	Chemical manufacture or processing
Micro-organisms	Pathogenic to humans	None	Increased need of treatment	Animal excrement	Intensive farming

SAQ 38

Which of the following is a true statement concerning the effects of both organic pollution and eutrophication?

A The depletion of oxygen occurs because of an increase in the activities of primary producers in both cases.

B In both cases it is the presence of the plant nutrients (nitrate and phosphate) that causes the death of green plants and depletion of oxygen.

C The difference in the proportion of producers and consumers between organically polluted water and eutrophic waters is negligible.

D A reduction of dissolved oxygen in both cases causes the depletion of species.

E Once the dissolved oxygen content is decreased, only the removal of the offending pollutant can allow an increase in species.

SAQ 39

Which two of the following are true statements?

A Organic pollutants such as domestic sewage cannot cause permanent damage to a watercourse as can toxic pollutants.

B Physical pollutants, especially a temperature rise from 15 °C to 30 °C, can be more damaging to game fish than to coarse fish.

C Effluents from fish farms can be badly polluted. Concern has arisen about these effluents mainly because they contain unconsumed food and faecal matter from fish.

D Substances can be clearly designated as synthetic, natural, toxic or non-toxic.

E Metals which exist as low molecular weight organic complexes are water soluble and as such are able to bioaccumulate by diffusing across biological membranes of organisms.

SAQ 40

Identify the false statements from the following:

A The toxicities of individual chemicals in a mixture can be summed up to give an overall toxicity figure. This is simpler than testing a complex mixture.

B In toxicity tests for a proposed discharge, the most sensitive species in the receiving watercourse should be used as the test organism.

C When suspended solids settle on the river bed, it is only benthic plants that are affected, as the light will not reach the leaves.

D *E. coli* is a species of bacterium that inhabits human intestines and is harmless.

E *Clostridium perfringens* is pathogenic causing gas gangrene but lives in the human gut.

F Control of the discharge of the culprit chemicals from industry will overcome the problem of endocrine disrupters.

SAQ 41

Indicate the causative agent (virus, bacteria, protozoa or helminth) of each of the following diseases:

cholera

poliomyelitis

typhoid

bilharzia

anthrax

cryptosporidiosis

tuberculosis

8   WATER QUALITY TESTS

Methods of analyses have become increasingly sophisticated so that they have very low limits of detection and it is now possible to carry out estimations for elements and compounds at extremely low concentrations, e.g. at micrograms and nanograms per litre. This ability to estimate low concentrations has allowed even stricter standards to be set for pollutants which may be present in water. To carry out analyses for low concentrations with precision and accuracy requires qualified and competent analysts and this is one of the requirements of the 1989 Water Act. It is also necessary to know if variation in the results is due to experimental error or to a real change in water quality. At low concentration levels it can be a difficult decision to make. To try to overcome this problem 'analytical quality control' has been introduced. Laboratories take part in interlaboratory exercises in which they are asked to analyse sample solutions prepared by a given laboratory for certain parameters. Since the instigating laboratory knows the concentration of the samples it is able to judge the quality of the analytical results. Laboratories also run in-house control checks so that they can see if the results of analyses on standard solutions of known concentration vary beyond acceptable limits or standard deviation. Laboratories in the UK aim to prove the quality of their work by being accredited under NAMAS (National Accreditation of Measurement and Sampling) operated by the United Kingdom Accreditation Service.

8.1   Oxygen demand

One of the most important measures of overall water quality is the dissolved oxygen content. Dissolved oxygen is essential to maintain most forms of aquatic life and to allow the decomposition of organic matter, including organic effluents, and thus to ensure the continued existence of rivers, streams and lakes in their natural state and as usable resources. The most significant impact on the oxygen resources of a river is the biodegradation of organic matter. It is this effect which is utilized in the measurement of the oxygen demand of an effluent.

The measurement of the oxygen demand of an effluent requires the determination of dissolved oxygen content. The two methods in general use are:

1   A chemical method, in which the dissolved oxygen in a sample is replaced by its chemical equivalent in free iodine, which can then be measured by reaction with sodium thiosulphate. (You will be carrying out a number of dissolved oxygen estimations by this method in the home experiments.)

2   A method using a detecting probe in which a potential difference is set up between two metal electrodes immersed in electrolyte (a solution that can carry an electrical current). Figure 57 shows the main elements of such a dissolved oxygen probe. When the probe is brought into contact with a sample solution, dissolved oxygen from the solution diffuses through the permeable membrane. The dissolved oxygen reacts by removing electrons from the electrolyte solution at the cathode. The electrons are replaced by a corresponding reaction at the anode where the anode metal goes into solution. These two reactions produce a current in the external circuit; the magnitude of the current is directly proportional to the rates of reaction at the

electrodes which are in turn proportional to the concentration of dissolved oxygen present. Since the probe consumes oxygen, the water near the probe becomes oxygen deficient. Hence the water must be gently stirred to get an accurate reading.

Once a method has been chosen for determining dissolved oxygen, the oxygen demand of an effluent sample can be simply measured as the difference between the initial dissolved oxygen content in the sample and the dissolved oxygen left after the effluent has taken up its required amount of oxygen. So if C_o is the concentration of dissolved oxygen in the sample initially and C_u is the final or 'ultimate' dissolved oxygen concentration after all the oxidizable matter in the sample has reacted, then the ultimate oxygen demand L_u of the effluent sample is given by

$$L_u = C_o - C_u \qquad\qquad (3)$$

We can think of L_u as a measure of the concentration of oxidizable matter present in the sample. By the end of the reaction, all the oxidizable matter has reacted, which causes a reduction in the dissolved oxygen in the sample.

However, things are not quite as simple as Equation (3) suggests. From Table 2, the saturation concentration of dissolved oxygen C_s at 20 °C is 8.99 g m^{-3}. Thus if demand for oxygen exceeds 8.99 g m^{-3}, a C_u value of zero will be recorded. In this event the value of L_u would not truly represent the amount of biodegradable matter in the sample because more dissolved oxygen could have been taken up had there been a sufficient supply.

In many oxygen demand tests, therefore, samples are diluted so that there is at least 2 g m^{-3} dissolved oxygen left in the diluted sample at the end of the reaction. Naturally, with an unknown sample many different dilutions must be tried in the hope that at least one will satisfy the above criterion. This standard procedure is known as the 'dilution method'. A 'blank' comprising only dilution water is also incubated to allow for the oxygen demand of the dilution water.

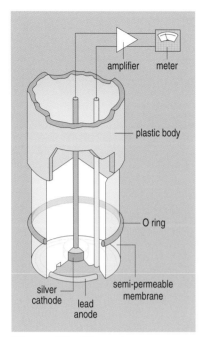

Figure 57   The main components of a dissolved oxygen probe

EXERCISE

An effluent has an ultimate oxygen demand of 50 g m^{-3}. A sample is made up for testing by diluting 1 part effluent by volume with 9 parts clean water by volume.

What is the ultimate oxygen demand of the diluted sample?

ANSWER

When an effluent is diluted with clean water, the ultimate oxygen demand of the resulting mixture is less than that in the original effluent. However, the principle of mass conservation applies to the oxidizable material which is present both before and after dilution, i.e. mass of oxidizable material *before* dilution = mass of oxidizable material *after* dilution.

Mass of material = volume × concentration, so if Lu is the 'concentration' of oxidizable material in the sample after dilution, then the mass balance gives

$$1 \times 50 = (1 + 9)(L_u) \text{ g m}^{-3}$$

$$L_u = 5 \text{ g m}^{-3}$$

which is the ultimate oxygen demand of the diluted sample.

EXERCISE

If the initial concentration of dissolved oxygen in the diluted sample is measured as 8.2 g m^{-3}, what will be the final dissolved oxygen concentration after oxidization is complete?

ANSWER

From Equation (3), where C_u is the final dissolved oxygen concentration,

$$C_u = C_o - L_u$$

$$= 8.2 - 5 \text{ g m}^{-3}$$

$$= 3.2 \text{ g m}^{-3}$$

SAQ 42

An effluent is diluted in the ratio one part effluent to 49 parts clean water by volume. In an oxygen demand test, this diluted sample gives the following results:

$$C_o = 7.6 \text{ g m}^{-3}; \; C_u = 1.3 \text{ g m}^{-3}$$

What is the ultimate oxygen demand:

(a) of the diluted sample;

(b) of the original effluent?

In principle, the measurement of oxygen is straightforward. In practice, the major problem is to know how long to leave the sample to ensure that all the required oxygen has been taken up. One way to find out is to plot the change in dissolved oxygen concentration with time. Figure 58 shows how such a plot might look. At the start of the test, the dissolved oxygen concentration is C_o. As the test proceeds the oxygen concentration drops rapidly at first, but more slowly later. This makes sense if we think about what is happening during the oxidation reaction. At the start, there is a lot of oxidizable material present, so the rate of oxygen uptake is high and the oxygen concentration drops rapidly. Later, after most of the material has been oxidized, the reaction rate is lower and the oxygen concentration drops more slowly.

Does the shape of the curve in Figure 58 look familiar?

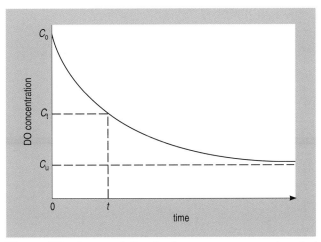

Figure 58   Decay of dissolved oxygen concentration during oxidation reaction

You might recognize that the curve in Figure 58 is very like an *exponential decay curve*. In fact, it is helpful to describe oxygen demand tests by assuming that the rate of oxygen uptake follows this exponential decay behaviour. At any time t, the dissolved oxygen concentration in the sample C_t is given by the following equation:

$$\frac{C_t - C_u}{C_o - C_u} = e^{-kt}$$

(4)

where k is a constant, called the decay constant.

Equation (4) describes the way in which the dissolved oxygen concentration varies with time during the reaction. At the start $t = 0$, and since $e^0 = 1$, Equation (4) becomes $C_t - C_u = C_o - C_u$, in which case $C_t = C_o$.

How long does it take for C_t to drop to C_u according to Equation (4)?

If $C_t = C_u$, then $e^{-kt} = 0$. This can only happen if t is infinitely large. So Equation (4) predicts that the dissolved oxygen concentration never actually falls to the ultimate value C_u. Of course, Equation (4) is just a mathematical model for the oxidation reaction and we cannot expect real reactions to behave precisely in this way. Nevertheless, we might expect to have to leave the sample for a very long time to ensure that the reaction is complete. It would obviously be expedient to set a fixed time after the start of a test at which to measure the oxygen demand of a sample and then standardize on that time.

The most common oxygen demand test for organic pollution is the biochemical oxygen demand (BOD) test, which is standardized on a 5-day reaction time. This test requires measurement of the dissolved oxygen content of a given sample.

SAQ 43

An effluent sample has an initial dissolved oxygen concentration of $8.0\ \text{g m}^{-3}$ and an ultimate dissolved oxygen concentration of $2.3\ \text{g m}^{-3}$. If the decay constant for the oxidation is $0.2\ \text{d}^{-1}$, what is the dissolved oxygen concentration 14 hours after the start of the test? (The unit d^{-1} means reciprocal days; it is usual in oxygen demand tests to measure time in days or fractions of a day.)

8.1.1   The BOD test

The *biochemical oxygen demand* (BOD) test measures the oxygen required by micro-organisms during the biodegradation of an effluent sample. In its simplest form the BOD test is carried out by incubating a sample effluent in a sealed bottle for 5 days at $20\,^{\circ}\text{C}$.

The Royal Commission on Sewage Disposal (set up in 1912) chose an incubation period of 5 days for the BOD test because that is the longest flow time of any British river to the open sea. An incubation temperature of $20\,^{\circ}\text{C}$ was chosen because at that time it was similar to the long-term average summer temperature in Britain). During incubation of the sample in the BOD test, the dissolved oxygen concentration of the sample decreases.

$\text{BOD}_t =$ initial dissolved oxygen $-$ dissolved oxygen after t days

$$= C_o - C_t$$

(5)

For 5 days at 20 °C

$$BOD_5^{20} = C_o - C_5$$

In Europe the 7-day BOD is quite common. This modification frees the analyst from having to come into the laboratory at the weekend to take measurements. The 7-day BOD is also used for analysis of intractable industrial effluents such as those from pulp and paper mills.

$$BOD_7^{20} = C_o - C_7$$

As mentioned earlier, you will be carrying out a BOD test as part of the home experiments. However, instead of incubating the sample for 5 days, you will be monitoring the changing dissolved oxygen concentration over a period of about 24 hours and extrapolating these results to give an estimated BOD_5^{20}.

Figure 59 shows the general form of a graph of BOD for a typical effluent sample incubated for different times. Initially, the BOD rises rapidly as the rate of oxygen uptake by the sample is high. With time the rate of oxygen uptake becomes lower until eventually the sample has been completely biodegraded, having satisfied its required oxygen demand. This is shown by the approach of the BOD curve in Figure 59 to the horizontal dotted line representing the 'ultimate' oxygen demand L_u of the sample.

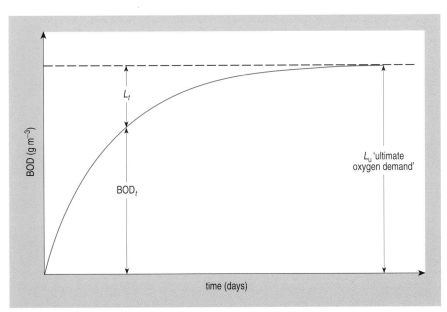

Figure 59 Form of the BOD–time curve

The relationship between the BOD_t at any time t and the ultimate oxygen demand L_u can be expressed as a mathematical model by rearranging Equation (5). Thus:

$$BOD_t = C_o - C_t$$

$$= (C_o - C_u) - (C_t - C_u)$$

$$= (C_o - C_u) \left[1 - \frac{C_t - C_u}{C_o - C_u} \right]$$

But

$$C_o - C_u = L_u$$

and

$$\frac{C_t - C_u}{C_o - C_u} = e^{-kt}$$

Therefore

$$\mathrm{BOD}_t = L_u \left(1 - e^{-kt}\right) \tag{6}$$

The decay constant k in Equation (6) is often called the BOD rate constant and its value will depend on the type of effluent sample under test. Some effluents (e.g. washings from a syrup plant) oxidize very rapidly and have large values of k. Effluents which oxidize slowly have small values of k. Figure 60 shows a series of BOD–time curves for three effluents with the same $L_u = 500$ g m^{-3}, but with different rate constants: $k = 1$ d^{-1}, $k = 0.1$ d^{-1}, and $k = 0.01$ d^{-1}. The values of the 5-day BOD for each of the effluents will show this difference:

(a) $\mathrm{BOD}_5^{20} = 500\left(1 - e^{-5}\right) = 497$ g m^{-3}

(b) $\mathrm{BOD}_5^{20} = 500\left(1 - e^{-0.5}\right) = 197$ g m^{-3}

(c) $\mathrm{BOD}_5^{20} = 500\left(1 - e^{-0.05}\right) = 24$ g m^{-3}

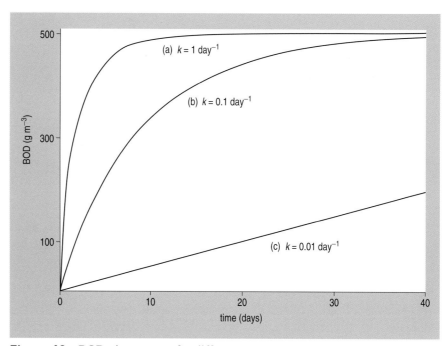

Figure 60   BOD–time curves for different rate constants

EXERCISE

An effluent sample from a whisky distillery has a BOD$_5^{20}$ of 7000 g m^{-3}. Calculate the ultimate oxygen demand (L_u) for a rate constant of 0.3 d^{-1}.

ANSWER

$$\mathrm{BOD}_t^{20} = L_u \left(1 - e^{-kt}\right) \ \text{g m}^{-3}$$

For a 5-day BOD, $t = 5$

$$BOD_5^{20} = L_u \left(1 - e^{-5k}\right) \text{ g m}^{-3}$$

From information given,

$$BOD_5^{20} = 7000 \text{ g m}^{-3} \text{ and } k = 0.3 \text{ d}^{-1}, \text{ i.e.}$$

$$7000 = L_u \left(1 - e^{-5(0.3)}\right) \text{ g m}^{-3}$$

Rearranging the equation,

$$L_u = \frac{7000}{1 - e^{-5(0.3)}} \text{ g m}^{-3}$$

$$= \frac{7000}{0.78} \text{ g m}^{-3}$$

$$= 8974 \text{ g m}^{-3}$$

SAQ 44

A sample of wastewater gave a BOD_5^{20} of 150 gm^{-3}. Calculate the ultimate oxygen demand for a BOD rate constant $k = 0.4$ d^{-1}.

The observed BOD rate constant for many sewage effluents is quoted as $k = 0.4$ d^{-1}. This value actually represents an average degradation rate for the many different kinds of materials present in sewage. Figure 61 shows that the BOD curve for $k = 0.4$ d^{-1} and $L_u = 400$ g m^{-3} (upper curve) can be considered as the summation of the oxygen demand curves of materials, between those that are degraded rapidly like simple sugars ($k = 1$ d^{-1} or greater) and those which are degraded slowly like fats and oils ($k = 0.1$ d^{-1} or less). At any time the total observed oxygen demand expressed as the BOD curve represents the summation of all the individual oxygen demand curves. (Note that only the oxygen demand of the different materials can be added together, not the various rate constants k.)

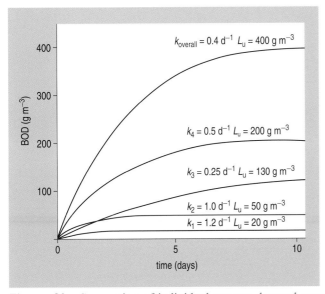

Figure 61   Summation of individual oxygen demand curves

SAQ 45

Use the values of k and L_u from Figure 61 to complete the table below.

Material	BOD_5^{20}	Proportion of ultimate oxygen demand after five days (BOD_5^{20}/L_u)
1		
2		
3		
4		
Overall		

SAQ 46

The experimental results below are from a test in which the BOD of an effluent sample was monitored at regular intervals of time.

BOD (g m^{-3})	0	2.5	4.4	5.8	7.0	8.1
Time t (day)	0	0.5	1.0	1.5	2.0	2.5

(a) Plot the results on a BOD–time graph.

(b) Plot the results in the form BOD_t vs $(1 - e^{-kt})$ assuming a BOD rate constant $k = 0.4$ d^{-1}. Estimate the ultimate oxygen demand of the sample.

(c) Calculate the BOD_5^{20}.

Of course this whole analysis should be considered as a simplified overview. The many reactions occurring in the biological degradation of waste materials include complex series of interlocking mechanisms. The assumption of an exponential relationship is a convenient empirical model to explain gross experimental results.

The BOD test is widely used as the most important indicator of organic pollution. The BOD value forms the basis of discharge standards for effluents and is fundamental to the design and operation of effluent treatment plants. Because the BOD test relies on biological action and is a simulation of the actual processes which occur in a receiving water or in an aerobic treatment plant, it has been adopted universally as the most trustworthy index of organic pollution. However, the test is slow, normally taking five days to yield a result, which does not make it suitable for rapid process control in a wastewater treatment plant. Also, BOD is not a good indicator of industrial pollutants. Industrial wastes are often toxic or inhibiting to the micro-organisms on which the BOD test depends. In some effluents there may not be all the nutrients required for microbial degradation to take place so essential trace elements have to be added. The BOD test is used to determine the oxygen required for the oxidation of carbonaceous material. Oxygen is also used up when ammonia is oxidized to nitrate (nitrification). To prevent this reaction taking place, a chemical such as allylthiourea is used to suppress the nitrifying organisms.

BOD through self-check measurements

This is a simplified means of measuring the BOD. This method utilizes the fact that reduction of the oxygen level in a sample bottle results in a pressure reduction.

Samples of effluent are put in bottles on which a pressure-measuring device with a data logging capability is used as a cap (Figure 62). The microelectronics in the cap can be set to convert pressure reading to residual oxygen. During incubation of the sample, oxygen is used up by micro-organisms degrading the organic pollutants in the effluent. Oxygen from the headspace diffuses into the effluent.

Carbon dioxide generated by the micro-organisms is released into the headspace, and is absorbed by sodium hydroxide pellets in the cap of the bottle.

The net result of the above is a reduction in pressure in the headspace of the sample bottle. Each day a measurement of the headspace air pressure is made. After 5 days, the BOD_5^{20} can be read off directly.

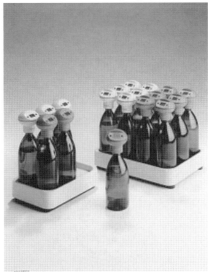 

Figure 62 Apparatus for measuring BOD through the reduction of oxygen level (and hence pressure); the right-hand photograph shows the electronics within the cap

8.1.2 The COD test

Another chemical method frequently used is the ***chemical oxygen demand*** (COD) test. For this test the effluent is boiled for two hours with potassium dichromate ($K_2Cr_2O_2$) and concentrated sulphuric acid in the presence of silver as a catalyst. Because of the extremely strong oxidizing conditions, the COD represents the oxidation of most organic and inorganic compounds. For this reason the COD value is virtually always higher than the BOD_5^{20}. The BOD–COD ratio is often used to assess the treatability of an effluent. If there are two effluents with BOD–COD ratios of 3.5:1 and 2.0:1, the former would be more amenable to biodegradation.

The COD test is quicker than the BOD test, taking about 2 hours, and is often used for routine monitoring of an effluent once its BOD–COD ratio has been established. This is because the BOD–COD ratio remains relatively constant for a particular waste, though it may vary from one waste to another. For domestic sewage, this ratio is about 1:2.

Charges are levied on industrial wastes received and treated by water and sewerage companies on the basis of the COD values of the waters after settlement of suspended solids (see Appendix 2).

Table 20 gives an indication of the values of BOD and COD for different effluents.

Table 20   Typical oxygen demand values in terms of BOD and COD for various effluents

Type of waste	Main pollutants	BOD_5^{20} $(g\ m^{-3})$	COD $(g\ m^{-3})$
Slaughterhouse	suspended solids, protein	2600	4150
Sugar beet	suspended solids, carbohydrate	850	1150
Board mill	suspended solids, carbohydrate	430	1400
Brewery (cask washing)	carbohydrate, protein	550	770
Cannery (meat)	suspended solids, fat, protein	8000	17 940
Chemical plant	suspended solids, extremes of acidity or alkalinity, organic chemicals	500	980
Distillery	suspended solids, carbohydrate, protein	7000	10 000
Domestic sewage	suspended solids, carbohydrate, oil/grease, protein	250	500
Maltings	suspended solids, carbohydrate	1240	1480
Pulp mill	suspended solids, carbohydrate, lignin, sulphate	25 000	76 000
Petroleum refinery	phenols, hydrocarbons, sulphur compounds	850	1500
Tannery	suspended solids, protein, sulphide	2300	5100

SAQ 47

What do you conclude from the BOD–COD ratios of domestic sewage and pulp mill effluent?

8.1.3   Total organic carbon

The total organic carbon (TOC) content of a sample is a measure that is also available. Analysis of the TOC in a sample can be carried out by burning a small amount of the sample with air in a high-temperature (1000 °C) platinum catalyst furnace. The total carbon is first measured by injecting a sample onto the catalyst. The carbon compounds are converted into carbon dioxide, which is measured by an infrared detector. (The carbon dioxide absorbs the infrared radiation, just as in the greenhouse effect that we experience on Earth.)

The inorganic carbon is then measured by adding hydrochloric acid to the sample and sparging it with air (i.e. blowing air through the sample). The resulting carbon dioxide is measured by an infrared detector. The total organic carbon will be total carbon minus inorganic carbon. The TOC test takes only 15 minutes and is useful for testing industrial wastes containing toxins. It is also valuable for measuring organic pollution in highly saline water where the salinity makes other methods unreliable. However, the TOC value does not relate to the biodegradability of the sample. For example, a piece of plastic would register a value of TOC but not of BOD_5^{20}.

The TOC content is a useful means of determining small, adverse changes in drinking water quality which, being small, are not easily detected by BOD measurement.

8.1.4 The Royal Commission Standard

As a result of extensive investigations (see Section 8.1.1) by the Royal Commission on Sewage Disposal in 1912, the 5-day BOD_5^{20} was adopted as a standard measure for regulation of sewage effluent. The standard which was set reflects the ideal of ensuring that the BOD_5^{20} of a receiving water does not exceed 4 g m^{-3}, so that a value of dissolved oxygen above about 5 g m^{-3} is maintained in the stream to support the aquatic ecosystem.

Let

$x = BOD_5^{20}$ of sewage effluent

$y = BOD_5^{20}$ of a river just upstream of an effluent outfall

$z = BOD_5^{20}$ of the river just downstream of the effluent outfall

$n = BOD_5^{20}$ dilution ratio, i.e. ratio of upstream river water flow to effluent flow

Then the principle of mass conservation applies at the outfall point (Figure 63) where the effluent enters the river:

Mass of oxidizable + mass of oxidizable = mass of oxidizable material
material in *effluent*   material *upstream*   *downstream*

(1) (x) $+ (n)(y)$ $= (n+1)z$

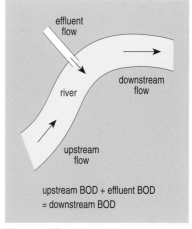

Assuming that the upstream BOD is given by $y = 2$ g m^{-3} (the BOD of clean river water) and that the downstream BOD is $z = 4$ g m^{-3}, then for an eightfold dilution ratio (i.e. $n = 8$)

$$x + (8)(2) = (9)(4) \text{ g m}^{-3}$$

$$x = 20 \text{ g m}^{-3}$$

Hence the BOD_5^{20} of the treated effluent should not exceed 20 g m^{-3}. Similar arguments require that the concentration of suspended solids released should not exceed 30 g m^{-3}.

Figure 63 Mass balance at effluent outfall

This was the basis of the ***Royal Commission Standard***, whereby for effluents discharged to clean streams giving a dilution ratio of at least 8, the BOD_5^{20} should not exceed 20 g m^{-3} and the concentration of suspended solids should not exceed 30 g m^{-3}. This was referred to as the '30/20 standard'. The quality of treated effluent now has to comply with the requirements of the EU Urban Waste Water Treatment Directive passed in 1991. Secondary treatment is normally required for all discharges serving greater than 2000 population equivalent (p.e.) to inland waters and estuaries, and greater than 10 000 p.e. to coastal waters. The limits are shown in Table 21 below. In addition, use-related criteria may be set for watercourses and then more stringent limits may be set.

Table 21   Requirements for discharges from wastewater treatment plants under the Urban Waste Water Treatment Directive

Parameter	Maximum concentration	Minimum percentage reduction
BOD$_5$	25 mg O$_2$ l^{-1}	70–90
COD	125 mg O$_2$ l^{-1}	75
Suspended solids	35 mg l^{-1}	90
Total phosphorus (discharges to sensitive areas)	1 mg P l^{-1a} 2 mg P l^{-1b}	80 80
Total nitrogen	10 mg N l^{-1a} 15 mg N l^{-1b}	70–80 70–80

a, >100 000 p.e.; b, 10 000–100 000 p.e.

Routine monitoring of river water (by the Environment Agency in England and Wales, by the Scottish Environment Protection Agency in Scotland, and by the Environment and Heritage Service in Northern Ireland) includes measurements of the temperature (taken at the time of sampling), pH value, dissolved oxygen, amount of suspended and total solids, and alkalinity. If the presence of pollution due to sewage effluent is known or suspected, tests for ammonia, nitrates, nitrites, chlorides, phosphates and organic matter would also be made. Other substances (e.g. toxic metals, oil or particular organic compounds such as pesticides) might be measured if the water is polluted directly with industrial or farm wastes, or with effluent from a plant treating sewage which has been mixed with industrial waste.

Analyses are not only tailored to the source of the sample, but also to the standards set for the water or effluent. Special tests may be necessary if the water is to be used for a particular purpose, for which specific standards have been set. A typical example would be the measurement of iron and manganese in water for textile processing, which requires water free of these elements. For water intended for potable use, other parameters such as hardness, turbidity, colour and the detection of coliform organisms would be important. Salinity is another parameter, measured in groundwater intended for irrigation.

8.2   Estimation of physical, chemical and microbiological components

8.2.1   Temperature

Temperature in °C or °F can be recorded using mercury-in-glass thermometers. For robustness in the field, however, metallic temperature probes are preferred. Equipped with digital readout, these are convenient to use.

8.2.2   pH value

pH is usually measured using an ion-selective probe which has been calibrated using buffers (usually at pH 4 and pH 7). The temperature of the solution being analysed has to be measured first and this value is used in setting up the probe. (The home experiments will give you practical experience with a pH probe.) Titration can also be used. A third method, often used for rapid measurements, is the use of chemical-impregnated paper strips which develop a colour which can then be compared with a colour-coded standard strip. You may be familiar with litmus paper and the 'litmus test'. Chemical strips are a variation of these.

8.2.3 Suspended solids

The suspended solids present in a river can reduce light penetration and may even smother organisms on the river bed. The quantity of suspended solids is estimated gravimetrically – by filtering a given volume of water and measuring the dry weight of solids present after all the water in the filtered solids has evaporated in an oven. The concentration of suspended solids is expressed in $g\ m^{-3}$.

8.2.4 Dissolved solids and salinity

The concentration of dissolved solids can affect the ecology of a particular site, and also affect the usefulness of a water supply for humans, animals and plants. The dissolved solids content of a water sample can be estimated gravimetrically but is more usually estimated by measurement of the electrical conductivity of the water sample. The electrical conductivity (in mmho cm^{-1} or mS cm^{-1}, millisiemens per cm) is measured using a conductivity meter and this is converted (by multiplying with an appropriate factor) to an approximate value of the dissolved solids concentration in $g\ m^{-3}$. Where the concentration of dissolved solids is high (above, say, 10 000 $g\ m^{-3}$), the term 'salinity' is used: e.g. we refer to the salinity of sea water, rather than to its dissolved solids content.

Conductivity is inversely proportional to resistance. Hence the use of 'mho' which is the reverse of 'ohm', the unit of electrical resistance.

8.2.5 Total solids

The total solids content of a water sample (made up of the sum of suspended solids and dissolved solids) is estimated by gravimetric means by evaporating a given volume of sample, and weighing the residue. The result is expressed in $g\ m^{-3}$.

8.2.6 Hardness

Water hardness is caused by the presence of calcium and magnesium salts as we saw in Section 2.4. High levels of hardness inhibit the formation of lather with soap and can cause scaling in water systems. By contrast, hardness has been shown to be beneficial to health, reducing the onset of cardiovascular disease (see Section 2). Hardness can be measured by titration, and the results are expressed in units of $g\ CaCO_3\ m^{-3}$. (You will be trying out this method in your home experiment on hardness.)

8.2.7 Alkalinity

You will recall from Section 3.3 that *alkalinity* of a water is a measure of its capacity to neutralize acids. It is due to the presence of alkaline substances such as bicarbonates, carbonates, hydroxides, and the salts of weak acids such as borates, silicates and phosphates. Such substances act as buffers to resist a drop in pH resulting from acid addition. In polluted water, ammonia and the salts of weak acids such as ethanoic acid, propionic acid, and hydrosulphuric acid may also be present, contributing to alkalinity. It is also an important test parameter in a number of industrial water uses, notably in boiler water treatment. Boilers and steam-generating plant are normally operated under conditions of high alkalinity in order to minimize corrosion. Alkalinity is measured by titration and is expressed in units of $g\ CaCO_3\ m^{-3}$.

8.2.8   Ammonia

Ammonia occurs as a breakdown product of nitrogenous material and is harmful to fish and other forms of aquatic life. It can be measured using a colour comparator. Reagents are added to the water sample and the colour that develops is compared with the colour of glass which has the colour of a solution of known concentration of the substance under investigation. This method can easily be used on site. A paper colour chart can be used in a similar way. (You will be using one in your home experiment on river water analysis for ammonia, nitrite and nitrate.) Other methods include using an *ion-selective electrode* specific for ammonium ions. Values are usually expressed in terms of the nitrogen content in the form of ammonium ions (i.e. g NH_4^+–N m^{-3}, grams of nitrogen present). This can be converted to the ammonium concentration since 14 g of N gives rise to 18 g of ammonium ions. Ammonium content can also be measured by titration and spectroscopy (determination of the absorption of light).

8.2.9   Nitrites

Nitrites can be found in rivers as intermediates in the conversion of ammonia to nitrate. (Nitrites are produced by the bacterium *Nitrosomonas* in biological nitrification.) Nitrites are harmful to fish and other aquatic organisms. They can be measured using a colour comparator, colour chart or spectroscopy. Values are expressed in g NO_2^-–N m^{-3}.

8.2.10   Nitrates

Nitrates enter water sources from the breakdown of natural vegetation, the excess use of inorganic fertilizer, and from the oxidation of nitrogen compounds in domestic and industrial effluents. Excess nitrate levels can lead to eutrophication in waterways, and cause methaemoglobinaemia in infants. Nitrates can be measured using a colour comparator (or a colour chart), an ion-selective electrode, by titration or by spectroscopy. Results are usually expressed in g NO_3^-–N m^{-3}.

8.2.11   Phosphates

Inorganic phosphates contribute to eutrophication. Their presence also indicates the possibility of contamination by sewage. Measurement is by colour comparator or spectroscopy, with the results in g PO_4^{3-}–P m^{-3}.

8.2.12   Chlorides

Almost all the chloride we consume in the form of table salt (sodium chloride) ends up in sewage (about 1% of urine is sodium chloride). The concentration of chloride ions is unaffected during sewage treatment. Thus the detection of chloride in a river can indicate pollution by sewage or treated sewage. It can sometimes be that road run-off in winter contributes salt, so one has to be a little cautious in arriving at conclusions. Chlorides, being present in sea water, are also used to detect the occurrence of seawater intrusion into aquifers near the coast. Chlorides are corrosive and their monitoring is vital in the prevention of corrosion. Measurement of chloride concentration is by titration with the results expressed in g Cl^- m^{-3}.

8.2.13   Metals

Metal ions can have a range of effects on water: some (e.g. zinc) impart taste and turbidity, while others (such as the *heavy metals*) make it toxic. In the laboratory, atomic absorption spectrophotometry can be used to quantify metals present in water (the method uses light of a specific wavelength absorbed by the metal species to give an indication of its concentration). In the field, colour comparators are commonly used for several metals of concern. The concentrations of the metals, usually being low, are expressed in mg m^{-3}.

8.2.14 Oil

The presence of oil on water can affect the rate of oxygen transfer into the water body. Oil can also cause taste, odour and toxicity in water. It is extracted using organic solvents and then quantified using infrared and ultraviolet spectroscopy, and expressed in units of g oil per m^3.

8.2.15 Pesticides

Increased use of pesticides has led to their appearance in run-off waters and consequently in rivers. Limits on pesticide levels in sources used for drinking water have been formulated by the EU. The measurement of pesticide levels requires sophisticated chromatographic equipment coupled with a mass spectrometer. The concentration of individual pesticides is measured, in g m^{-3}.

8.2.16 Phenols

Phenols are toxic to aquatic organisms. They also impart odour and taste to water. As mentioned in Section 7.4, this can be exacerbated when chlorination takes place and chlorophenols are formed. Phenols can be measured by titration, or by spectroscopy, with the results in g phenol m^{-3}.

8.2.17 Radiation

Radiation can lead to cancer, and there are strict guidelines on the emission of radioactive compounds. As mentioned in Section 2.4.2, a limit exists as regards tritium. Tritium levels are measured by chemical analysis. Essentially, the water sample is distilled after addition of potassium permanganate. This ensures that only tritium is carried away in the vapour. A sample of the distillate is then mixed with a scintillation solution. This is a solution that emits light upon receiving radiation. The tritium emits beta particles and these cause the scintillation solution to emit light, which is then measured with a liquid scintillation spectrometer. The results are related back to a graph giving the radiation levels for standard solutions, and the radiation level of the water sample is then ascertained. The results are expressed in becquerels per litre (Bq l^{-1}).

8.2.18 Odour, colour and turbidity

Physical aspects such as odour, colour and turbidity affect the acceptability of the water, regardless of their possible health effects. The presence of specific substances may be indicated by their odours, although the lowest concentration of a substance detectable in this way varies widely (Table 22). Odours can be measured by sensory methods and specific odorant concentrations can be measured by instrumental methods. It has been shown that under carefully controlled conditions the sensory measurements of odours by the human olfactory system can provide meaningful and reliable information. Therefore, the sensory method is now used most often to measure the odours emanating from wastewater treatment facilities. In this method, a panel of human test subjects is exposed to a sample of the odorous air which is progressively diluted with odour-free air, until 50% of the panellists cannot detect any odour. The number of dilutions to this *odour threshold* value is reported as the threshold number. The threshold number may also be called the number of odour units (see Block 6: *Air quality management*).

Table 22   Odour thresholds of some compounds in sewage and trade wastes

Compound	Approximate concentration having faint odour $(g\ m^{-3})$	Odour	Typical sources
Ammonia, NH_3	0.037	pungent, alkaline	coal carbonization, farm wastes
Chlorine, Cl_2	0.010		chemical processes, swimming pools
Chlorophenol, ClC_6H_4OH	0.00018	'medicinal'	chlorination of water containing phenol
Hydrogen sulphide, H_2S	0.0011	rotten eggs	anaerobic decomposition
Skatole, C_9H_9N	0.0012	faecal, nauseating	raw sewage
Sulphur dioxide, SO_2	0.009	pungent, acid	chemical processes, during striking of a match

Following cases of spillage or ingress of solvents into raw water in rivers and their subsequent passage into supply, in some water treatment plants 'smell bells' are used to monitor raw and final (chlorinated) water. The water sample is disinfected by UV for operator safety and heated to 60 °C (to volatilize organics for odour detection) and then sprayed into a bell jar. Any smell present can be detected. Operators are given sensory training and are made familiar with compounds whose tastes and/or odours are representative of those that cause problems at the treatment works. This enables any contamination to be rapidly dealt with, preventing unacceptable water going into the supply system.

The *true* colour of water (that which excludes the effect of any scattering of light due to suspended solids) depends on the substances dissolved in it but this can be modified to an *apparent* colour resulting from the effect of both suspended and dissolved material. Large amounts of organic material impart greenish, yellowish or brownish colours to water. The apparent colour of water may be measured by filtering a sample through a 0.45-μm filter and comparing it with the colours of solutions of a known standard chemical composition. A widely used standard for such colour grading is the **Hazen** scale, one Hazen colour unit being the colour produced by $1\ g\ m^{-3}$ platinum (as chloroplatinic acid) in the presence of $2\ g\ m^{-3}$ cobaltous chloride. Alternatively the filtered sample can be analysed using spectrophotometry with light of 400 nm wavelength, and the absorbance reading related to the Hazen scale. Colour is pH-dependent, normally, and so this has to be recorded too.

Absorbance is the capacity of a material to absorb light of a specified wavelength.

Turbidity gives a rough indication of the quantity of undissolved matter in water and is easily measured; hence it is an important initial test. Many types of analyses were used in the past. The presently preferred method is to determine turbidity by measuring the scattering of light of a specified wavelength in a laboratory instrument. The sample is put into a small measuring cell. Turbidity is quoted in nephelometric turbidity units (NTU).

8.2.19 The coliform organisms

Coliforms are deemed to be present in a water sample if bacterial growth occurs in a medium containing bile salts, and if the sample is shown to be capable of fermenting lactose within 48 hours at 37 °C with the production of acid and gas. The production of gas (CO_2) can be shown by the use of Durham tubes (miniature test tubes which can trap any gas produced).

This is referred to as a 'presumptive test', based on the presumption that all the tubes which show acid and gas production contain coliform organisms.

A confirmatory test for *E. coli* is normally carried out after coliforms are found in the presumptive test. A loopful of culture from each positive tube in the presumptive test is transferred to each of two tubes, one containing Tryptone Water and the other typically Lactose Ricinoleate Broth. Both tubes are incubated in a water bath at 44.5 °C for 24 hours. *E. coli* is the only coliform that produces indole from tryptophan, and ferments lactose at 44.5 °C. To confirm the presence of *E. coli* in a presumptive positive tube, both tubes must give a positive reaction.

An alternative confirmatory test is to plate out a loopful of culture from each presumptive positive tube on Eosin Methylene Blue Agar. After incubation for 24 hours at 37 °C, colonies of *E. coli* exhibit a green metallic sheen.

Membrane techniques are often used to quantify faecal coliforms. A measured volume of sample, or an appropriate dilution of it, is filtered through a 0.45-μm pore size membrane filter. Micro-organisms are retained on the filter surface which is then incubated in a petri dish on a medium containing lactose. The visible colonies which develop (Figure 64) after 24 hours incubation at 44.5 °C are counted and expressed in terms of the number present in 100 ml of the original sample. Samplers have been developed which comprise 0.45-μm membranes bonded to absorbent pads containing dehydrated nutrient media (Figure 65). Each sampler (called a dipslide) is contained in a transparent plastic case. The entire assembly is sterilized at manufacture. When the dipslide is immersed in the water to be analysed, it absorbs 1 ml of sample. The dipslide is then put back into its plastic case and the case is put into an incubator maintained at 44.5 °C. After 24 hours, the faecal coliform colonies that develop are counted. The surface of the dipslide has grid squares to ease the process of counting.

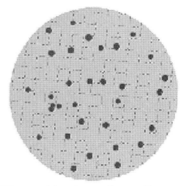

Figure 64   A membrane filter with bacterial colonies

An older method of enumerating faecal coliforms is by the multiple tube fermentation technique. This involves adding measured volumes of sample to sets of sterile tubes containing a liquid medium with lactose and bile salts and incubating at 44 °C for 24 hours. The production of gas (seen by its presence in the Durham tube) indicates that faecal coliforms are present (a positive reaction). The numbers of tubes showing positive and negative reactions are recorded and an estimate of the most probable number (MPN) of faecal coliforms present in the original sample is obtained by using appropriate statistical tables relating to the volumes of sample inoculated.

Figure 65   A membrane-type sampler (courtesy of Millipore (UK) Ltd)

A further development has been the manufacture of portable battery-powered incubators. These enable analysis for faecal coliforms to be undertaken in remote locations where laboratory facilities are not at hand.

There are also simple 'colour change' test kits for coliforms. These consist of standard bacterial media with enzymes that react to the presence of certain chemicals in the bacteria. One millilitre of the sample water is put into a sterilized bottle and a sachet of media is added. After 18–24 hours of incubation, the presence of coliforms will be shown by a colour change. Faecal coliforms will be indicated by fluorescence. A special counting tray can be used to estimate the numbers of bacteria present.

Other coliform organisms, closely related to *E. coli*, can also occur in water, especially under tropical conditions. They need not be of faecal origin, but their presence indicates the existence of some pollution, even though at the time of sampling typically faecal organisms were not present. *E. coli* itself also occurs in the faeces of organisms other than humans.

8.2.20   Faecal streptococci

With the MPN method, an incubation period of 5 days is required for *Streptococcus* using Glucose Azide Broth. The tubes are incubated for a maximum period of 72 hours at 37 °C. As soon as acidity is observed in a tube by a colour change (purple to yellow) of the pH indicator in the medium, three loopfuls of the culture are transferred to a fresh tube of the same medium. These tubes are incubated in a water bath at 44 °C for 48 hours. Tubes showing acidity at this temperature are deemed to contain faecal streptococci and are used to calculate the MPN.

The confirmatory test for faecal streptococci involves plating out a loopful of culture from a positive second stage MPN tube, onto MacConkey's Agar. Minute magenta-coloured colonies should be formed after incubation at 37 °C for 24 hours.

8.2.21   *Clostridium perfringens*

A two-stage MPN technique is generally used to enumerate *Cl. perfringens* in water. The sample is heated to 75–80 °C in a water bath and held at this temperature for 10–15 minutes.

Different volumes of sample, when cool, are used to inoculate Differential Reinforced Clostridial Broth. These are transferred to screw-capped bottles containing double-strength medium. The bottles are topped with single-strength medium to leave only a small air space. The cap is screwed on tightly to ensure sufficiently anaerobic conditions. The medium also contains a reducing agent.

After incubation for 48 hours at 37 °C, bottles containing clostridia turn black, due to the precipitation of iron sulphides resulting from the reaction between iron salts in the medium and the sulphite produced by the action of the organisms on the sulphate in the medium. Each positive black bottle is then examined for the presence of *Cl. perfringens,* since blackening can be produced by any clostridium.

On Egg Yolk Agar, all strains of *Cl. perfringens* produce zones of opalescence round their colonies and this fact is used to confirm the presence of this organism.

8.2.22   Viruses

The detection and measurement of viruses is a complex and time-consuming operation, and hence this is not routinely undertaken. It is, however, carried out when disease outbreaks occur. A representative sample is first acquired and the viruses concentrated through a technique such as absorption to, and removal (elution) from, a microporous filter. The concentrated viruses can then be identified using sensitive biological assays to detect viral genetic material or protein. This test involves the 'polymerase chain reaction' (PCR) and takes only a few hours. If virus particles are detected, quantification using tissue culture techniques and plaque formation (where areas of cell destruction in a tissue culture monolayer preparation are measured) is employed. This process can take about a week!

Virus detection poses several difficulties. Viruses are very small in size (20–100 nm), they are often at very low concentrations, and they can be of varied types. They are also inherently unstable as biological entities. To compound matters, the various dissolved and suspended impurities in water and wastewater can interfere with the analytical procedures to detect and quantify viruses. The results of assays for viruses are expressed in number of plaque-forming units (PFU) per unit volume (e.g. 5 PFU per litre).

8.3   Toxicity testing

As mentioned in Section 7.3.1, toxicity-based consents are seen as an effective way of protecting the environment.

The number of chemicals in the market is an ever-increasing figure. Further, the effects of these chemicals on the environment are not always known – it is said that environmental quality standards exist for only 0.1% of the chemicals currently registered!

In conventional toxicity testing, organisms are exposed to different dilutions (0–100%) of a chemical under standard conditions in a laboratory. Table 23 gives an indication of the species at different trophic levels which can be used for freshwater and marine/estuarine environments.

Table 23   Species of organisms commonly used in toxicity testing

	Fresh water	Marine/estuarine
Trophic level 1	Selenastrum (alga)	Skeletonema (alga)
Trophic level 2	Daphnia magna (crustacean)	Oyster embryo larvae (Crassostrea)
Trophic level 3	Juvenile trout	Juvenile turbot

For EC_{50} determinations, the accepted length of time of exposure of a test organism is 48 hours. This makes the assessment of the impact of a sample a very long process, especially when one takes into account the time taken to prepare the sample and process the data. There is also the complication that the test organisms may not be available when the test is required. Further, the sample (of, say, river water) tested will of necessity be a 'grab sample' and this may not be representative of the true situation.

EC_{50}: the concentration of the effluent at which 50% inhibition or elimination occurs compared with the control.

In order to overcome the above problems, on-line toxicity measuring devices have been developed. These can use bacteria, algae, marine invertebrates or fish. The devices provide a real-time result for the effect of a chemical or an effluent. They can be installed at potential 'trouble spots' and act as an early warning system should a pollution event occur.

Some toxicity measuring methods are described below.

8.3.1   Microtox™

This test utilizes the marine bacterium *Vibrio fischeri,* which is luminous. When exposed to a toxic sample, the amount of light emitted diminishes. A measure of the diminution of the light is a direct assessment of the toxicity of the sample. The test organism is supplied in freeze-dried form and thus has to be reconstituted for the test, with sterile diluent and chemicals (which are also supplied).

8.3.2   Amtox™

Amtox is an on-line nitrification inhibition monitor which uses nitrifying bacteria immobilized in a polyvinyl alcohol matrix. The bacteria are held in an aerated reactor at 30 °C and pH 6.5–8.5 (for optimum nitrification conditions). The sample requiring testing is added to the reactor where a built-in ammonia probe measures the conversion of ammonia to nitrate by recording the residual ammonia in the reactor. This provides an indication of inhibition or death of the bacteria and, hence, the toxicity of the sample.

The Amtox system has been applied to the River Trent catchment (Figure 66) in order to provide an early warning system for the drinking water abstraction point on the River Trent at Shardlow.

The River Tame discharges into the River Trent upstream of the abstraction point, after flowing through a highly urbanized catchment vulnerable to a wide variety of pollutants. In addition, Minworth Sewage Works, one of the largest in Europe, discharges into the River Tame after treating a range of industrial effluents.

A chain of Amtox monitors have been put in place. The first is at the inlet of the sewage works at Minworth (point a, Figure 66). This provides important information to the plant operators on the treatability of the incoming sewage.

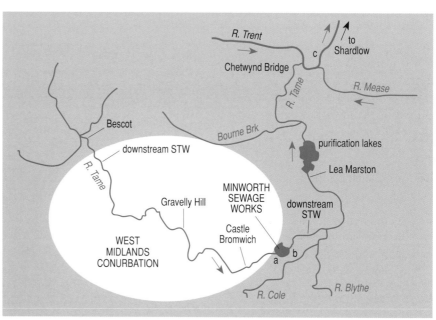

Figure 66   The River Trent catchment

The second monitor (point b, Figure 66) at the treated sewage discharge point indicates whenever potentially toxic compounds are discharged into the River Tame, thus providing an early warning for the abstraction point on the River Trent. The third monitor (point c, Figure 66) above the abstraction point on the River Trent ensures that any remaining toxicity passing through into the River Trent is identified and abstraction halted, if necessary.

Figure 67 shows a sample plot from the Amtox monitors placed on this river system. The trace line for the monitor upstream of the Minworth discharge on the River Tame (used as reference) shows no inhibition and, therefore, no toxicity, whereas downstream of the Minworth discharge, nitrification inhibition is apparent, showing that toxicity is present within the River Tame. The final line, however, is taken from the River Trent Amtox, placed nearer the drinking water abstraction point at Shardlow. Additional monitors are needed downstream to verify any toxic readings. Without this third Amtox, abstraction may have been stopped unnecessarily, based on the result from the monitor on the Minworth discharge.

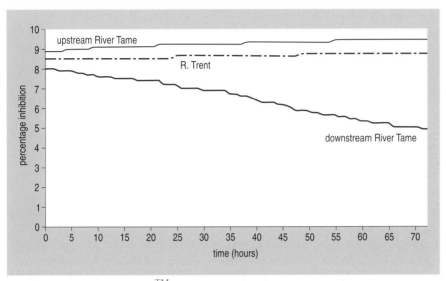

Figure 67   Sample Amtox^{TM} traces from the Rivers Tame and Trent

8.3.3   Fish monitors

Trout are kept in tanks in temperature-controlled rooms to test the quality of water, usually from an intake point. The breathing rates of the fish are measured every minute. By comparing these data with historical breathing rates, conclusions can be drawn as to the quality of the water. This method of monitoring water quality is not totally reliable.

SAQ 48

State whether the following statements are true or false, and give reasons for your answers.

A   Where chemical tests such as hardness, pH value and chloride concentration can be carried out, physical tests such as colour and turbidity need not be performed because physical tests do not measure true pollutants.

B   An analyst could distinguish river water from groundwater simply by measuring the chloride concentration.

C   Hardness, pH value, acidity and alkalinity are related to each other in water possessing bicarbonate hardness.

D   The Hazen scale is useful for measuring the concentrations of specific substances in water.

E   Odour detection and control is important in sewage treatment but in water treatment odour tests are a luxury.

SAQ 49

Which of the following tests (A–E) would be most useful in initially characterizing the organic matter in water polluted with: (a) dairy wastes; (b) wastes from a petroleum refinery?

A   Dissolved oxygen

B   BOD

C   TOC

D   pH

E   Ammonia

SAQ 50

What inferences can be made from bacteriological tests on samples of river water which show that:

(a) there are no bacteria which thrive at 22 °C;

(b) there are bacteria present which thrive at 45 °C.

SAQ 51

What might be the likely 'trouble spots' at which to install an on-line toxicity monitor?

8.4   Summary

The testing of water quality covers a range of different aspects – physical, chemical and biological. The two major parameters in the monitoring of effluent discharges are the oxygen demand and the suspended solids content. The historical '30/20' standard for suspended solids and biochemical oxygen demand assumed a dilution of the effluent of at least eight times in the receiving water.

These days effluent discharge standards are based on the EU Urban Waste Water Treatment Directive, or on water use criteria.

Table 24 summarizes the analytical methods for the various water quality parameters discussed in this chapter.

This is a good point at which to carry out the water-related experiments detailed in the Home Experiment Book. You will get a good idea of the types of analyses involved. I'm sure you'll find it fun (especially the river quality survey!).

Table 24 Some important water quality tests, their chief significance and general means of measurement

Quality parameter	Significance	General method of analysis (unit of measurement)
Dissolved oxygen	Quantity of oxygen in water sample indicates quality of water	Titration or electrode (per cent saturation or $g\,m^{-3}$)
Biochemical oxygen demand	Extent of biodegradable organic matter – indicator of pollution	Measurement of dissolved oxygen before and after incubation for 5 days at 20 °C (grams of oxygen consumed per cubic metre of sample)
Chemical oxygen demand	Estimate of organic matter – indicator of pollution	Oxidation with strongly acidic dichromate solution, followed by titration (grams of oxygen consumed from standard dichromate solution per cubic metre)
Total organic carbon	Estimate of organic matter – indicator of pollution	Combustion, followed by measurement of CO_2 by infrared (g organic carbon m^{-3})
Temperature	Measure of heat pollution	Thermometer (°C)
pH value	Intensity of acid or alkali present affects many chemical and biological properties	Titration; electrode; colorimetric (pH value 0–14)
Suspended solids	Turbidity; treatment efficiency may be affected	Gravimetric ($g\,m^{-3}$)
Dissolved solids	Salinity; may affect ecosystems and domestic and agricultural usefulness	Gravimetric ($g\,m^{-3}$, also units of electrical conductivity $mS\,cm^{-1}$)
Total solids	General polluting potential	Gravimetric ($g\,m^{-3}$)
Hardness	Soap consumption; scale formation	Titration (g $CaCO_3$ m^{-3})
Alkalinity	Amount of alkali present	Titration (g $CaCO_3$ m^{-3})
Ammonia	Estimate of decomposition of nitrogenous compounds (proteins); toxicity	Colour comparator, ion-selective electrode, titration or spectroscopy (grams of ammonia as nitrogen per cubic metre)
Nitrites	Toxic to fish and other aquatic organisms	Colour comparator or spectroscopy (grams of nitrite as nitrogen per cubic metre)
Nitrates	Estimate of oxidation of NH_3; plant nutrient; may serve as source of O_2; toxicity	Colour comparator or spectroscopy (grams of nitrate as nitrogen per cubic metre)
Inorganic phosphates	Plant nutrient	Colour comparator or spectroscopy (grams of phosphate as phosphorus per cubic metre)
Chloride ions	Degree of pollution with sewage; degree of salt water intrusion; taste; corrosion in hot water systems	Titration, colour comparator or spectroscopy (g Cl m^{-3})
Heavy metals	Toxic pollution	Colour comparator or spectroscopy (mg m^{-3})
Iron	Taste, discoloration; turbidity; growth of 'iron' bacteria	Colour comparator or spectroscopy (mg Fe m^{-3})
Magnesium	Hardness; taste; possible gastrointestinal irritation	Colour comparator or spectroscopy (mg Mg m^{-3})
Zinc	Taste; turbidity	Colour comparator or spectroscopy (mg Zn m^{-3})
Copper	Taste; discoloration; corrosion	Colour comparator or spectroscopy (mg Cu m^{-3})
Oil	Reduction in O_2 transfer; taste and odour, toxicity	Spectroscopy (g oil m^{-3})
Pesticides	Toxic pollution	Chromatography/mass spectroscopy (g pesticide m^{-3})
Phenols	Toxic pollution; odour; taste	Titration; spectroscopy (g phenol m^{-3})
Radiation	Carcinogen	Liquid scintillation spectrometer (Bq l^{-1})
Odour	Unaesthetic – indicator of pollution	Subjective perceived odour (threshold number)
Colour (apparent)	Suspended and dissolved solids; organic matter	Spectrophotometry or comparison with platinum-cobalt standard (Hazen colour units)
Turbidity	Estimate of suspended matter	Measurement of scattering of light (NTU)
Faecal coliforms	Faecal pollution	Membrane techniques (number in 100 ml); membrane dipslides (number in 1 ml); multiple tube fermentation (MPN) (number in 100 ml); colour change tests
Viruses	Faecal pollution	Concentration and use of cell culture techniques (PFU l^{-1})
Toxicity	Elimination of species in watercourse	Decrease in activity levels in bacteria, algae, invertebrates or fish

9   SEWAGE TREATMENT

9.1   Introduction

Water, after use, is discharged as waste. This is usually conveyed by drains and sewers to a treatment plant where the water is cleaned and reused or, as is more usual at the present time, discharged into a receiving water body such as a river. While this is the most popular discharge route, there are some discharges directed into estuaries and the open sea.

Domestic effluent or sewage consists of wastewaters from toilets and wastewaters from other activities such as bathing, clothes washing, food preparation and the cleaning of kitchen utensils. The non-faecally contaminated water, as mentioned earlier in the block, is referred to as greywater or sullage. Domestic sewage is up to 98.5% water, with the remaining 1.5% comprising 70% organic matter and 30% inorganic. The organic portion comprises protein (65%), carbohydrates (25%) and fats (10%), while the inorganic part consists of grit, metals and salts.

SAQ 52

Calculate the masses of the various components in 250 m^3 of domestic sewage using the information given above. Assume the density of the sewage to be 1000 kg m^{-3}.

In this chapter we consider the transport of sewage from its point of origin to the treatment plant, and the various processes carried out at the treatment plant to render the sewage suitable for discharge. We begin by considering drains and sewers.

9.2   Drains

Drains are pipes or other conduits which convey water away from a building or from an area to prevent it accumulating and causing a nuisance. The water drained from fields, roofs or paved surfaces may be relatively clean. However, the term 'drain' is also used specifically for the pipe which carries foul drainage (the wastes from toilets and washing facilities) to the public sewer.

In a building, waste pipes take the water discharges from various points to the main underground drain. In the UK the pipes above ground are now placed entirely within the building to avoid blockage by freezing. The drainage pipes in a house will be from the toilets and wash basins (Figure 68). A vertical extension of the waste pipe, opening at roof level, is often used to ventilate the underground drain in a building. Such a vent reduces air pressure fluctuation, prevents the build-up of offensive smells within the drain, and aids the drying and subsequent flaking-off of deposits from the drain walls. Smells from drains were once regarded as a principal health hazard. You will realize that this is not true, but that ventilation is retained as a consideration of amenity, as well as for the practical reasons mentioned.

Gutters, pipes and drains conveying rainwater away from all roofs, roads and paved areas, in many new developments, constitute a separate system from that used for sewage. This separation can continue in the *sewerage* system and subsequent treatment. However, it is often desirable to combine these systems when draining factories and abattoir yards, markets, etc., as these open areas are likely to be sources of pollution.

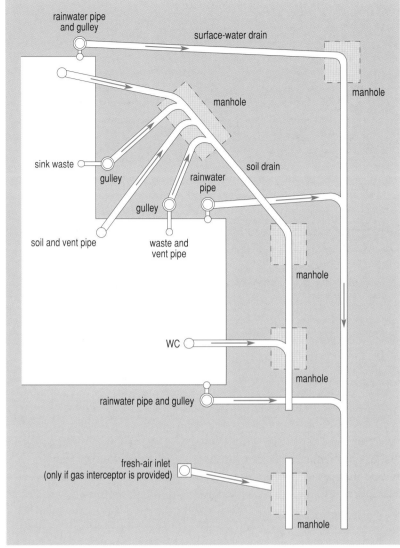

Figure 68 Drainage system for a house

Whether combined or separate, the drainage systems must include a facility for inspection and maintenance and this is provided by manholes or inspection covers. For ease of clearing blockages, drains should always be laid in straight lines between inspection points. This layout should ensure that drain-clearing rods can be introduced when necessary. Although there is no clear rule for the location of inspection points, it has been a tradition to provide inspection chambers at all junctions of drains into which soil pipes discharge. These chambers are also provided at intervals along straight (junctionless) lengths of drain to ensure that the whole length of drain can be 'rodded' satisfactorily.

9.3   Sewers

The flow of sewage from buildings is carried away by drains to the main sewers. These are large pipes or brick or concrete-lined tunnels which convey the combined flow to the treatment works or, in an isolated or coastal area, some other point of disposal. The primary function of the sewerage system is to maintain a healthy local environment. This includes the avoidance of local flooding and the minimizing of river pollution by preventing wastes from running directly into the rivers. Figure 69 shows a typical layout of drains and manholes used to connect a single household to the public sewer.

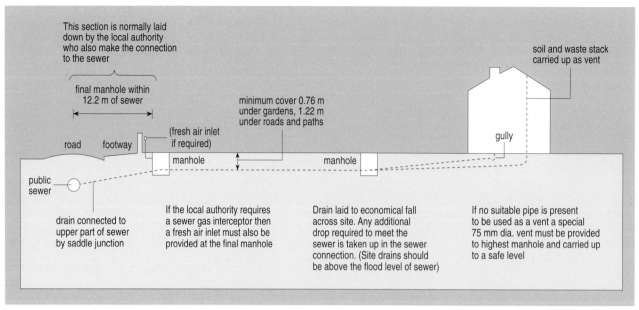

This section is normally laid down by the local authority who also make the connection to the sewer

soil and waste stack carried up as vent

final manhole within 12.2 m of sewer

minimum cover 0.76 m under gardens, 1.22 m under roads and paths

(fresh air inlet if required)

gully

road   footway

manhole

manhole

public sewer

drain connected to upper part of sewer by saddle junction

If the local authority requires a sewer gas interceptor then a fresh air inlet must also be provided at the final manhole

Drain laid to economical fall across site. Any additional drop required to meet the sewer is taken up in the sewer connection. (Site drains should be above the flood level of sewer)

If no suitable pipe is present to be used as a vent a special 75 mm dia. vent must be provided to highest manhole and carried up to a safe level

Figure 69 Drain connections to main sewer

Raw domestic sewage in a fresh state is typically light grey to brown in colour. In it, however, the biodegradation of its organic content is constantly in progress. Provided a measurable amount of dissolved oxygen is maintained in the wastewater, the biodegradation process will remain aerobic and the sewage will remain fresh. Should the rate of oxygen demand exceed the rate at which oxygen can be dissolved from the sewer atmosphere, anaerobic conditions will result – the wastewater will rapidly turn a black colour and hydrogen sulphide will be formed. Hydrogen sulphide gas evolved in sewers is a hazard to sewer maintenance personnel and is a major cause of corrosion of sewer structures. It also causes severe odour problems in the primary phase of the treatment works. These problems can be particularly severe in hot climates because of the reduced solubility of oxygen at higher temperatures, and the more rapid biological action. Aerobic conditions may be ensured by providing adequate sewer ventilation, by designing sewers with steep gradients and by minimizing the total time that the sewage remains in the collection system.

A considerable portion of the water supplied to a community does not reach the sewers. This includes water used by manufacturing industries and power plants, and water used in gardening and in actual consumption, i.e. in drinking and cooking. It also includes leakage and water used in extinguishing fires. Ignoring groundwater infiltration into sewers (discussed below), some 80% of the water supplied ends up as wastewater in sewers.

The size of a sewer (or underground drain) is calculated according to the flow that is to be carried.

The ratio of maximum and minimum flow rates varies with position along the sewer lines. In the smaller upstream sewers serving small areas the ratio can be large with wide fluctuations of flow. In the larger downstream sewers leading to the treatment plant, the extremes of flow will be less pronounced, due to the attenuation of the maximum and minimum flows as a result of differing travelling times from the various tributary areas.

In addition to flows from household sewage and trade wastes (effluents from industry), surface and groundwater will also influence the flow rate. During storms, rainwater run-off entering the sewer can dwarf the sewage flow. A properly laid sewer is watertight when laid and installed, but ground movement may cause it to be damaged and leak. If the groundwater level rises above the sewer, water will leak in (or infiltrate). This water is called infiltration water. On the other hand, if the groundwater level falls below the sewer, it is possible for sewage to leak out and contaminate underground water supplies.

The critical factors in calculating surface water discharges are the likely intensity and duration of rainfall, and the area and permeability of the surfaces from which the water is drained – that is, how much soaks in and how much runs off. This was discussed in Chapter 1.

Some small coastal communities discharge their sewage directly into the sea from submerged outfalls. The dispersion of the sewage as it rises to the sea surface is analogous to the dispersion of chimney plumes. The extent of dilution depends on the velocity of the jet of sewage leaving the end of the pipe, the depth of water over the outfall and the tidal velocity at this point. After the column of sewage and entrained sea water reaches the sea surface, it spreads as a layer of less dense material over the dense sea water. Final dispersion occurs by mixing of this layer due to the natural turbulence of the sea.

The combined total of average daily flows due to sewage and trade wastes to be expected in a sewer is called the dry weather flow, and other flows may be expressed in terms of this.

9.4   Dry weather flow

Strictly, the *dry weather flow* is the rate of flow of sewage and trade waste, together with infiltration, if any, in a sewer in dry weather. This is measured as the average flow during seven consecutive days without rain, following seven days during which the rainfall did not exceed 0.25 mm on any one day. Preferably, the flows during two periods in the year, one in summer and one in winter, should be averaged to obtain the average dry weather flow.

The dry weather flow (DWF) may also be calculated using the following formula:

$$\text{DWF} = PQ + I + E$$

where

P is the population served;

Q is the average daily per capita domestic water consumption (m^3 d^{-1});

I is the average rate of infiltration (m^3 d^{-1});

E is the average volumetric flow rate of industrial effluent discharged to the sewer (m^3 d^{-1}).

The expression for DWF takes the worst case scenario and assumes that all the water consumed in the home enters the sewer after use.

The dry weather flow is used in determining the capacity of the treatment works, typically specified as capable of treating the DWF up to three times. Allowance is usually made for the DWF to be treated a further three times for gross solids and grit removal only. This is to cater for storm waters. Guideline figures are available (Table 25) for the estimation of sewage flows from different establishments.

Table 25 Guideline per capita sewage volumes

Premises	Per capita volume (litres per day)
Domestic	150
Hotels	300
Restaurants	35
Campsites	100
Day schools	50
Boarding schools	300
Offices	50
Factories	70
Bars	15
Airports	15
Rest homes	300
Hospitals	500

9.5 Gravity flow

Almost all drainage systems are based on gravity flow and partially filled pipes. Foul drains and sewers slope downwards towards the treatment works or pumping stations, and the sewage flows in the bottom of the pipe rather than filling it completely. For example, foul drains are designed to contain flows to a depth of three-quarters of their diameter. With a sudden discharge, the level in the pipe rises, so the surge is stored temporarily and may flow away over a longer period.

Partially filled gravity sewers possess several advantages over pipes designed to be operated completely full for most flows. This follows particularly from their 'self-cleansing' operation, since, when designed properly, sewage is not delayed in transit, as it would be at low flow rates in full pipes. Further advantages are:

1 The maintenance of higher velocities at low flows results in less deposition of material and the sewage arrives at the sewage works 'fresher' than it would otherwise be, the organic matter having undergone relatively little decomposition.

2 At normal flows, maintenance work can be carried out in the sewers.

3 No power is needed for pumping.

Although local authorities have their own requirements for minimum sewer gradient, the larger the diameter that is chosen for the sewer, the less steep the fall that is required. The slope must be sufficient to provide a flow of water fast enough to sweep the solids along. A minimum self-cleansing velocity of 0.6 to 0.75 m s^{-1} is needed to avoid stranding solid matter, and the system should be designed so that this velocity is achieved at least once per day. The depth of flow is important since this affects not only the velocity of flow, but also the area inside the sewer that is cleansed. Moreover, the minimum gradients cannot be calculated by assuming that the drains or sewers are perfectly positioned. Irregularities of laying, ground movement and distortion of pipes mean that steeper gradients are needed in practice than would be proposed for ideal conditions. Occasionally, when flows in an existing foul sewer are low and give problems of inadequate self-cleansing, it is common practice to supplement the flow with rainwater run-off by connecting in some roof or road gutter flows to the sewer.

It is not always possible to design drainage and sewerage systems to allow effluent to flow under gravity all the way from its source to the treatment works. The difference in height between the drainage area and the treatment works may be insufficient or the topography might be unsuitable. For these circumstances it is necessary to pump the effluent to the works, i.e. to use a rising sewer main.

SAQ 53

Which of the following factors can be used to explain the difference between a sewer and an underground drain?

A Size

B Gravity flow

C Pipe material

D Jointing

SAQ 54

Which of the following parameters would you expect to differ between a rising sewer main and a gravity sewer of the same discharge flow rate? How will they differ?

A Diameter

B Pressure

C Type of effluent

D Gradient

E Speed of flow

SAQ 55

Estimate the maximum effluent flow rate to a treatment plant serving a population of 20 000. Assume that infiltration accounts for 20% of DWF and that the total per capita water consumption (domestic and industrial) is 250 litres per person per day.

SAQ 56

Calculate the volume of sewage expected from an industrial complex during a normal working day when 10 000 people work in various factories and 6000 work in offices.

9.6   Functions of sewage treatment

About 96% of the population of the UK is served by a sewer network which transports wastes away for disposal. The sewage is treated in sewage works before discharge into rivers or the sea. The remaining 4% of the UK population, mainly in rural areas, use septic tanks or small-scale package treatment plants (described later) to dispose of their sewage.

The functions of sewage treatment are:

1   to reduce the total biodegradable material, including suspended solids, to acceptable levels as measured by BOD and suspended solids concentrations;

2   to remove toxic materials;

3   to eliminate pathogenic bacteria.

Figure 70 shows a typical sewage treatment plant designed to produce what is called secondary effluent (effluent which has undergone biological treatment).

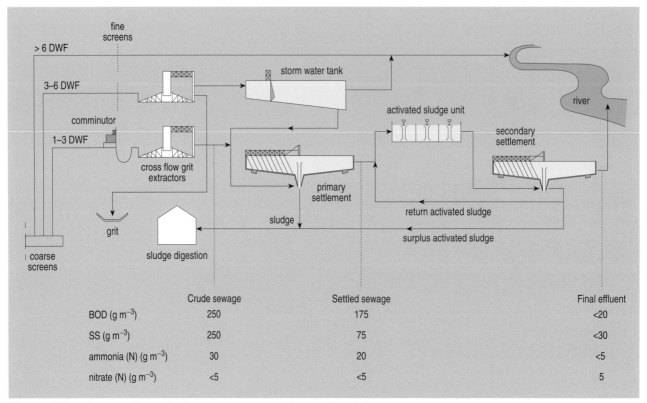

	Crude sewage	Settled sewage	Final effluent
BOD (g m^{-3})	250	175	<20
SS (g m^{-3})	250	75	<30
ammonia (N) (g m^{-3})	30	20	<5
nitrate (N) (g m^{-3})	<5	<5	5

Figure 70   Diagram of a typical sewage treatment plant designed for secondary treatment

A typical sequence of treatment is as follows:

1   Preliminary treatment

    (a) Removal of gross material by screening, or occasionally

    (b) Shredding of paper and rags by comminutors (rotating, slotted drums equipped with cutting blades – see Section 9.7).

    (c) Removal of grit.

2   Primary treatment

Removal of fine solids by settlement.

3   Secondary treatment

    (a) Biological oxidation of organic matter.

    (b) Removal of solids produced by biological treatment.

The quality of the secondary effluent can be improved by tertiary and advanced wastewater treatment.

4   Tertiary treatment

   (a) Reduction of the suspended solids content and the BOD concentration still further, typically to 10 g m^{-3} of each.

   (b) Removal of N, P and NH_3.

5   Advanced wastewater treatment

   (a) Removal of trace quantities of organics.

   (b) Disinfection.

The products of sewage treatment are:

■ an effluent of acceptable quality in relation to the receiving watercourse;

■ sewage *sludge*;

■ *screenings*;

■ *grit*.

In practice, it is not considered sensible to treat all the wastewater entering a sewage works at all times. We have seen that the flow in the sewer or rising main reaching a sewage works can fluctuate a great deal. To provide a treatment capacity for the maximum flow would mean that much equipment would be idle for long periods. Experience has shown that a plant capacity that can treat three times the dry weather flow is a reasonable compromise.

All sewage treatment works are provided with a safety device to avoid the plant being damaged by excessive flows. It is called the storm overflow or combined sewer overflow (mentioned in Section 6.1.1) and its function is to cause the excess flow above the treatment capacity to bypass the works. Typically, a trunk sewer carries the overflow to an open channel near the river serving as the receiving body. The side of the channel nearer to the river is lower than the other so that when the flow in the channel reaches the maximum capacity the mixture of storm water and sewage spills over it. There, another channel leads through coarse screens to the river. Combined sewer overflows are a serious cause of pollution, and efforts are under way to eliminate them.

> *Can you suggest a reason why this treatment would not be sufficient for storm water?*

When a storm occurs, the early part of the storm cleanses the roads and streets, and also flushes out the combined sewer system where a certain amount of sedimentation may have taken place. Thus the early flow of a storm can be considerably contaminated by oil and other materials from roads which have settled in the sewers; even in a river swollen by the storm it could prove to be a problem. To overcome this, sewage works also have storm tanks. These tanks, in series, are filled with the contaminated early storm flow and only when they are full can the now less-polluting storm water reach the river. In many instances the full capacity of the storm tanks is not reached during any one storm, so when the flow reduces, the storm tanks are emptied by pumping their contents back to the beginning of the treatment process. Under these circumstances no untreated sewage can reach the receiving water.

SAQ 57

What are the problems for sewage treatment posed by a combined sewerage system?

9.7 Preliminary treatment

The processes of screening, comminution (see below) and grit removal used in preliminary treatment remove the larger floating and suspended matter. They do not make a significant contribution to reducing the pollution load but they do make the sewage easier to treat by removing material which could cause blockages or damage equipment. Screenings may consist of pieces of wood, plastic materials, paper, rags, hygiene products and condoms. The screenings may be burnt in an on-site incinerator or buried in a landfill site. Raking of the screens on many small sewage works is still done manually – a job not many people like to do. Even if automatic raking is incorporated, the movement and disposal of screenings is a very unpleasant task. In very large works, screenings are often macerated and returned to the inflow.

In some treatment works, coarse screens are followed by comminutors (Figure 71) (instead of fine screens). A comminutor consists of a slotted, rotating drum fitted with cutting blades. Sewage with solids passes through the slots into the drum where the solids are macerated. Grit removal (see below) then follows. In sewage with a high proportion of grit, grit removal may precede comminution to save the comminutor blades from being prematurely worn down.

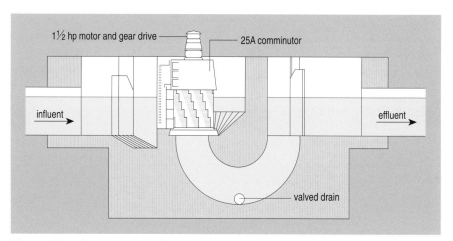

Figure 71 Cross-section of a comminutor

Screening does not remove small stones or grit which will be present. Grit comes from having been spread on roads in winter. To a lesser extent it is due also to erosion of roof tiles and cemented areas and may also contain pieces of metal and glass. These abrasive materials increase the rate of wear of mechanical plant and can also settle easily, causing blockages in pipes.

Grit is usually removed in a parabolic-shaped grit channel (Figure 72) where the sewage flow is reduced to 0.3 m s^{-1} to allow the grit to settle by gravity. This velocity does not allow the (lighter) organic material to settle and this material is carried forward. The grit deposited in the grit channel is removed daily using manual and/or mechanical methods, and put into a skip for disposal, usually at a landfill site.

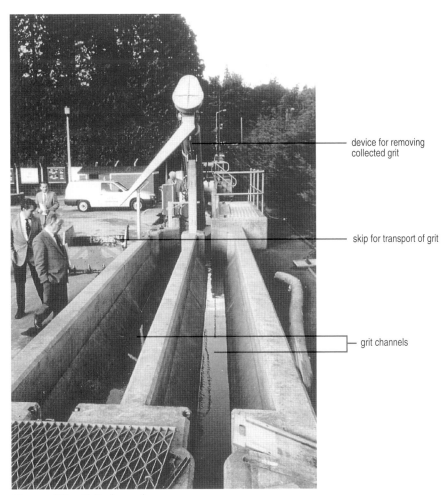

device for removing
collected grit

skip for transport of grit

grit channels

Figure 72 Grit channels

Other types of grit removal systems are available. In the cylindrically shaped Pista^{R} grit trap (Figure 73) centrifugal action is used to enhance separation of the grit. In the crossflow grit extractor (Figure 74), grit-laden sewage flows into a large square tank at a velocity less than 0.3 m s^{-1}. This allows even fine grit to settle. In addition, some organic solids settle out. In this system, the grit is collected and washed before disposal. It can be used for road gritting if it is thoroughly washed. The washwaters containing the organic matter are returned to the sewage inflow downstream of the grit extractor.

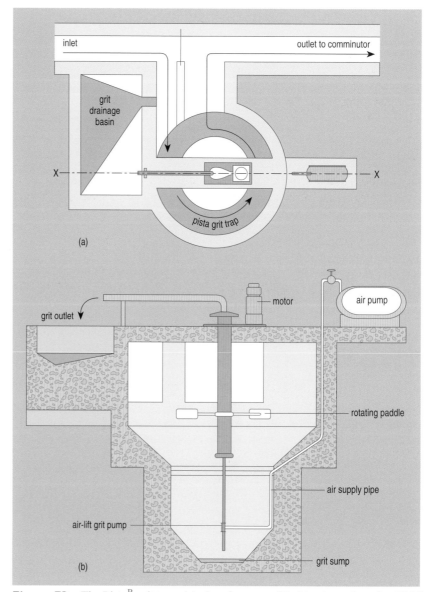

Figure 73 The Pista^R grit trap: (a) view from top; (b) side view of section X–X

Figure 74 An empty crossflow grit extractor

9.8 Primary treatment

Now that most of the coarse particles have been removed, only fine particles remain in suspension in the sewage, and the next stage in sewage treatment allows the sewage to travel at low velocity through large tanks so that most of the remaining particles can fall out of suspension. This process is called primary sedimentation. The effluent emerging from the primary sedimentation tank is referred to as settled sewage, and the sludge produced is called *primary sludge*.

Primary sedimentation removes approximately 70% of the suspended matter. Because some of these solids are biodegradable, the BOD is also reduced, by some 30% (see Figure 70).

The tanks used in primary sedimentation are similar to those used for sedimentation in water treatment (Section 3.4). Thus the tanks could be circular with radial flow, rectangular with horizontal flow, or hopper-bottomed with upward flow. In contrast to water treatment, however, the upward flow tanks usually have their inlet near the surface (Figure 75).

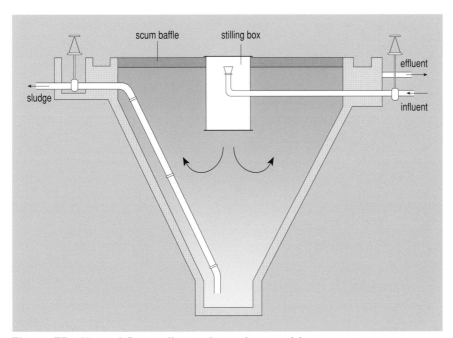

Figure 75   Upward flow sedimentation tank as used in sewage treatment

Circular tanks are not as compact as rectangular tanks but do provide a longer weir length. Hopper-bottomed tanks are popular on small sewage works where the extra cost of construction is more than offset by the absence of any scraping mechanism which would require maintenance. The sludge obtained from primary sedimentation is drawn off and can be sent on for further treatment (e.g. *anaerobic digestion*) or dewatered before disposal. The subject of sludge disposal will be looked at in Chapter 10.

Retention time in primary sedimentation tanks is generally between 2 and 6 hours and the tanks used have depths of between 2 m and 4 m.

9.9 Secondary (biological) treatment

Before a sewage works can discharge its effluent, the BOD and other polluting factors of the effluent must be reduced. This is achieved by using the process of biological oxidation, which uses the same reactions as occur in natural self-purification. The main difference in the treatment process compared with natural water purification is that the former attains a higher level of purification through providing optimum conditions.

In *sewage treatment* the two major categories of processes which use biological oxidation are the *activated sludge process* and biological filtration (see *biological filter* in Set Book).

The principal parameter in biological treatment is the ratio of food to micro-organisms (F/M) in a process. This can be defined as follows:

$$F/M = \frac{\text{mass of BOD applied to the biological stage each day (kg BOD d}^{-1})}{\text{mass of micro-organisms in the biological stage (kg biomass)}}$$

(7)

Figure 76 shows a typical biological growth curve which indicates how the concentration of micro-organisms (biomass) varies with the food supply. When food supply is present in excess (region A) the growth rate of micro-organisms is high. When food supply declines (region B) the rate of organism growth slows down till at point M, with food supply exhausted, the concentration of organisms reaches a maximum. Without food the organisms die and the total cell mass declines (region C). In practice, biological treatment processes operate continuously, either in the high growth rate region A with high values of organic loading rate (F/M>1.0), or in the low growth rate region B with low values of F/M (<0.1).

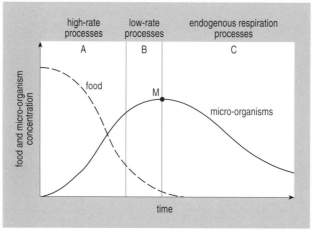

Figure 76   The biological growth curve

Selection of the F/M ratio to be used in the treatment gives the required size of the biological unit needed, since the size of the unit will be proportional to the quantity of biomass present. Low-rate processes (low F/M) require a larger quantity of biomass than high-rate processes (high F/M) for the same BOD input and are consequently of a larger size.

EXERCISE

After sedimentation, a settled sewage with 200 g m^{-3} BOD is to be treated biologically at a flow rate of 2500 m^3 per day.

(a) Calculate the amount of biomass needed if a low-rate process with an organic loading rate of 0.07 kg BOD per kg biomass per day is used.

(b) Calculate the amount of biomass needed if a high-rate process with an organic loading rate of 1.8 kg BOD per kg biomass per day is chosen instead.

ANSWER

Mass of BOD added to biological stage per day = flow rate $\times$ BOD

$$= 2500 \times \frac{200}{1000} \text{ kg d}^{-1}$$

$$= 500 \text{ kg d}-1$$

(a) Biomass = 500/0.07 = 7143 kg

(b) Biomass = 500/1.8 = 278 kg.

Another feature of biological systems is the net mass increase in biological solids (sludge). It is not feasible to operate biological processes to produce zero net growth of biological solids because a certain proportion of cell material is always relatively resistant to further degradation. Cells grow and in turn die and are used as food by other organisms, but some poorly degradable cell residues will remain. This increase in organism mass will be larger for high-rate processes than for low-rate processes, since in the high-rate region (see Figure 76) a large fraction of the food supply is used for increasing total cell mass. In the low-rate region, the limited food supply tends to be used mostly for sustaining the energy requirements of the cells, with little increase in total cell mass. The implication of these phenomena is that high-rate biological treatment processes impose larger demands for the withdrawal and disposal of sludge resulting from the net mass increase of biological solids.

There are two principal methods of bringing the micro-organisms into contact with the effluent. In *biological filters* the active mass of micro-organisms grows on a solid support, typically a bed of loose material. This is referred to as a fixed film system. In activated sludge systems the micro-organisms are suspended in the wastewater and such systems are termed dispersed growth systems.

9.9.1   Biological filters

In the early days of sewage treatment the sewage was allowed to 'soak away' through large areas of land and this gave rise to the term 'sewage farm'. It was found, however, that about ten times the volume of sewage could be treated if the sewage was passed through a granular medium of stone or clinker in a biological filter.

Biological filters can be circular (Figure 77) or rectangular in shape and are also known as percolating filters, trickling filters or bacteria beds. They operate by oxidation and not by filtration. The rectangular shape tends to be used in large works to reduce the land area required. The principal idea is that the settled sewage is slowly sprayed over the surface of the stone or clinker so that it is able to trickle down. In this way, oxidizing bacteria on the media are able to come into contact with the organic constituents of the sewage, and oxidation can take place. These bacteria are able to use the ample supply of atmospheric oxygen as long as the material in the beds has a large surface area and the beds are well ventilated, by allowing air to enter at the base. The process contains five important parts:

1   a dosing system or distributor for applying the settled sewage;

2   a filter bed in which the oxidation takes place;

3   an underdrainage system for collecting the treated effluent;

4   a ventilation system to provide oxygen;

5   a sedimentation tank to remove biological solids washed through the filter media.

Figure 77   A biological filter

1   The *dosing system*, or distributor, sprays the settled sewage over the surface of the bed. Circular beds use a rotating arm distributor. Here, the settled sewage enters at the central column of the filter and is discharged through nozzles spaced along low tubular arms which are supported by the central column. The arms rotate slowly, parallel to the surface of the bed and so distribute the sewage evenly over the whole surface. In rectangular filters the distributor sprays the settled sewage across the width of the bed and moves slowly down the length of the filter.

2   The *filter bed* must have an adequate depth to ensure that the incoming liquid receives sufficient time for the bacteria to act. Usually the depth of the medium is greater than 1.2 m and less than 2.0 m. The material forming the filter beds must be durable, strong enough to resist crushing, and frost resistant. Hard-burnt clinker, blast furnace slag, gravel or crushed rock can be used. Clinker and slag tend to give the best results.

The ideal filter medium should have the following:

(a) a large surface area on which the biomass can grow;

(b) voids which are large enough to allow the growth of the biomass without clogging and also to permit the passage of air;

(c) a structure which will distribute the sewage over all the surfaces of the bed with a maximum of turbulence so that oxygen transfer can take place.

The surface area of the medium is an important parameter, and is related to the porosity of the medium. Note, however, that a high porosity is an indication of a large exposed surface only if the pores are open and also interconnected. The parameter that is used to compare the suitability of different media for filters is the specific surface area which is defined as the exposed area per unit volume of material.

Media may also be made from plastic sheets, tubes or other shapes, forming regular modular or random patterns (Figure 78). Plastic filter media have the advantage over clinker and slag in that they provide a larger specific surface area, and so smaller, lighter and more compact 'packs' may be used for a given flow of sewage. Against this must be set the facts that they are more expensive than conventional filter media and that it is not possible to achieve as high a degree of treatment using them.

Filters can be distinguished by the flow rate of effluent being treated. High-rate filters treat 10–40 m³ of effluent per m² of filter bed area per day. Low-rate filters treat 1–4 m³ m⁻² d⁻¹. Most high-rate filters use plastic media and can be expected to remove only 15–50% of pathogenic

Figure 78 Plastic filter media: (a) Surfpac^{TM} (standard); (b) Surfpac^{TM} (crinkle-close); (c) Flocor^{TM}; (d) Cloisonyle^{TM}

bacteria in the sewage. BOD reduction may be up to 85%. They are most useful for relieving some of the load at an existing overloaded works and for treating certain industrial effluents. Low-rate filters use conventional media and can be expected to remove 99% of the pathogenic bacteria as well as reducing the BOD of the sewage by up to 95%.

As liquid passes through a filter it loses a considerable height. For this reason it is preferable for filters to be built on sloping sites since this allows gravity to assist flow between the different stages. On flat sites it may be necessary to raise the flow to the filter by pumping.

Aerobic bacteria grow as a film on the surface of the media in the filter. This will be a mixed population of bacteria, different from the *Schmutzdecke* mentioned in Section 3.6. (The latter is a few millimetres thick and contains higher life forms than bacteria, such as algae and plankton.) The flow of sewage through the bed entrains air, and up-draughts circulate because bacterial decomposition creates temperature differences. The air movement provides oxygen for the bacteria, which break down the organic matter in the settled sewage to provide energy and make new cell material. Some toxic material can be treated at this stage but the overall efficiency of the bacteria is much reduced if any toxic material is present. Bacteria would proliferate and eventually block the filter were it not for the activities of other forms of predatory life such as protozoa, worms and larvae from aquatic flies. These live in the filter and graze on the bacteria. When the larvae hatch and emerge as flies, however, they tend to be a nuisance.

A variety of methods can be employed to control the flies. These include using bacterial insecticides (bacteria that attack the fly larvae), controlled flooding of the filters to drown the larvae, and fine netting to prevent the emerging flies leaving the filters. It is also possible to use naturally occurring parasitic worms that attack and kill fly larvae.

The micro-organisms which make up the gelatinous film at the surface of the filter appear to be made up of three layers: an upper fungal layer, a main algal layer, and a basal layer of algae, fungi and bacteria. The fungi are efficient at oxidizing organic matter. The blue-green algae are able to remove nitrogen and minerals. Beneath the surface where there can be no sunlight, algae are absent. Protozoa remove any free-swimming bacteria which, if present, give the effluent a turbid appearance. Biological filtration produces high levels of nitrate produced through the bacterial action of *Nitrosomonas* and *Nitrobacter*.

Some bacterial cell material is shed and discharged from the filter with the effluent, along with solids which had not settled out in the primary sedimentation tank. This material is known as ***humus*** and is removed in the final sedimentation tank. The debris which settles out is called humus sludge.

3   The *underdrainage*, which collects the effluent, is constructed as an impervious base beneath the perforated filter floor. The filter floor slopes towards collecting channels. The underdrainage system should be capable of accommodating the maximum flow rate.

4   *Ventilation* is achieved by natural air circulation. Sufficient openings are provided at the bottom of the filter to allow air to flow in. In cold climates the air inflow is controlled so that the temperature in the filter does not dip so low as to reduce biological activity.

5   The *sedimentation tanks* used to remove the humus are similar to those used for primary sedimentation. The settled solids are not recycled (unlike in the activated sludge process, discussed later) but are returned to the works inlet where they settle in the primary sedimentation tank.

It is difficult to estimate the total biomass in a biological filter. Although the total surface area of the media gives some indication of the amount of biomass that could be supported, the active mass cannot be easily determined. So it is customary to take the volume of the bed as the most practical measure of biomass and to express the organic loading rate as the BOD applied per day per unit volume of filter medium. If Q is the sewage flow rate in $m^3\ d^{-1}$ distributed over a filter of cross-sectional area A m^2 and bed depth H m, and if the BOD of the influent is Y kg m^{-3} (not g m^{-3}), then

$$\text{organic loading rate} = \frac{(Q)(Y)}{(A)(H)}\ \text{kg BOD } m^{-3}\ d^{-1}$$

EXERCISE

A biological filter for the treatment of the sewage from a small group of houses in a remote area in the countryside has a diameter of 2.5 m and a depth of 2 m.

If the filter each day treats 5 m^3 of sewage with a BOD_5^{20} of 210 g m^{-3} after primary settlement, what is the organic loading rate?

ANSWER

$$\text{Organic loading rate} = \frac{(Q)(\text{BOD})}{(A)(H)}\ \text{kg BOD } m^{-3}\ d^{-1}$$

where

$$Q = 5\ m^3\ d^{-1}$$

$$\text{BOD} = 0.21\ \text{kg } m^{-3}$$

$$A = \pi\frac{(2.5)^2}{4}$$

$$H = 2\ m$$

Therefore, organic loading rate

$$= \frac{(5)(0.21)}{\frac{\pi(2.5)^2(2)}{4}} \text{ kg BOD m}^{-3}\text{ d}^{-1}$$

$$= \frac{1.05}{9.82} \text{ kg BOD m}^{-3}\text{d}^{-1}$$

$$= 0.11 \text{ kg BOD m}^{-3}\text{ d}^{-1}$$

In the UK it has been customary to use low-rate filters in a single pass (Figure 79a) in which the sewage is applied at the top and treated effluent discharged at the bottom. This reduces the BOD by 90–95%.

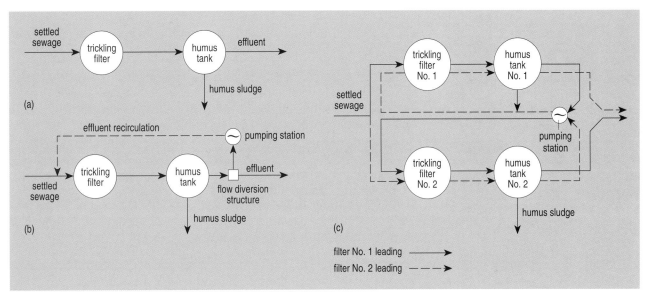

Figure 79   Flow arrangements for biological filters: (a) single-pass; (b) recirculation; (c) alternating double filtration

High-rate filters have organic loading rates which are significantly higher than those of low-rate filters. In order to achieve the necessary higher flow rates through the filter, alternatives to the single-pass system have been introduced.

1   The settled filter effluent is recirculated: purified effluent, which has passed through the filter once, is added to the inflowing settled sewage, thereby diluting it up to a maximum flow depending on the speed of action of the filter (Figure 79b).

2   A number of filters are used in series: for example, two filters are used in series with first and second stage settling tanks. Settled sewage is applied at a high rate to the primary filter, and its effluent, after settlement, is passed to the secondary filter (double filtration) and then to the second settling tank. After a period of operation the flow of sewage is changed so that the first stage filter becomes the second and vice versa. This is known as alternating double filtration (Figure 79c).

Both of the above systems enable a greater volume of sewage to be applied to a given volume of medium than with a single-pass filter. Indeed, in an alternating double filtration system up to 20 times the normal loading can be applied to the primary high-rate filter as a partial treatment stage, resulting in a reduction of up to 70% of the BOD.

Table 26 gives typical values of the different parameters for variations of biological filters.

Table 26   Typical design values for biological filters

Filter type	Organic loading ($kg\ BOD\ m^{-3}d^{-1}$)	Depth of filter medium (m)	Effluent SS/BOD ($g\ m^{-3}$)
Low-rate	0.07–0.3	1.5–2	30/20
High-rate	up to 1.0	1–2	30/30 and greater
High-rate plastic media	1.8	several metres	BOD removal 60–70%
Alternating double filtration	0.24	2	30/20

High-rate filters have a relatively low capital cost and they are easy to install. For this reason they are considered for the treatment of crude sewage (i.e. before primary sedimentation). The main problems with high-rate filters occur with the disposal of the resulting sludge.

Alternating the filters for double filtration is needed because the first filter becomes organically overloaded, i.e. the organic loading rate becomes too high. Overloading of filters may be indicated by *ponding* – a situation in which the bacterial growth on the media becomes so thick that the air spaces are blocked and the settled sewage is unable to trickle through, causing 'ponds' on the surface. By regularly alternating the first and second stage filters, the bacterial growth is never allowed to build up to such an extent.

SAQ 58

Which of the following statements are false?

A   Comminutors (where used) are always placed after coarse screens but before grit removal in the preliminary treatment of sewage.

B   In a biological filter, nitrification takes place due to the bacterial activity of *Nitrosomonas* and *Nitrobacter.*

C   One advantage of using biological filters is that they do not require final sedimentation tanks.

D   In a biological filter, bacteria and algae reduce the BOD of the settled sewage.

E   In alternating double filtration, treated effluent from the primary filter is fed to the secondary filter. When the primary filter shows signs of overloading, the position of the filters in the process is reversed.

SAQ 59

Which of the following considerations is most important (apart from cost) in choosing a medium for a filter?

A   Whether the medium is to be used in a high-rate or a low-rate filter.

B   Whether the filter is to be used for crude sewage or a sewage that has been partially treated by screening and primary sedimentation.

C   The ratio of surface area to volume of the filter medium.

D   Regularity of shape of the particles of the medium.

E   The size of the particles of the medium.

SAQ 60

A settled sewage flow of 1200 m^3 per day with 180 g m^{-3} BOD is applied to a low-rate biological filter of 40 m diameter and 1.8 m depth. What is the organic loading rate? What is the rate of removal of BOD in kg per day if the outlet BOD is 20 g m^{-3}?

9.9.2 The activated sludge process

This process was developed in Manchester in 1913–14. It has become extremely popular in sewage treatment as it occupies less space than a biological filter and it has proved useful for treating organic industrial wastes which were once thought to be too toxic for biological treatment. The activated sludge process produces a flocculent, microbial culture which is easily settled. The process (Figure 80) has the disadvantage of being more costly to operate due to its demand for power and maintenance.

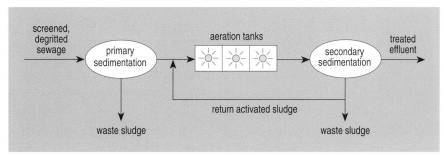

Figure 80   Schematic of an activated sludge system, with mechanical aerators

The process consists of the following elements:

(a) an aeration tank;

(b) an aeration system;

(c) a final sedimentation tank;

(d) a return activated sludge system;

(e) a system to remove the excess activated sludge produced.

Air is introduced into the settled sewage as it arrives from primary sedimentation by either bubbling compressed air through the liquid, or by mechanically agitating the liquid surface. (More information on these systems is given in the next section.) The oxygen 'feeds' aerobic bacteria suspended in the sewage and the bacteria use the organic matter in the sewage to form new cell material. The activated sludge unit also contains protozoa which remove free-swimming non-settleable bacteria, and rotifers which remove small biological floc particles, and so help to produce a clear effluent. Protozoa also play an important role in the reduction of pathogenic bacteria, e.g. those that cause diphtheria, cholera and typhoid.

The mixture of sewage and micro-organisms in the activated sludge unit is called the mixed liquor. The total suspended solids content determined by filtration and drying is a measure of the microbial mass and the inert substances present, and is referred to as the mixed liquor suspended solids (MLSS). If the MLSS is volatilized at 600 °C, any organic fraction will be decomposed to water, oxides of carbon, and ammonia, while the inorganic material will remain as oxides, carbonates or other salts. The volatile fraction is referred to as the mixed liquor volatile suspended solids (MLVSS) and gives a closer indication than the MLSS of the biomass in the biological reactor. In routine analysis at treatment plants, it is usually the MLSS that is measured. This is used in calculating the organic loading rate or F/M ratio, which was defined earlier (Equation 7) as follows:

organic loading rate $= $ F/M

$$= \frac{\text{mass of BOD applied to the biological stage each day}}{\text{mass of micro-organisms in the biological stage}}$$

$$= \frac{\text{flow rate } (\text{m}^3 \ \text{d}^{-1}) \times \text{BOD} (\text{kg m}^{-3})}{\text{volume of aeration tank } (\text{m}^3) \times \text{MLSS} (\text{kg m}^{-3})}$$

Settling is not possible in a liquid which is constantly agitated and so when the treated sewage containing the activated sludge leaves the aeration unit it is allowed to settle in a final sedimentation tank similar in design to that used for primary treatment. The treated effluent from the final settlement tank flows over a weir to be discharged to a watercourse, while the sludge settles to the bottom of the tank. A portion of the settled sludge is returned to the aeration unit. This is known as return activated sludge and it is often mixed in the ratio 1:1 with the incoming settled sewage. The settled sludge which is not reused is the surplus sludge and this is usually pumped away for treatment and disposal. It can, however, also be used to aid settling in the primary settlement tank, and is in this case pumped to the inlet of that tank.

It is necessary to maintain a concentration of 1–2 mg l^{-1} of dissolved oxygen in the mixed liquor. This is particularly important in the final settlement tanks: if there is insufficient oxygen present, the settled activated sludge may become anaerobic before it is returned, and this would lead to poor settlement due to gas production, and to the death of the organisms present.

The return activated sludge must be present in sufficient volume to give stabilization in the aeration unit. If insufficient is returned, poor purification will be achieved, and if too much is returned then poor settlement will result in the final settlement tanks.

Because of the importance of maintaining good quality sludge, several indices have been developed to give a guide on sludge quality. Examples are:

1   The sludge volume index (SVI). This can be defined as the volume occupied by sludge containing 1 g of solids (dry weight) after 30 minutes' settlement.

$$\text{SVI} = \frac{\text{settled volume of sludge in 30 mins (ml l}^{-1})}{\text{mixed liquor suspended solids (g l}^{-1})}$$

2   The sludge density index (SDI).

$$\text{SDI} = \frac{\text{mixed liquor suspended solids (g l}^{-1}) \times 100}{\text{settled volume of sludge in 30 mins (ml l}^{-1})}$$

Values of SVI vary from 40 to 100 ml g^{-1} for a good sludge, while sludges which have poor settlement and 'bulk' (see Section 9.9.6) in the final settlement tank have values in excess of 180. For SDI, the figures vary between 2.0 for a good sludge and 0.3 for a poor sludge.

EXERCISE

The sludge solids in 1 litre of mixed liquor are found to be 1850 mg l^{-1} and settle into a volume of 150 ml.

Find the SVI of the activated sludge.

ANSWER

$$SVI = \frac{150 \text{ ml } l^{-1}}{1.85 \text{ g } l^{-1}}$$

$$= 81.08 \text{ ml g}^{-1}$$

The retention time of the activated sludge in the aeration unit is typically 6–8 hours. The sludge is, however, recycled for several days before it is finally removed from the system. The sludge age is a value which tells a great deal about the type of activated sludge plant. For instance, a plant with a long sludge age of 25 days would be likely to produce a nitrified effluent. The sludge age varies according to the type and strength of sewage to be treated.

The sludge age is the ratio of the mass of cells in the bioreactor to the mass of cells wasted per day.

$$\text{sludge age} = \frac{\text{volume of aeration tank (m}^3) \times \text{MLSS (g m}^{-3})}{\text{flow rate of surplus sludge (m}^3 \text{ d}^{-1}) \times \text{solids concentration of sludge (g m}^{-3})}$$

EXERCISE

An aeration unit has a volume of 13.5×10^3 m^3, with a mixed liquor suspended solids concentration of 1850 g m^{-3}. Daily, 320 m^3 of surplus sludge with a solids concentration of 7500 g m^{-3} are wasted. What is the sludge age?

ANSWER

$$\text{Sludge age} = \frac{13.5 \times 10^3 \times 1850}{320 \times 7500} = 10.4 \text{ days}$$

In *extended aeration* systems, the retention time of the effluent in the aeration tank is typically 24–48 hours. The sludge produced in this type of system is highly stabilized (oxidized) and the amount of inert sludge left for disposal is reduced to a minimum.

9.9.3 Aeration systems

The main functions of the aeration system in an activated sludge plant can be summarized as follows:

1 to ensure a continuous and adequate supply of dissolved oxygen for the bacteria;

2 to keep the activated sludge solids in suspension;

3 to mix the incoming sewage and the activated sludge;

4 to remove from solution excess carbon dioxide resulting from the oxidation of the organic matter;

5 to assist the flocculation process by which the smaller particles adhere together to settle out later (in the sedimentation tank).

The two main methods by which activated sludge units are aerated are:

■ the introduction of air into the wastewater through pipes or porous diffusers – called diffused air aeration; and

■ the agitation of the wastewater by mechanical means such that air from the atmosphere dissolves in it – called mechanical aeration.

(a) *Diffused air aeration.* In this mode of aeration, there are three categories – coarse, medium and fine bubble aeration. In coarse and medium bubble aeration, air is pumped through open-ended pipes (Figure 81a) or pipes with holes often placed along one side of the aeration tank. As the name implies, large air bubbles are formed, with the aeration efficiency less than that of fine bubbles. A circulation pattern is set up in the tank. In fine-bubble aeration, filtered air is pumped to porous dome diffusers (Figure 81b) made of ceramic or plastic material. Fine air bubbles (approx. 2.0 mm in diameter) are generated. With porous diffusers it is essential that the air supplied is free of dust particles as these can clog the diffusers. The dome diffusers are placed in a network on the base of the aeration tank. Although coarse and medium bubble systems have slightly lower aeration efficiencies than fine bubble systems, their lower cost, easier maintenance and the absence of stringent air purity requirements have made them more popular.

(b) *Mechanical aeration.* Mechanical aerators consist of submerged or partially submerged impellers attached to motors which are mounted on floats or on fixed structures. The impellers agitate the wastewater vigorously, entraining air from the atmosphere into the wastewater. Partially submerged units, called surface aerators (Figure 81c), are popular. A variant of these is the brush aerator (Figure 81d). This is commonly used to provide both aeration and circulation in oxidation ditches (described later). It is also possible to have submerged turbine-sparger systems (Figure 81e). These disperse air which is introduced beneath the impeller, and also mix the tank contents.

Jet aerators (Figure 81f) are a variant of aerators where oxygen transfer is achieved by mixing pressurized air and water within a jet nozzle, and then discharging the air-liquid mixture into the effluent. The velocity of the air-liquid mixture discharged from the nozzle and the rising plume of fine air bubbles that form after discharge result in mixing of the wastewater within the tank.

For means of comparison, typical oxygen transfer rates for the aeration systems described above are given in Table 27.

Table 27   Typical oxygen transfer rates for a selection of aeration systems at standard conditions (tap water at 20 °C, 101.3 Pa) with initial dissolved oxygen concentration at 0 mg l^{-1}

Aeration system	Oxygen transfer rate(kg O_2 kWh^{-1})
Diffused air:	
fine bubble	1.2–2.0
medium bubble	1.0–1.6
coarse bubble	0.6–1.2
Low speed surface aerator	1.2–2.4
Brush aerator	1.2–2.4
Turbine-sparger system	1.2–1.4
Jet aerator	1.2–1.4

Source: Metcalf & Eddy Inc., revised by Tchobanoglous, G. (1987) *Wastewater Engineering: Treatment, Disposal, Reuse* (2nd edn), McGraw-Hill, New York.

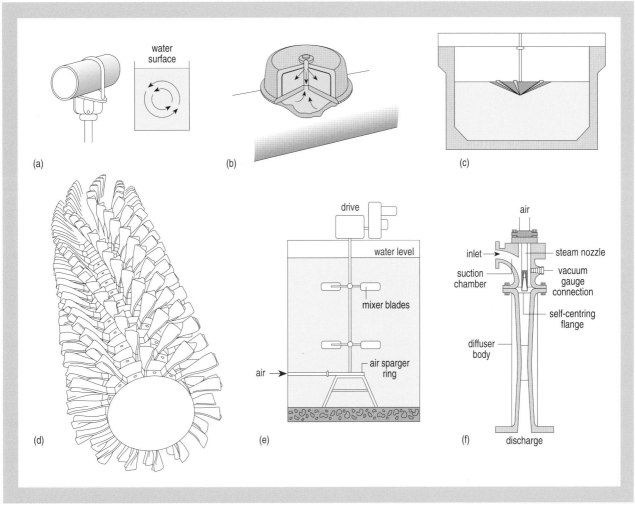

Figure 81 Various aeration systems: (a) a coarse air diffuser, with water circulation pattern set up in tank; (b) a fine air diffuser; (c) a surface aerator; (d) a brush aerator; (e) a turbine-sparger system; (f) a jet aerator

It is possible to express the BOD loading of an activated sludge unit in terms of an aeration tank loading rate, which is defined as:

$$\text{aeration tank loading rate} = \frac{\text{BOD entering aeration tank per day (kg BOD d}^{-1})}{\text{volume of aeration tank (m}^3)}$$

9.9.4 BOD removal in activated sludge units

Conventional activated sludge processes are 'medium rate' treatment processes with values of organic loading rate (F/M) of about 0.5 kg BOD kg^{-1} MLSS day^{-1}. With an adequate supply of oxygen in the aeration tanks, the rate of BOD removal depends only on the concentration of active micro-organisms in the tanks (Figure 82).

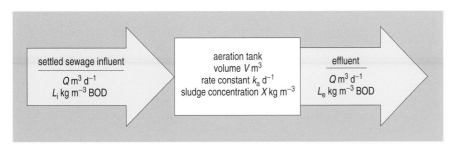

settled sewage influent

$Q\,\text{m}^3\,\text{d}^{-1}$
$L_i\,\text{kg m}^{-3}$ BOD

aeration tank
volume $V\,\text{m}^3$
rate constant $k_a\,\text{d}^{-1}$
sludge concentration $X\,\text{kg m}^{-3}$

effluent

$Q\,\text{m}^3\,\text{d}^{-1}$
$L_e\,\text{kg m}^{-3}$ BOD

Figure 82 Mass balance for aeration tank in the activated sludge process

That is:

rate of BOD removal (kg d^{-1}) $\propto$ mass of micro-organisms or mass of activated sludge

or

$$Q(L_i - L_e) = k_a XV \qquad (8)$$

L_i is the BOD concentration entering the plant (kg m^{-3})

L_e is the BOD concentration leaving the plant (kg m^{-3})

Q is the sewage flow rate (m^3 d^{-1})

X is the concentration of activated sludge (kg m^{-3})

V is the aeration tank volume (m^3)

k_a is a constant, the activated sludge rate constant (d^{-1}).

Equation (8) should be compared with the equation for BOD removal in the BOD test. The BOD test was a batch process, while the activated sludge process is a continuous one. Nevertheless, the biological reactions in both situations are similar.

EXERCISE

Settled sewage at a flow rate of 1500 m^3 d^{-1} and 200 g m^{-3} BOD is treated in an activated sludge plant which is equipped with an aeration tank 25 m long $\times$ 5 m wide $\times$ 4 m deep and with a sludge concentration $X = 2000$ g m^{-3}. The activated sludge rate constant k_a is 0.28 d^{-1}.

(a) Calculate the overall percentage BOD removal.

(b) Calculate the retention time in the tank.

(c) Calculate the aeration tank loading rate in kg BOD m^{-3} d^{-1}.

(d) Calculate the organic loading rate in kg BOD kg^{-1} MLSS d^{-1}.

ANSWER

From Equation (8)

$$L_i - L_e = \frac{k_a XV}{Q}$$

$$= \frac{(0.28)(2)(25)(5)(4)}{1500} \text{ kg m}^{-3} \text{ BOD}$$

$$= 0.18667 \text{ kg m}^{-3} \text{ BOD}$$

$$= 186.67 \text{ g m}^{-3} \text{ BOD}$$

Therefore, % BOD removal $= \dfrac{186.67}{200} \times 100$

$$= 93.3\%$$

Retention time $t = \dfrac{V}{Q}$

$$t = \frac{(25)(5)(4)}{1500} \, \text{day}$$

$$= 0.33 \ \text{day}$$

Aeration tank loading rate $= \dfrac{QL_i}{V}$

$$\frac{QL_i}{V} = \frac{(1500)(0.2)}{(500)} \, \text{kg BOD m}^{-3} \, \text{d}^{-1}$$

$$= 0.6 \, \text{kg BOD m}^{-3} \, \text{d}^{-1}$$

Organic loading rate $= \dfrac{QL_i}{VX}$

$$\frac{QL_i}{VX} = \frac{(1500)(0.2)}{(500)(2)} \, \text{kg BOD kg}^{-1} \, \text{MLSS d}^{-1}$$

$$= 0.3 \, \text{kg BOD kg}^{-1} \, \text{MLSS d}^{-1}$$

SAQ 61

A litre of activated sludge is found to settle in 30 minutes to a volume of 280 ml, and has a concentration of solids of 1050 mg l^{-1}. What is the SVI of the sludge, and is this acceptable?

SAQ 62

Sewage from a primary settling tank has a BOD of 250 g m^{-3}. It is to be treated in an activated sludge plant to reduce the BOD to 20 g m^{-3}. The aeration tank volume is 250 m^3 and the activated sludge rate constant k_a is 0.3 d^{-1}.

(a) What concentration of activated sludge is required in the aeration tank to process 1000 m^3 d^{-1} of sewage?

(b) Suggest what actions might be taken to meet the output BOD specification if, for some reason, the primary treatment fails and the BOD of the sewage entering the activated sludge plant rises to 1000 g m^{-3}?

9.9.5   Secondary sedimentation

The settling tanks in which the activated sludge is separated from the mixed liquor are similar in design to the primary sedimentation tanks. Usually the tanks are circular, and most have floors that slope to the centre, although large tanks have flat floors. In small- and medium-sized tanks the sludge is scraped to the centre by helical blades. The sludge then flows through an outlet pipe to the sludge well, from which most of it is pumped back to the aeration tank (the rest being taken away for disposal as surplus sludge). Sludge is removed from flat-floored tanks by suction pipes.

9.9.6   Sludge bulking

The situation can arise in activated sludge plants when the outflow from the activated sludge tank does not settle in the secondary sedimentation tank to produce a sludge and clear water. Instead, the biological flocs remain suspended throughout the sedimentation tank and are carried out in the overflow. The sludge in this situation is referred to as bulking sludge.

Bulking sludge is attributed to two factors:

1 the presence of filamentous organisms or organisms that grow in a filamentous form under adverse conditions;

2 the incorporation of water (bound water) in the bacterial flocs of activated sludge, causing a reduction in the density of the flocs.

Neither the filamentous organisms nor the reduced-density flocs settle easily, resulting in a bulking sludge.

Bulking is caused by fluctuations in wastewater flow and strength, pH and temperature, excessive organic loading, and an inadequate supply of oxygen or nutrients, e.g. N, P, and trace elements.

Remedial measures include adding chlorine or hydrogen peroxide to the sludge recycle stream to eliminate the filamentous organisms. The filamentous organisms, due to their larger surface area, are more affected by these biocides than are the normal activated sludge micro-organisms. This is followed by measures to stabilize the inflow and other conditions, e.g. pH and temperature. Steps to reduce the organic loading (e.g. by balancing the inflow, increasing the content of mixed liquor suspended solids to have a favourable F/M ratio, etc.) can then be taken. Nutrient addition (e.g. N, P, trace elements such as Fe, Cu, Zn and Mn) may be required. It is valuable to identify the species of bacteria causing the problem, as the reason for their excessive growth (e.g. O_2 deficiency, nutrient deficiency, low F/M ratio) varies between species.

A lack of dissolved oxygen has been noted more frequently than any other as the cause of bulking. If the oxygen transfer rate with aerators is limited, pure oxygen may be injected into the activated sludge tank to increase the available oxygen as in the Vitox system (see Section 9.9.14). This technique is employed to overcome sludge bulking at the Newbridge Sewage Treatment Works in Edinburgh where highly polluting organic wastes from a wide variety of food manufacturing and processing establishments constitute a major proportion of the flow treated at the works.

9.9.7   Elimination of pathogens in biological treatment

As we have seen, one of the objectives in treating sewage is the elimination of pathogenic organisms present in the effluent. More than 99% of the pathogenic organisms present in sewage are removed in the treatment process. The pathogens can be grouped broadly into viruses, bacteria and protozoa.

1 *Viruses.* The viruses are usually adsorbed onto bacterial flocs which are in turn removed by sedimentation in the secondary sedimentation tank. Some of the viruses are also consumed by protozoa.

2 *Bacteria.* Bacteria are killed by a number of methods. Some are killed by viruses. Others are consumed by protozoa, or are eliminated by toxins produced by other species of bacteria. Many of the pathogenic bacteria are simply enveloped by the rapid growth of non-pathogenic bacteria around them such that they become enmeshed in flocs of non-pathogenic bacteria. The bacterial flocs are then removed in the sedimentation process following biological treatment.

3 *Protozoa.* Most of the protozoa become bound to bacterial flocs which are later removed in sedimentation.

9.9.8   Comparison of activated sludge and biological filter systems

Advantages of the activated sludge process include the following:

1   In the event of a poorer than normal quality influent entering the works, the ability to vary the proportion of sludge that is recycled offers a degree of control over the quality of effluent finally discharged, which is not possible with a normal filter bed.

2   The nuisance of filter flies is avoided.

3   Loss of head through an activated sludge plant is significantly less than that through a filter bed, which may save on pumping.

4   Considerable space is saved. Where it is necessary to produce an effluent of particularly high quality, the area of land required for an activated sludge plant is about ten times less than that needed for a conventional filter scheme to treat the same pollution load. For plants required to treat large flows, the smaller area required for activated sludge is the deciding factor. On the other hand, the area required by biological filters is much reduced when high-rate filtration is used, and in recent years the maximum size of new plants that include biological filters has been decreasing.

Disadvantages of activated sludge plants are:

1   They require continuous attention.

2   They consume large amounts of energy and labour – in comparison, the biological filter is simple and requires little attention.

3   They are not tolerant of peak loads, whether of flow or composition.

4   They are noisy in comparison with filters, which can be important when the plant is sited in an area which is otherwise quiet.

5   The annual costs (including operating and maintenance expenses) are higher than for biological filters.

6   Activated sludge systems are more vulnerable than filters to toxic materials present in the influent.

7   Unlike biological filters, the activated sludge process does not convert ammonia to nitrate unless very high concentrations of oxygen are maintained. This requires extra costs and longer retention times in the aeration unit. Nitrification occurs during the later stages of the biological treatment, i.e. at the bottom of a biological filter and at the 'effluent end' of an activated sludge aeration tank. Nitrification puts a heavy demand on the available dissolved oxygen. Indeed, one of the first signs of overloading of a biological treatment system is the loss of nitrification due to the inability of the system to reach a high enough dissolved oxygen concentration.

9.9.9   Monitoring and control of biological filters

Due to the simplicity of biological filter systems, little analysis of the biological stage takes place. The only moving mechanical part is the rotating distributor and this is powered by the incoming wastewater flow. Maintenance of the system consists largely of lubricating the bearings and 'rodding' of the distributor arms to remove any solids that may have come in with the wastewater. Excess algal growth (as a result of organic overloading and 'ponding') may occur as sheets blocking the filter bed; these are removed manually using rakes. Organic overloading leads to a loss in nitrification and hence is to be avoided at all costs. The pH of incoming effluent to the plant would be measured to verify that it is within the tolerable range of 6.5–8.0. Analyses would also include measurement of the suspended solids content and the BOD values of the final effluent (after secondary sedimentation) to verify compliance with discharge consent conditions. Nitrification may also be monitored. If effective BOD removal were not taking place, it is likely that the incoming BOD, N and P levels would be measured and the N and P levels adjusted, if necessary, to give a BOD:N:P ratio of 100:5:1. This relationship is used as a rule of thumb in the treatment of wastewater. Alternatively, the presence of toxic compounds might be suspected and these would be sought out and eliminated, preferably at source. BOD data take five days to acquire, so for immediate feedback a measurement of the chemical oxygen demand is often also made and the related BOD value obtained from this using the COD/BOD relationship determined for the particular effluent. Other parameters recorded would be pH, temperature, ammonia–nitrogen content, nitrate–nitrogen content, chloride and the dissolved oxygen level. If metal-bearing effluents were being treated, the concentrations of the metals in the outflow would also be determined. Similar specialist data would be acquired if pesticides, etc. were present in the incoming wastewater. The frequency of sampling and analysis would depend on the size of the works. Many of the smaller sewage treatment works would be sampled only weekly or even monthly.

Temperature affects the performance of biological filters, with reduced removal efficiencies at low winter temperatures (including nitrification) and the opposite at high summer temperatures.

9.9.10   Monitoring and control of the activated sludge process

Activated sludge systems are more complex than biological filters and a number of tests are made to monitor the treatment process and to pre-empt any upsets that may occur. Measurements of dissolved oxygen, pH, mixed liquor suspended solids and the sludge volume index are taken. The suspended solids content of the return activated sludge also needs to be measured. Very often process upsets can be detected by a change in the normal colour or smell of the mixed liquor or the return activated sludge. The parameters measured are discussed below.

Dissolved oxygen
Most dissolved oxygen control systems work by controlling the concentration of dissolved oxygen in the mixed liquor leaving the aeration tank, and a commonly chosen range is 0.5–2.0 mg l^{-1}. Measurements with a portable dissolved oxygen meter can be undertaken to verify that the required level is being maintained.

Mixed liquor suspended solids (MLSS)
The maximum concentration of MLSS which can be achieved depends on the settleability of the sludge and the surface area of the settlement tank. The optimum concentration is usually in the range 2000–3000 mg l^{-1}, though in an aeration tank providing full nitrification it is higher, e.g. 6000 mg l^{-1}. The MLSS concentration in the aeration tank affects the organic loading (F/M) which is crucial to the required performance of the plant. The MLSS concentration may be changed by altering the amount of sludge which is returned from the final sedimentation tank.

Sludge volume index (SVI)
The SVI is measured to gauge the settleability of the sludge. As mentioned in Section 9.9.2, an SVI below 100 ml g^{-1} indicates a good

settling sludge, whereas a result in excess of 180 ml g^{-1} would suggest that further investigation is needed.

Suspended solids content in the return sludge

The suspended solids content needs to be known in order to estimate how much sludge has to be recycled to maintain a given (F/M) ratio in the aeration tank. All the suspended solids are assumed to be composed of microbial mass which would add to the MLSS level in the aeration tank.

Microscopic examination

Microscopic examination by an experienced eye is an excellent method of judging the condition of an activated sludge system. Examination of the activated sludge for floc size and diversity of organisms can give an indication of the performance of the aeration tank. Filamentous organisms are undesirable. The presence of protozoa in the final effluent indicates a clear effluent.

SAQ 63

Compare the activated sludge process with the biological filter in terms of the merits and demerits of each.

9.9.11   Industrial effluents

It can often be advantageous to treat industrial effluents (usually called 'trade effluents' or 'trade wastes' in the UK) after mixing with domestic sewage: the final composition of the mixed industrial/domestic sewage stream may reach the BOD:N:P ratio of 100:5:1 required for biotreatment.

Industrial effluents come from a variety of manufacturing processes such as those producing textiles, metals, food and dairy products. They usually have a wider range of characteristics than domestic sewage and are more likely to contain toxic and non-biodegradable compounds that require physico-chemical treatment rather than biological oxidation. Treatment usually takes place in a series of unit operations designed to remove or to modify the characteristics of the pollutants in the effluent. There are many trade wastes, however, which can be biodegraded, provided any toxic components present are first removed. This is usually achieved using chemical treatment, e.g. oxidation of high concentrations of cyanides (see below).

In a mixed industrial/residential area, there can be significant savings in capital and operating costs if a single wastewater treatment plant is installed.

In many cities, industrial effluents (especially from the smaller industries) are discharged into the sewer system, after pretreatment where necessary. The industry concerned pays a charge to the authority responsible for the sewers and the receiving treatment plant. The magnitude of the fee depends on the polluting potential of the effluent (based on its COD), its suspended solids content and the volumetric flow rate. The fee is calculated using the Mogden formula (which you will learn about in the third-level course). The receiving plant dictates what can be put into the sewers by issuing a consent to discharge limiting the value of these three parameters and the content of any components of concern (e.g. metals) that may affect the biotreatment process. The toxic content of trade effluent discharged into sewers also has to be controlled in order to safeguard men working in the sewers and to protect the piping and equipment in the sewerage system from chemical attack.

Typical pretreatment operations carried out on industrial effluents prior to despatch to a sewage treatment plant include the following (also see the entry for *effluent, physico-chemical treatment* in the Set Book):

1   solids removal, e.g. by screening, sedimentation, filtration or microstraining;

2   pH adjustment, using acid or alkali to bring the wastewater to a pH value in the range 6.5–8.0;

3   chemical oxidation, e.g. oxidation of the highly toxic cyanide ion (CN^-) to the much less toxic cyanate ion (CNO^-);

4   chemical reduction, e.g. reduction of the toxic Cr^{6+} ion to the Cr^{3+} ion using SO_2;

5   removal/recovery of heavy metals, e.g. precipitation of Cd using lime;

6   oil/fat/grease removal, e.g. using an oil *interceptor* (Figure 83) or by flotation;

7   trace organics removal, e.g. adsorption of pesticides using activated carbon.

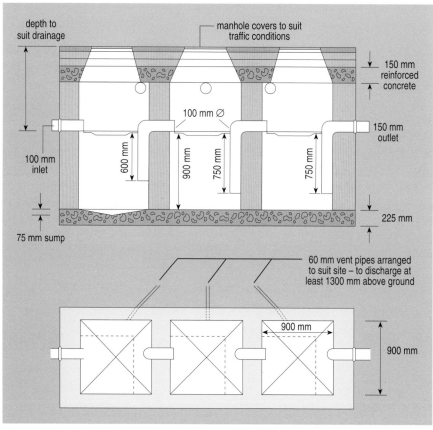

Figure 83   Plan and section of an oil interceptor – the retention time is sufficient for any oil to rise to the surface from where it is removed during periodic inspections

SAQ 64

Table 28 lists industrial and manufacturing activities, pollutants and pretreatment options. For each activity, select the pollutant you would expect to find and the pretreatment operation necessary before the effluent could be discharged into a domestic sewer.

Table 28

Industrial activities	Pollutants	Pretreatment options
Ceramic works	oil and fat	chemical reduction
Distillery	chromium (VI)	neutralization
Chicken processing plant	acid mine waters	sedimentation
Electroplating works	china clay	microstraining
Copper mining	spent grain	flotation

9.9.12 Treatability of effluents

If industrial effluents are to be discharged to municipal sewers for treatment at the local sewage works, it is important to ascertain if the effluents are amenable to treatment, and also that they are not going to inhibit the normal biological processes at the treatment works. Some of the methods utilized to verify this are described below.

The activated sludge respiration inhibition test

This test is based on the fact that activated sludge respires rapidly in the presence of synthetic sewage but that the respiration rate decreases in the presence of a toxic chemical, with the decrease being proportional to the toxicity of the chemical. In the test, activated sludge from a sewage treatment plant is continuously aerated and fed with a stream of synthetic sewage containing varying concentrations of the effluent being tested, for a period of 30 minutes.

The activated sludge concentration (expressed as MLSS) should be maintained at 3000 mg l^{-1}, with the respiration rate expressed in mg O_2/g MLSS/h. The oxygen concentration is recorded over the test period. From data of the dissolved oxygen concentration over time, the respiration rates of the test samples and the control (activated sludge fed with only synthetic sewage) can be calculated. The oxygen uptake of the sample by physico-chemical action, when no activated sludge is added, is also measured. The percentage inhibition can then be calculated using the expression

$$\% \text{ inhibition} = \frac{R_c - R_t}{R_c} \times 100$$

where

R_c is the respiration rate of the control with activated sludge and synthetic sewage only;

R_t is the respiration rate of the test sample.

Compact computerized systems to analyse and present the data are available (Figure 84).

The percentage inhibition values can be plotted against the various dilutions of the effluent. From this, the concentration of the effluent at which 50% inhibition of the control occurs (the EC_{50}), can be ascertained.

The system has been utilized for testing industrial effluents before they are accepted for treatment at a sewage works. Discharges may be direct to the sewer or brought by tanker to the treatment plant. The test takes about 30 minutes to complete.

With the emphasis being placed on compliance with consent conditions, the system has also been purchased by installations such as paper mills to

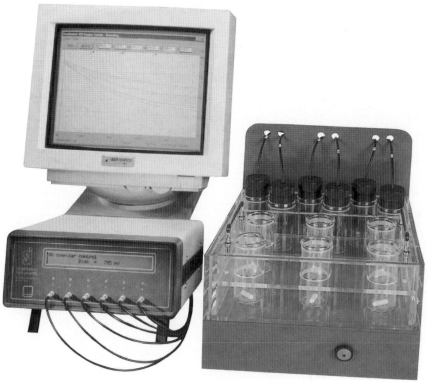

Figure 84   A system used for the activated sludge respiration inhibition test

ensure that their in-house activated sludge plants are not put out of action by effluents from various parts of their site. Based on the consent conditions, some degree of inhibition may be tolerated at the plant.

SAQ 65

The manager of a large effluent treatment plant in Scotland was approached by an industrialist in the area wanting to discharge trade effluent to it. The laboratory staff at the treatment plant carried out a respiration inhibition test which revealed the following:

Respiration rate of control = 14.67 mg O_2/g MLSS/h

Respiration rate of test samples

Concentration of trade effluent (%)	Respiration rate (mg O_2/g MLSS/h
20	13.47
40	12.00
60	9.07
80	8.20
100	6.53

(a) Calculate the percentage inhibition at each of the dilutions tested.

(b) Plot the percentage inhibition against dilution, and determine the EC_{50} for the effluent.

(c) If the treatment plant manager calculates that 15% inhibition of his activated sludge units is tolerable without compromise to the quality of final effluent from the plant, estimate the dilution of the trade effluent that would be necessary before treatment.

The BOD inhibition test

In this test, the new effluent is assessed by measuring its effect on the oxygen utilization by heterotrophic micro-organisms growing in a readily degradable substrate. The standard 5-day BOD test is used with a substrate consisting of a mixture of glucose and glutamic acid. Various dilutions of the effluent are tested and the percentage inhibition calculated. The standard substrate is made up of 0.15 g l^{-1} glucose and 0.15 g l^{-1} glutamic acid, giving a BOD of 220 mg l^{-1}. A standard bacterial seed is used.

The percentage inhibition is calculated using the following expression:

$$\% \text{ inhibition} = \frac{BOD_c - BOD_t}{BOD_c} \times 100$$

where

BOD_c is the BOD of the control;

BOD_t is the BOD of the test solution.

From a plot of percentage inhibition against dilution, the value of the EC_{50} can be determined.

The Microtox^R test

The Microtox test referred to in Section 8.3 has also been used to derive EC_{50} values. This is defined as the concentration of the effluent (or test chemical) which reduces the light production by *Vibrio fischeri* by 50%, with reference to the control. Microtox has been used at sewage treatment plants to screen new effluents entering the works for toxicity and treatability.

9.9.13 Bioaugmentation

Commercially produced microbial species are sometimes used in wastewater treatment to break down difficult-to-degrade substances such as complex hydrocarbons. This is referred to as bioaugmentation. The desired micro-organisms are usually obtained from areas contaminated with the chemical of concern, as natural selection would have ensured that those microbes which adapted to the chemical would be present. For instance, it is said that up to half the micro-organisms in coastal waters can degrade hydrocarbons, while meat-processing plants can be a source of microbes capable of degrading fats and proteins. The microbes collected from such sites are grown in a medium rich in the chemical under investigation. The strains growing best are then isolated and cultured on a larger scale. The microbes are harvested and freeze-dried for sale. They are sold in powder form with the formulation usually containing nutrients, wetting agents and emulsifiers to aid dispersion.

In addition to the main purpose of degrading difficult compounds, bioaugmentation can be utilized to reduce the inhibitory effects of toxic compounds in effluents entering a treatment plant.

SAQ 66

When I was working on a research project for an oil refinery in Kuwait we were trying to find a microbial culture that would degrade the residual alkanes in its effluent, to be treated in a plant at high ambient temperature.

Where would be a good place to find such organisms?

9.9.14 Variants of the biological treatment system

Although activated sludge units and biological filters are probably the most common forms of biotreatment used in effluent treatment, variations do exist. Each of these variations has distinct advantages in treating a particular wastewater and/or for a particular situation. A few examples of processes currently in use are given below.

Contact stabilization

The contact stabilization process takes advantage of the adsorptive properties of activated sludge. It has been postulated that BOD removal in the activated sludge process occurs in two phases. The first is the adsorptive phase, taking some 20–40 minutes, in which soluble and colloidal, finely suspended organic matter is adsorbed by the activated sludge. In the second phase, the adsorbed organics are assimilated metabolically. In the conventional activated sludge process, the two phases occur in the same tank. In contact stabilization the two reactions take place in separate tanks. In this process (Figure 85) screened, degritted, settled effluent is mixed with return sludge and aerated in a contact tank for about 60 minutes. The sludge is then separated and aerated in a separate sludge stabilization tank for 3–6 hours, where oxidation of the adsorbed material occurs. At the end of the aeration period the sludge is devoid of 'food' and thus readily adsorbs organic pollutants when put into the contact tank with fresh effluent. By concentrating the sludge before oxidation, total aeration tank volumes are reduced by approximately 50% compared with the conventional process. The contact stabilization process is particularly suitable for wastewaters in which a high proportion of the BOD is in suspended or colloidal form.

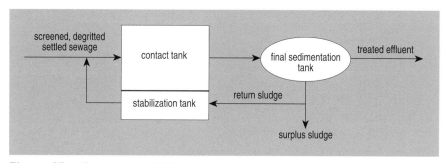

Figure 85 The contact stabilization process

Oxidation ditch

In this system, biological oxidation takes place in a continuous 'race track'-shaped channel (Figure 86) in which the mixed liquor is circulated and aerated by brush aerators, which maintain a liquid velocity sufficient to prevent the settlement of sludge. The ditches may be constructed in concrete or be plastic sheet-lined earth channels, and have a water depth of 1–2 m. They are trapezoidal in cross-section to maintain a uniform horizontal velocity throughout the depth of liquid. Large plants generally have channels of rectangular section and water depths of 3–4 m. Retention time in the ditch is in excess of 24 hours (extended aeration). The sludge age in oxidation ditches is normally 20–30 days. Consequently, the sludge solids undergo a considerable degree of stabilization and aerobic digestion; the surplus sludge yield is said to be about 50% of the combined primary and secondary sludge from conventional activated sludge systems.

Nitrification usually takes place, owing to the long retention time and high sludge age provided, and the presence of an adequate supply of oxygen. Because there are time intervals between the passage of mixed liquor through successive aeration zones, denitrification can also occur. In a number of cases the period allowed for passage through an anoxic zone (a zone devoid of oxygen) is deliberately increased (e.g. by switching off an aerator) to achieve a substantial reduction in the concentration of nitrate in the final effluent.

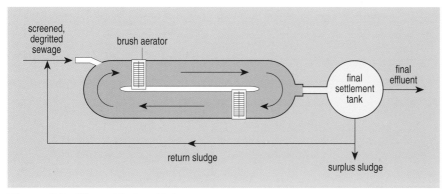

Figure 86   The oxidation ditch system

In the oxidation ditch system no primary sedimentation is required; thus screened, degritted effluent is fed straight into the ditch.

The pure oxygen activated sludge process
Look at the definition of ***pure oxygen activated sludge process*** in the Set Book.

It has been recognized that the use of pure oxygen rather than air in activated sludge systems can result in higher concentration driving forces and hence higher oxygen transfer rates per unit reactor volume. This allows a higher organic loading of the oxygen-fed reactor compared with an air system. Thus an increase in plant capacity can be achieved without a corresponding increase in reactor volume. This feature would be attractive where severe space limitations are present. The oxygen required in the treatment process can be purchased as liquid oxygen or produced by on-site generation. In the latter, pressure swing adsorption is often utilized to adsorb nitrogen from air onto a molecular sieve, to give 80% oxygen-enriched air as a product. Typically, for a conventional air system the design organic loading would be 0.2–0.6 kg BOD per kg MLVSS per day, while for an oxygen system it would be 0.4–1.0 kg BOD per kg MLVSS per day. An added advantage with pure oxygen systems is that the high dissolved oxygen levels enable nitrification to take place.

A commonly used pure oxygen activated sludge is the UNOX^{TM} process developed by the Union Carbide Corporation (Figure 87). This system consists of a series of completely mixed, roofed tanks, with the wastewater and oxygen gas moving concurrently through them. In each stage mechanical aerators are used to distribute the oxygen throughout the wastewater. The exhaust gases (containing carbon dioxide which inhibits bacterial action and which can also acidify the wastewater) are withdrawn from the headspace.

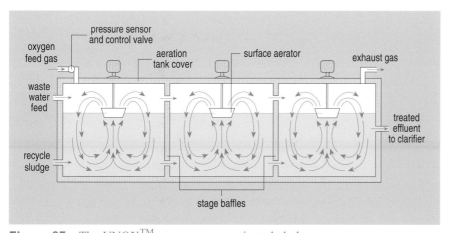

Figure 87   The UNOX^{TM} pure oxygen activated sludge process

The pure oxygen process has been shown to be particularly applicable where:

1   the available space for the construction of the treatment facilities is limited;

2   wide fluctuations occur in the organic loading to the plant;

3   strong wastewaters are to be treated.

Care must be taken in pure oxygen systems to prevent explosive atmospheres arising from the possible discharge of hydrocarbons to the treatment plant. Materials of construction have to be carefully selected as corrosion proceeds more rapidly in an oxygen-rich environment.

The pure oxygen system has been shown to have the following additional advantages over the conventional activated sludge process:

1   a sludge with improved settleability is produced;

2   lower quantities of sludge are produced;

3   there is a reduced risk of creating an odour nuisance when treating malodorous wastewaters.

Pure oxygen can also be used within conventional activated sludge units. One possibility for this is the Vitox System.

The Vitox System®

In the Vitox System (Figure 88) pure oxygen is pumped directly into the aeration tank in an activated sludge unit via an expansion nozzle. The process involves pumping settled wastewater through a venturi where gaseous oxygen is injected under pressure. Millions of fine bubbles are formed and dissolve under high pressure. The oxygenated wastewater, which now contains a high concentration of dissolved oxygen (20–30 mg l^{-1}), is then distributed via a multi-nozzle sparge system into the mixed liquor at the bottom of the aeration tank. The high-velocity jetting action of the nozzles shatters the undissolved gas into micro-bubbles, and entrains the surrounding effluent. Intimate mixing of the oxygenated effluent and the tank contents results. In order to achieve maximum effectiveness, the Vitox System is normally installed at the inlet end of the aeration tank where the demand for oxygen is greatest. It is often used to supplement the existing aeration system by providing extra oxygen at peak flows, or when seasonal overloading occurs. The Vitox System is also ideal where restricted land availability precludes the construction of new aeration tanks to cope with a sustained increased load.

The Deep Shaft™ process
Look at *sewage treatment, deepshaft process* in the Set Book.

The Deep Shaft process is a form of high-intensity activated sludge treatment carried out in an underground shaft. The process was a spin-off from research into the production of protein from methanol, carried out by ICI in the 1970s. In the Deep Shaft process, raw sewage or strong biodegradable effluent, together with activated sludge, enters a vertical shaft (30–150 m deep; 0.7–6.0 m diameter) made of steel or concrete, where biodegradation takes place. Although the shaft can treat raw sewage, screening and grit removal is first undertaken to prevent blockages and damage to pumps and other equipment. Solids are kept in suspension at the high flow velocity within the shaft and are carried out with the outflow. Allowing the solids to go through with the effluent results in a portion of them being degraded.

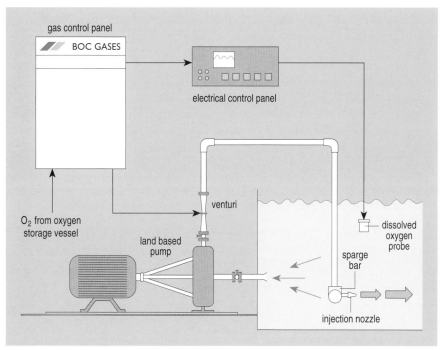

Figure 88 Diagram of a Vitox unit

The shaft consists of an upflow section (the 'riser') and a downflow section (the 'downcomer') which may be concentric or side by side (Figure 89). To start the circulation of the mixed liquor, compressed air is injected into the riser, reducing the density of the liquor and acting as an airlift. Since the header tank provides a common water level above both the riser and the downcomer, circulation begins. The supply of compressed air to the riser is then gradually reduced and transferred to the downcomer and, because the downward velocity of the liquid is greater than the upward velocity of the air bubbles, the entrained air is forced downwards. The air is rapidly dissolved in the water in the high pressure in the depths of the shaft and is readily available for use by the micro-organisms. As the mixture travels up the riser and the pressure falls, bubbles of residual dissolved gases come out of solution, serving as an airlift, sustaining the circulation velocity of about 1.5 m s^{-1}. The effluent retention time is 1–2 hours.

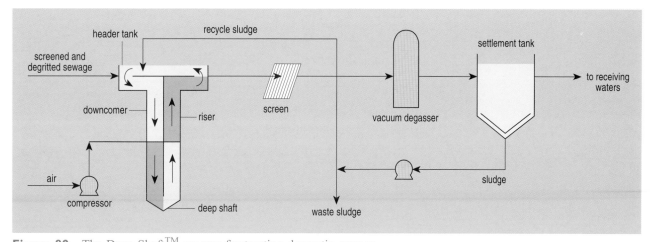

Figure 89 The Deep Shaft^{TM} process for treating domestic sewage

The outflow of treated effluent from the shaft contains bubbles of nitrogen and carbon dioxide attached to the sludge flocs which hinder their settlement. The liquid is therefore degassed by passage through the header tank, and is usually assisted by a vacuum device or by coarse or fine bubble aeration. The mixed liquor, now free from entrained gases, passes forward to the settlement tank, where sludge settles, to be recycled or taken away for disposal.

In the treatment of sewage in the Deep Shaft process, oxygen utilization may be as high as 90% (compared with 20% in the conventional activated sludge system) and the oxygen uptake intensity as high as $1 \text{ kg O}_2 \text{ m}^{-3} \text{ h}^{-1}$ at peak flow (compared with $<0.2 \text{ kg O}_2 \text{ m}^{-3} \text{ h}^{-1}$ in the conventional activated sludge process). This high oxygen uptake results from the greater dissolution of the oxygen at the high pressure in the shaft and the long bubble contact time (about 90 seconds, compared with about 15 seconds in conventional diffused air systems). This results in a lower power consumption and a lower aeration volume requirement. It has been observed that in the Deep Shaft process the amount of sludge generated is less than in the conventional system, due to the complex microbiological reactions occurring in the shaft. This has a positive effect on the operating costs of the treatment process, since sludge disposal is a major cost item in wastewater treatment. Another major advantage of the Deep Shaft process is that it requires much less land area than a conventional system treating the same load. For this reason it has found acceptance in densely populated cities where land availability is at a premium.

The largest Deep Shaft plant in the world is at Tilbury, on the north bank of the River Thames. The diameter of the shaft is 5.7 m, and its depth 60 m. It treats sewage from a population equivalent of 540 000, with the BOD of the influent 1100 mg l^{-1}, and a flow rate of 32 000 $\text{m}^3 \text{ d}^{-1}$.

SAQ 67

What is the BOD loading per capita assumed in the Deep Shaft plant at Tilbury?

The rotating biological contactor

The rotating biological contactor (RBC) is a system which combines the advantages of both the activated sludge system (long retention time in the active area, small space needed for plant) and the biological filter (sludge return not necessary, easy to operate and needing little maintenance or supervision). It has been employed as a sewage treatment plant for small communities. The sewage influent, after passing through a primary settlement tank, goes into a tank in which an assembly of vertical discs (usually made of glass-reinforced plastic) is slowly rotated by an electric motor at a speed of about three revolutions per minute (Figure 90). Usually about 40% of the area of these discs is submerged. The discs serve as physical support surfaces for the growth of micro-organisms and the rotation provides alternate immersion and aeration of the organisms. The discs are fluted or otherwise designed to increase the surface area available for the biological film to grow on. Nitrification can also be achieved with RBCs.

The RBC is similar to a biological filter in that both rely on microbes attached to a surface for biotreatment, but the RBC is more compact and does not result in a fly problem: because the biological film is immersed periodically in the sewage, flies do not colonize the discs. RBCs either have covers or are housed in buildings.

RBCs are quiet, require little attention, and can be made unobtrusive by being positioned partly below ground level. These factors make them suitable for small groups of houses, or for caravan and camp sites, and

Figure 90   A rotating biological contactor, with cover removed

there are large numbers in the UK. The RBC has been restricted to relatively small installations due to its high construction cost relative to an activated sludge system.

Biological aerated filters

Biological aerated filters (BAFs) (Figure 91) are fixed-film systems in which a support medium for micro-organisms is submerged in wastewater, providing a large surface area for biological treatment of the effluent to take place. Air (or sometimes oxygen) is introduced at the base of the reactor by aeration domes or diffuser pipes. BAFs can treat crude or settled sewage.

The support medium is usually of modular construction. Random packing has also been used, as has expanded polystyrene, porous stone, and expanded shale. The surface area offered is 140–1500 m^2 m^{-3}. The support medium may be submerged or floating, and reactors may be operated as either upflow or downflow systems.

The high specific surface area of the medium leads to a high density of micro-organisms, making BAFs very efficient. Low shear (tearing force) is exerted on the film of micro-organisms, and this results in its rapid build-up. To prevent the medium getting clogged, regular backwashing is required. The solids are separated from the effluent by filtration.

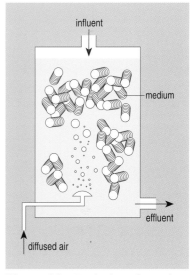

Figure 91   Typical configuration of a downflow BAF reactor

Organic loadings for BAFs are in the range 3000–8000 g BOD m^{-3} d^{-1}. Nitrification is usually carried out in a separate reactor where backwashing is not conducted. The BAF is a high rate system with a small space requirement. It is said to be stable to shock loads, and has cost advantages over conventional activated sludge systems in that there is no need for a return sludge flow.

There are non-backwash BAFs, called submerged aerated filters (SAFs), which utilize high voidage media, with specific surface areas typically less than 400 m^2 m^{-3}. These do not require backwashing because accumulated solids in the reactor are controlled by biomass sloughing and air-scouring. Due to the elimination of backwashing, SAFs are simpler and, therefore, more reliable than BAFs. SAFs normally treat settled sewage and require secondary sedimentation. The loading in SAFs is typically 430 g BOD m^{-3} d^{-1}.

Membrane bioreactors

Membrane bioreactors (MBR) are enclosed biological treatment units with ultrafiltration membranes for separating the biomass from the treated effluent prior to its discharge. This means of separation is very effective, and the biomass is returned to the aeration tank, where its concentration is around 20 000 mg l^{-1}.

Two different reactor configurations are possible:

1   Sidestream MBR. Here, the mixed liquor is pumped out of the biological reactor and put through a membrane filtration unit. The permeate is discharged while the biomass is returned to the bioreactor (Figure 92).

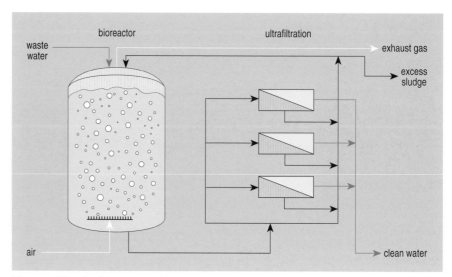

Figure 92   A sidestream MBR system

2   Submerged MBR. In this variant, the membrane unit is contained within the biological unit such that treated effluent is continuously filtered out, while the biomass remains within the bioreactor. In one design of this system, the membrane unit is mounted on top of a coarse bubble diffuser. The mixed flow of activated sludge and air bubbles is channelled between the membrane plates. The bubbles generate an upward flow of the mixed liquor over the membrane surface and minimize fouling.

The MBR process uses smaller reactors than a conventional activated sludge system and produces a higher quality of treated effluent. The avoidance of foaming, sludge bulking and odours is claimed. There is no need for a secondary sedimentation tank. Against the MBR process, however, is its high cost.

SAQ 68

(a)   How is the MBR process able to operate with a smaller reactor than a conventional activated sludge system?

(b)   In what ways would you expect the treated effluent quality to be higher?

(c)   Why might the claim of odour-free operation be true?

Sequencing batch reactors
Sequencing batch reactors are a batch process (as opposed to continuous) variant of the activated sludge process where there is no separate secondary sedimentation tank. Aeration and settlement take place in the same tank. Their main attraction is their smaller space requirement, and

for this reason they are becoming popular for small and medium-sized plants. The process comprises five different stages (Figure 93), which are carried out repeatedly.

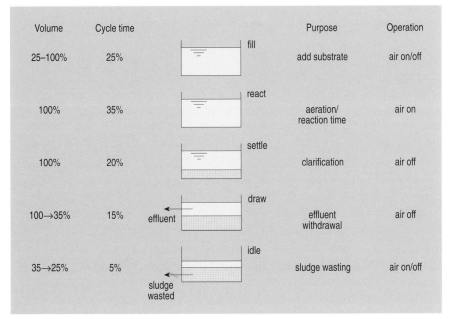

Volume	Cycle time		Purpose	Operation
25–100%	25%	fill	add substrate	air on/off
100%	35%	react	aeration/reaction time	air on
100%	20%	settle	clarification	air off
100→35%	15%	draw effluent	effluent withdrawal	air off
35→25%	5%	idle sludge wasted	sludge wasting	air on/off

Figure 93 The stages of operation in a sequencing batch reactor

In the first stage (top of Figure 93), effluent is fed into the tank. It is then aerated for 4–48 hours, longer periods being used for strong effluents. Following aeration, the effluent undergoes settlement in the same tank. The clarified effluent is then withdrawn. Some of the sludge is also removed for disposal. The reactor is then replenished and the cycle is repeated.

Waste stabilization ponds

Waste stabilization ponds are a simple means of treating wastewater biologically by harnessing the power of sunlight and wind. In this type of system, screened, degritted effluent is passed through a series of ponds with a total retention time of 10–50 days. In the ponds, bacteria oxidize the pollutants and work symbiotically with algae which provide oxygen through photosynthesis. The algae also utilize the carbon dioxide, ammonia and phosphate that are released by the bacteria. Aeration also occurs through the action of wind. No mechanical equipment is used in the ponds and hence operation and maintenance costs are very low. A typical layout for a waste stabilization pond system treating domestic sewage is shown in Figure 94.

The major part of the biodegradation of the sewage takes place in the *facultative* ponds (1–1.5 m deep), which are aerobic at the top and anaerobic at the bottom. *Maturation* ponds are usually about 1 m deep and serve to inactivate pathogenic bacteria and viruses through the action of UV radiation from sunlight and the greater algal activity in these shallow ponds, which raises the pH (above pH 8.5, pathogens are rapidly killed off) and the dissolved oxygen content. The long retention time in each of the ponds also enhances the sedimentation of parasite eggs and dormant forms of some parasitic organisms. In instances where the wastewater has a very high BOD (e.g. effluent from the intensive rearing of animals), *anaerobic* ponds are often used ahead of the facultative ponds. Anaerobic ponds are 2–5 deep and are nearly totally devoid of oxygen. They are commonly used for treatment of animal slurry (see Chapter 11 Agricultural pollution).

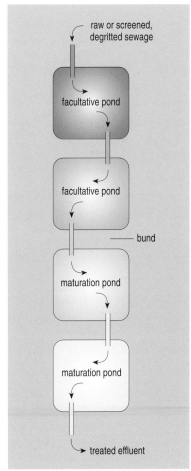

Figure 94 Layout of a waste stabilization pond system treating domestic wastewater

In an anaerobic pond, a floating crust some 40–60 mm thick forms, insulating the pond (preventing heat loss), maintaining anaerobic conditions and preventing odours from escaping. Solids settle to the bottom of the pond forming a sludge. Methane production can be high in the summer, with pockets of gas breaking through the crust.

Waste stabilization ponds are especially efficient in hot climates but are also used in colder areas: for example, in France there are about 2500 waste stabilization pond systems, in Germany there are about 1100, and in the USA about one-third of all wastewater treatment plants are of this type. Most of the systems in France and Germany serve populations of less than 1000. Though they require large areas of land, this need can be satisfied by locating the ponds at the outer perimeter of cities, or on disused land.

Treated sewage can be reused in irrigation if safe limits of faecal coliforms and intestinal nematode eggs are achieved in the treatment process. Waste stabilization ponds have been found capable of attaining these standards at low cost and are actively encouraged as a means of supplementing the water supply available for irrigation, especially in developing countries and in southern Europe, e.g. in Portugal. At the same time as treating wastewater, pond systems have been used to increase protein production through the rearing of fish and ducks in maturation ponds. Maturation ponds are also a tempting source of recreation – we had to rapidly put a fence around a set of these in Malaysia to stop children paddling in them!

The use of plants in wastewater treatment
Floating plants, such as water hyacinth and duckweed, have been used to treat effluents. Water hyacinth is a native of Florida and tends to be invasive, even blocking waterways. Grown in ponds, it can use the pollutants in the effluent as nutrients whilst absorbing the requisite oxygen and carbon dioxide from the air. The water hyacinth has an unbranched root system with rhizomes which supports a heterotrophic microbial population. The plant exhibits 'luxury' uptake of nutrients (absorbing far in excess of its requirements). It also absorbs heavy metals. Water hyacinths are mostly used as a polishing step in tertiary treatment (see Section 9.10), though they have been used in the secondary treatment of sewage.

Apart from floating plants, there are reed beds, or artificially constructed wetlands with emergent plants, for secondary or tertiary treatment. The plants (typically *Phragmites australis* or *Phragmites communis*) are grown in rows in beds of soil or gravel lined with an impermeable clay or synthetic liner (Figure 95). The effluent requiring treatment is fed into the bed. The depth of the beds is typically 600 mm.

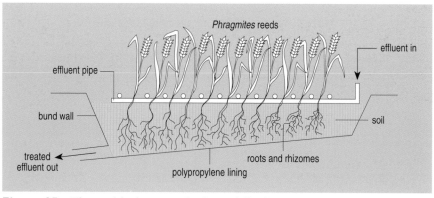

Figure 95   The reed bed system (horizontal flow)

The effluent to be treated is distributed through pipes and nozzles onto the reed bed and percolates down to the roots and rhizomes of the reeds. Oxygen is taken through the stomata (apertures) in the underside of the *Phragmites* leaves and passes down the hollow stem of the plant to the rhizome and root system.

However, there are also anoxic zones in the vicinity of the rhizomes. This mixture of environments permits the survival of both aerobic and anaerobic bacteria. Thus the processes of carbonaceous oxidation, nitrification, denitrification and anaerobic biodegradation can all take place. The treatment stages all occur in the root zone of the plants, hence the name root zone treatment.

The base of the reed bed has a slope of 2–8% to enable collection of the effluent after treatment.

Owing to the great diversity of microbial species in the soil, greater potential treatment is possible here: for example, the fungal species *Actinomyces*, *Streptomyces* and *Basidiomyces*, which are capable of biodegrading many synthetic chemicals such as the common pesticides and chlorinated hydrocarbons, are found in soil but are not normally in effluent treatment plants.

Root zone treatment has been used for landfill leachate, acid mine drainage, contaminated surface run-off, and for effluents from chemical plants containing traces of phenol, methanol, acetone and amines. They have been used for the treatment of screened, degritted domestic sewage from small communities, especially in Denmark and in Germany. There is even one in the Botanical Gardens in Carmarthen, Wales (Figure 96).

Figure 96 Part of the reed bed system at the Botanical Gardens in Carmarthen, Wales

At maturity, the reeds are 1.5–3.0 m high. Unlike mechanical treatment plant they are not unsightly or noisy. They are almost as expensive as mechanical treatment plant to set up but their running costs are low (since no electrical or mechanical equipment is needed) and they have no sludge disposal costs.

An equation relating the area of reed bed to the removal of BOD in sewage is:

$$A = Q \left(\frac{\ln C_o - \ln C_1}{k_1} \right)$$

where

A is the area of reed bed (m^2)

Q is the influent flow rate (m^3 d^{-1})

C_o is the influent BOD concentration (g m^{-3})

C_1 is the required final BOD concentration (g m^{-3})

k_1 is a constant (has a value of 0.067–1.0 m d^{-1} in the UK) for horizontal flow reed beds.

Due to their low loading rate, reed beds take up large areas of land. Also, in order to give the desired level of treatment to chemical wastes which are difficult to dispose of, the reeds may require several years to grow to full maturity. They are, however, able to withstand shock loads, and also offer a haven for wildlife, particularly for transmigratory birds. This has often been seen as advantageous by the local community.

SAQ 69

A small community of 16 houses in a village contemplates having a reed bed to replace the septic tanks presently treating its effluent. If the total population is 72 people, calculate the area of land required. Take the domestic wastewater generation as 150 l/person/day, the BOD as 230 mg l^{-1}, the final BOD to be 20 mg l^{-1}, and k_1 as 0.08 m d^{-1}.

Septic tanks
Septic tanks (Figure 97) are often used for partial treatment of sewage in areas which, for practical reasons, are not sewered (for instance, the effluent flow generated in the area may be small and intermittent, such as from farms or individual residences dispersed in the countryside).

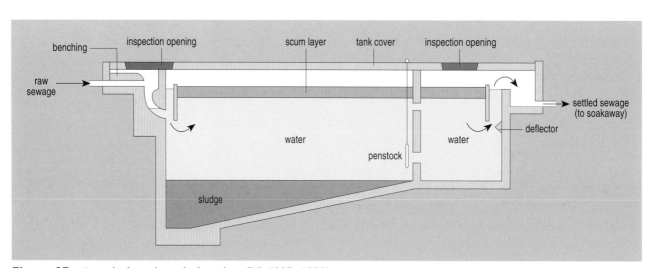

Figure 97   A typical septic tank (based on BS 6297: 1983)

Septic tanks usually have two compartments and are buried underground. The first compartment (which is usually twice the size of the second) provides for sedimentation, sludge digestion and sludge storage. The second compartment provides additional sedimentation and sludge-storage capacity and thus serves to protect against the discharge of sludge and other material that might escape the first chamber. A thick crust of scum usually forms at the water surface of the tank. The organic solids that settle out are partially digested by anaerobic bacteria. Sludge accumulates and the tank must be desludged occasionally, typically every 12 months, depending on loading. The sludge is tankered to a wastewater treatment plant for treatment and disposal. Experience has shown that in order to provide sufficiently quiescent conditions for effective sedimentation of the sewage solids in septic tanks, the liquid retention time should be at least 24 hours. Two-thirds of the tank volume is usually reserved for the storage of accumulated sludge and scum, so the size of the septic tank should be based on a 3-day retention time at start-up.

Effluent from a septic tank (which should be low in suspended solids but could be high in BOD) usually flows into a soakaway (a chamber with perforated or open-jointed walls), from where it percolates into the ground. In selecting a site for a soakaway it is important to consider the ability of the ground to absorb water, its permeability and the varying level of the water table with the seasons of the year.

9.9.15   Package treatment plants

The sewage from small groups of houses in remote locations is often treated in package treatment plants. These are compact, complete treatment systems which are prefabricated and hence easily installed. They are relatively simple to operate. They have all the unit operations of a full-scale sewage treatment plant except that they are smaller in size (to treat the low flows present).

Both activated sludge and biological filters can be made as package units. Being small in size, package treatment plants are able to use non-concrete tanks, e.g. tanks made of glass-reinforced plastic. This also makes them easy to transport. Rotating biological contactors are particularly favoured for package plants as they can be built partially below ground level and therefore do not significantly visually impair the landscape.

9.9.16   Chemical treatment of sewage

The various biological processes of sewage treatment could be replaced by chemical processes, such as coagulation and flocculation.

Advantages of chemical methods include their ability to process sewage at a faster rate, and they are also unaffected by toxic substances and changes in loading and temperature, whereas the organisms responsible for the effectiveness of biological processes are very susceptible to these factors.

The two main disadvantages are cost and the volume of sludge produced. Chemical reagents are very expensive – oxidizing bacteria can be exploited for approximately 5% of the cost of the cheapest oxidizing agent. Chemical methods, operating by precipitation, produce large volumes of sludge that contain both the solids removed from the sewage and most of the added chemicals. Chemical precipitation will not remove soluble BOD, only suspended and colloidal BOD. In biological treatment, the quantity of sludge produced is less because bacterial oxidation also results in the formation of carbon dioxide from organic carbon.

In the final analysis, however, it is economics that dictates the treatment process to be adopted. For biodegradable pollutants, biodegradation works out as the more favourable of the two.

9.9.17   Waterless sewage treatment

Water-borne disposal of sewage uses up vast quantities of water. Using the traditional lavatory flush system, each person utilizes some 50 litres every day of *clean, potable water* to transport 135–270 g of solid waste and 1.0–1.3 litre of liquid waste to the sewage treatment plant. The sewers and treatment plants needed to handle the tremendous volumes of wastewater generated by communities of people are costly, both in capital and in operation and maintenance. It would be much more prudent for sewage to be disposed of at source (i.e. within the compound of the house, factory, etc. where it is generated) using dry methods such as *composting*. Then sewers and treatment plants need only handle sullage (and rainwater run-off) and can be smaller and cheaper. The composting of the sewage could take place with other biodegradable domestic wastes, such as food waste. The composted material (free of pathogenic organisms) can be used beneficially in agriculture or horticulture, thus recycling valuable nutrients. Well-designed, dry composting toilets are being marketed at the present time.

If we are to conserve water and recycle nutrients usefully, the path to follow is perhaps the increased adoption of waterless sanitary disposal systems. The obstacle to be overcome, however, is the perceived nature of sewage by the public. The idea that sewage is an obnoxious waste has to be replaced by the view that is a valuable resource.

9.9.18   Relative costs

It is often difficult to get comparative costs for different treatment options because a lot depends on the scale of the plant, its location, etc. However, as a rough guide, the bandings 'low', 'medium' and 'high', can be allocated to the capital and operating costs of different systems. An attempt at this has been made in Table 29 but do not hold this against the author!

Table 29   Relative costs of different treatment options

System	Capital cost	Operating costs
Biological filters	High	Low
Conventional activated sludge	Medium	Medium
Contact stabilization	Medium	Medium
Oxidation ditch	Medium	Medium
Pure oxygen activated sludge process	High	High
Vitox	Medium	High
Deep Shaft	High	Medium
Rotating biological contactor	Medium	Low
Biological aerated filters	Medium	Low
Membrane bioreactors	High	High
Waste stabilization ponds	Low (if land cheap)	Low
Reed beds	High	Low
Septic tank	Low	Low
Chemical treatment	Medium	High
Composting toilet	High (for the individual)	Low

SAQ 70

Consider the different types of effluents given in Column A and select from Column B the most appropriate treatment technique or techniques for each of the effluents.

Column A	Column B
(a) Domestic sewage from a single cottage in the countryside	Pure oxygen activated sludge process
(b) An effluent with a high concentration of colloidal particles	Reed beds
	Vitox System
(c) Domestic and farm wastewaters in a sparsely populated rural area with a lot of land available	Rotating biological contactor
	Oxidation ditch
	Membrane bioreactor
(d) A high-BOD effluent from a food processing plant in a built-up area with little available land	Contact stabilization
	Septic tank
(e) Domestic effluent from a remote group of houses in an area of low soil permeability	Deep Shaft process
	Waste stabilization ponds
(f) An effluent with a high ammonia content from a fertilizer plant which has extensive land available	
(g) An industrial effluent with traces of mixed organics not easily degraded in a conventional mechanical plant	
(h) A mixed industrial–sanitary wastewater with a high and fluctuating organic load, in a city site	
(i) Domestic sewage which occasionally has peak loads from a sugar beet processing plant	
(j) Domestic sewage which has to be treated for reuse in watering a golf course	

BACK TO THE DOME

We saw in Section 5.6.2 that water from the different sources was treated for toilet flushing in the Millennium Dome. Now that you've learnt about the different treatment methods available, you will understand the reasons for the choices made at the site. The three types of water used were greywater, rainwater and groundwater.

The greywater from hand wash basins ($120 \ m^3 \ d^{-1}$) was treated by a biological aerated filter. A maximum volume of $100 \ m^3$ a day of rainwater was also collected and treated in two $250 \ m^2$ reed beds.

Finally, a 110 m borehole was used to pump out groundwater. The site was previously occupied by a gas works, and the groundwater was contaminated by hydrocarbons (such as benzene, toluene and pyridine) and hydrogen sulphide. Being located near to the tidal portion of the River Thames, the water was also hard and saline. Treatment was as follows:

The water was dosed with hydrogen peroxide (H_2O_2, a very strong oxidizing agent) and then passed through granulated activated carbon. The water was then mixed with the treated greywater and the treated rainwater, and the total flow passed through an ultrafiltration membrane before being processed in a reverse osmosis unit. The output was then suitable for use in toilet flushing.

SAQ 71

List the pollutants that would have been removed in each of the following treatment stages at the Millennium Dome:

(a) Biological aerated filter

(b) Reed beds

(c) Addition of hydrogen peroxide to groundwater

(d) Passage through a granulated activated carbon (GAC) column

(e) Ultrafiltration membrane

(f) Reverse osmosis unit.

9.10   Tertiary treatment

The processes so far described can produce an effluent containing no more than $30 \ g \ m^{-3}$ of suspended solids and $20 \ g \ m^{-3}$ of BOD. Sometimes more stringent standards may be necessary as, for example, when the effluent forms such a substantial part of a river flow that a dilution of less than 8:1 results, or when required by the conditions in the Urban Waste Water Treatment Directive, or by catchment management considerations, for example when the river is used for a public water supply. In such cases the effluent should not contain suspended solids greater in concentration than $10 \ g \ m^{-3}$, or have a BOD greater than $10 \ g \ m^{-3}$, or contain ammonia-nitrogen in excess of $10 \ g \ m^{-3}$. This standard is often referred to as the 10/10 standard (strictly speaking, the 10/10/10 standard). The additional processes beyond secondary treatment required to reach such a standard comprise tertiary treatment.

9.10.1   Suspended solids removal

Systems typically used to remove suspended solids in tertiary treatment are described below. The reduction in suspended solids also results in a lowering of the BOD because some of the solids are organic in nature and contribute to the BOD.

Microstraining

The microstrainers you met in Section 3.2 are also used in sewage treatment to retain solids with diameters larger than about 45 μm. The trapped solids are returned to the inlet of the treatment works. To reduce costs, the final effluent is often used as the washwater. To prevent biological growth on the fabric of the microstrainer (as a result of nutrients present in the treated effluent), a UV light is usually mounted alongside the washwater jets.

Sand filtration

The effluent from biological treatment is passed through rapid gravity sand filters, and the solid matter which has been trapped in the bed is removed by backwashing. The washings are pumped back to the inlet of the works.

Further settlement

Settlement of the final effluent will improve its overall quality. This may be carried out in special settlement lagoons similar to maturation ponds (see 'Waste stabilization ponds' in Section 9.9.14). During storage in the lagoons, the quality of the water improves as a result of some of the solids settling and the activity of bacteria, protozoa and algae. Suspended solids, BOD, pathogenic bacteria, nitrate and phosphate can all be reduced. The construction of such lagoons will, however, take up a considerable area of land and add to the total costs of the treatment works. This cost can be avoided if storm tanks are used instead. The procedure would be always to have one storm tank empty. During storm conditions, this empty tank would be filled first. While it is filling, the other storm tanks would be emptied to allow them to receive the storm water. Once the storm is over, the tanks can be emptied and returned to their tertiary treatment function.

> *The use of extended settlement seems simple and not overcostly. Can you think of any drawbacks in the process?*

In water with a good supply of oxygen, nitrate and phosphate, there is a strong possibility of algal growth and this could result in the effluent having a higher suspended solids content than the influent to the tertiary treatment process. But the presence of algae in the discharge is not altogether undesirable. The algae, if able to continue photosynthesizing, can contribute to the oxygenation of the receiving water. The algae could also increase the productivity of the receiving water. (For instance, algae would be 'food' to shellfish in coastal waters.) Finally, the non-toxic algae from the tertiary treatment process may be able to multiply and out-compete toxic algal species such as the blue-greens present in the receiving waterway. As an aside, lagoons can also develop into attractive semi-natural habitats that can be valuable for wildlife.

Grass plots

In this method the treated effluent is allowed to trickle slowly over grassland, resulting in a further reduction of the BOD and solids, but it has the disadvantage of requiring large areas of land with the correct characteristics, e.g. a slope of not greater than 1 in 60. Each cubic metre of effluent flow per day requires an area of 1.2 m^2 of grassland.

Reed beds can also be used to improve the quality of a 30/20 effluent. Lagoon, grass plot and reed bed treatment also remove the nitrate and phosphate nutrients, and so reduce the possibility of eutrophication in the receiving watercourse.

Specific processes for N, P and NH_3 removal can also be considered to be tertiary treatment operations.

SAQ 72

Which of the following processes is/are likely to remove more components than just suspended solids and BOD?

A Microstrainers

B Grass plots

C Lagoons

D Rapid gravity sand filters

E Reed beds

9.10.2   Nutrient removal

Under the Urban Waste Water Treatment Directive, new requirements were introduced for the control of nutrients in discharges. The aim is to reduce the level of phosphorus and nitrogen in effluents to concentrations at which excessive algal growth is not encouraged in the receiving water. For inland waters, nitrogen is abundant and phosphorus is considered to be the limiting nutrient. The converse is true for the sea. Where waters are defined as being sensitive with respect to a particular nutrient, discharges to these waters should not exceed 2 mg l^{-1} total P and/or 15 mg l^{-1} total N as annual averages for wastewater treatment plants of between 10 and 100 000 population equivalent, and 1 mg l^{-1} total P and/or 10 mg l^{-1} total N for plants above 100 000 population equivalent.

Ammonia and its removal

Domestic sewage typically contains 25 mg l^{-1} of ammoniacal nitrogen, most of it originating from the urea in urine. If high-ammonia wastewaters (e.g. abattoir effluents, landfill leachate, liquors from the dewatering of sludges from anaerobic digesters) are treated, a high residual quantity may be present in the secondary-treated effluent. Ammonia in the discharged effluent is undesirable for several reasons:

■ it has an oxygen demand;

■ it contributes to algal blooms;

■ in the free form it is toxic to fish and other aquatic animals;

■ if present in water used as a source of potable supply, it combines with chlorine in the disinfection stage, reducing its effectiveness as a disinfectant and increasing the chlorine demand of the water;

■ it accelerates corrosion of structures (e.g. bridges, water intake systems) in contact with the water;

■ it can be converted to nitrate, which would cause other problems.

Ammonia nitrogen exists in aqueous solution as either the ammonium ion (NH_4^+) or free ammonia (NH_3), depending on the pH of the solution, in accordance with the following equilibrium reaction:

$$NH_3 + H_2O \rightleftharpoons NH_4^+ + OH^-$$

At pH levels above 7, the equilibrium is displaced to the left and free ammonia predominates; at pH levels below 7 the equilibrium is shifted to the right and the ammonium ion predominates. An increasing level of pH above 7 results in a higher level of NH_3 being formed.

Ammonia can be removed from wastewater in several ways. The methods commonly used are described below.

Biological nitrification/denitrification   In this method, probably the most economical means of removing ammonia, micro-organisms are used (usually in an attached growth system) to convert the ammonia to nitrite and then to nitrate

$$2NH_4^+ + 3O_2 \xrightarrow{\textit{Nitrosomonas}} 2NO_2^- + 2H_2O + 4H^+$$

$$2NO_2^- + O_2 \xrightarrow{\textit{Nitrobacter}} 2NO_3^-$$

This is exactly the same process that normally takes place in biological filters during secondary treatment. It also occurs in soil and natural waters. The nitrates formed are then converted to nitrogen gas in an anoxic reactor because the denitrifying bacteria needed are anaerobic. A carbon source (typically methanol, CH_3OH) is added to facilitate the conversion:

$$6NO_3^- + 2CH_3OH \longrightarrow 6NO_2^- + 2CO_2 + 4H_2O$$

$$6NO_2^- + 3CH_3OH \longrightarrow 3N_2^- + 3CO_2 + 3H_2O + 6OH^-$$

Common denitrifying bacteria are *Pseudomonas denitrificans* and the *Hyphomicrobium* species.

Nitrification is an aerobic process, requiring 3.76 g of oxygen for every gram of ammonia oxidized. Denitrification, on the other hand, occurs under anoxic conditions. The energy required for denitrification is drawn from the organic content of the wastewater. In the event of the carbon content being low, external sources (most commonly methanol) are added. The facultative denitrifying bacteria reduce the nitrate to N_2 gas. With every gram of nitrate reduced, 0.65 g of oxygen are released. This can be used in nitrification. Similarly, the carbon content in nitrified effluent can be used for denitrification. Figure 98 shows one possible configuration of treatment units to achieve both nitrification and denitrification.

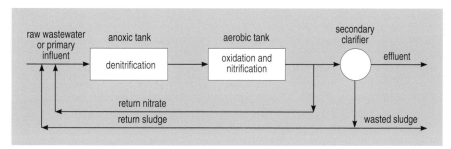

Figure 98   Schematic of the nitrification–denitrification process

In the anoxic tank, no aeration takes place, and denitrification occurs with a bacterial population high in denitrifiers. From the anoxic tank, the effluent flows to the aerobic tank where the oxygen level is maintained in excess of 2 mg l^{-1}. A sufficiently long retention time in this tank ensures that carbonaceous oxidation and nitrification take place. A part of the nitrified effluent is returned to the denitrification tank while the remainder goes for secondary settlement.

Nitrification–denitrification can be incorporated into oxidation ditch systems (Figure 99). Influent is fed to the anoxic zone and removed at the end of the aerobic zone.

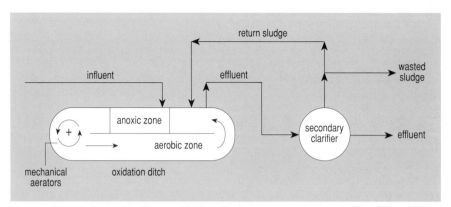

Figure 99   Schematic of an oxidation ditch incorporating denitrification

Non-biological means of removing ammonia

Air stripping   As mentioned earlier, at pH values above 7, ammonium ions are converted to free ammonia. In air stripping, the wastewater pH is increased using lime to about 11.0 (when 98% of the ammonia content is in the free form, i.e. NH_3 gas) and the wastewater then passed through a packed tower in which air is blown countercurrently (Figure 100). The ammonia gas is stripped out of solution by the air. The process requires large volumes of air and can be problematic during cold weather.

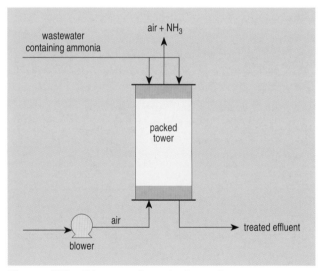

Figure 100   Diagram of a stripping column to remove ammonia from wastewater

Breakpoint chlorination   In this method, chlorine, which is an oxidizing agent, is used in excess to oxidize the ammonia nitrogen in solution to nitrogen gas, according to the equation

$$2NH_3 + 2HOCl \rightarrow 2NH_2Cl + 2H_2O$$
$$2NH_2Cl + HOCl \rightarrow N_2 + H_2O + 3HCl$$

Overall reaction: $\quad 2NH_3 + 3HOCl \rightarrow N_2 + 3H_2O + 3HCl$

The optimum pH operating range for breakpoint chlorination has been found to be 6–7. Outside this range, the chlorine dosage required to reach the breakpoint increases significantly and the rate of reaction slows. The chlorine dose required for breakpoint chlorination is about ten times the concentration of ammonia present. It is thus economically prohibitive except for special situations and where the ammonia concentration has already been significantly reduced. There can also be problems of chlorination by-products being generated and these can be of concern if the receiving watercourse is used for potable water abstraction downstream.

SAQ 73

Which of the following processes results in ammonia in an effluent eventually being expelled as ammonia gas to the atmosphere?

A   Nitrification

B   Denitrification

C   The oxidation ditch system

D   Air stripping

E   Breakpoint chlorination.

Phosphorus removal

Phosphorus may be present in wastewater as orthophosphates (e.g. PO_4^{3-}, HPO_4^{2-}, $H_2PO_4^-$ and H_3PO_4, which are available for biological metabolism without further breakdown), polyphosphate, and as organic phosphorus. Polyphosphates comprise two or more phosphorus atoms, oxygen atoms and, in some cases, hydrogen atoms combined in a complex molecule. Polyphosphates can interact with water and revert to the phosphate form. This hydrolysis is, however, slow. Organically bound phosphorus is not of major importance in domestic waste but can be significant in industrial effluents. Typically the phosphorus concentration in domestic wastewater is 8 mg l^{-1} and it originates from human body wastes (primarily urine), food wastes, and from household detergents and cleaning compounds. About 10% of the phosphorus in domestic wastewater is insoluble and is removed in primary sedimentation. A further 20% or so is incorporated into new bacterial cells in biological oxidation, with the remainder being in solution. In the biological oxidation stage of treatment most of the organic phosphorus and the polyphosphates are converted to orthophosphate.

Biological phosphorus removal in activated sludge systems can be enhanced by applying a sequence of anaerobic and aerobic conditions (Figure 101) which induce polyphosphate storage. The typical phosphorus content of microbial cells is 1.5–2% (dry basis) but with a system comprising an anaerobic and an aerobic zone, species which survive are capable of taking up phosphorus at levels above the normal requirement for growth (4–12% by weight). The *Acinetobacter* spp. is especially effective in this luxury uptake of phosphorus (see below).

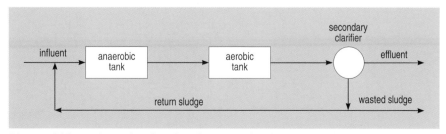

Figure 101   Schematic of a plant incorporating biological phosphate removal

In the anaerobic zone, the *Acinetobacter* spp. are stressed and utilize stored polyphosphate as an energy source. They also absorb volatile fatty acids (produced during anaerobic degradation) and store it as food in the form of polyhydroxybutyrate, a short-chain fatty acid (Figure 102). Phosphorus is released from the cells into solution.

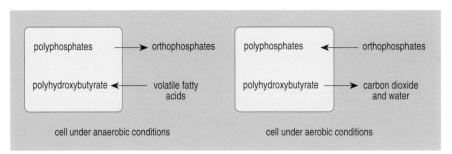

Figure 102   The principles in biological phosphate removal

When the bacteria are put into an aerobic environment, they oxidize the absorbed polyhydroxybutyrate, and take up further phosphate to be stored as polyphosphate granules. This storage is termed luxury phosphorus uptake, since an excess amount over that required for growth is taken up.

Phosphorus removal is achieved when these bacteria are settled out as sludge and withdrawn for disposal. The sludge, with its high phosphorus content, is ideal for agricultural land. Biological phosphate removal is largely independent of temperature over the range 5–20 °C. Final levels of under 1 mg l^{-1} of P are possible if the BOD:P ratio in the effluent is greater than 20. Chemical coagulation (see later) will be necessary to achieve minimal levels of phosphorus if this ratio is not reached.

Anaerobic conditions only occur in activated sludge when all dissolved oxygen has been removed, and no nitrate is present. In a conventional activated sludge plant, the return activated sludge will normally contain nitrate and, possibly, dissolved oxygen, and these components thus have to be removed. If this is not done, the process of denitrification will consume volatile fatty acids, which would otherwise be available for the production of polyhydroxybutyrate. The removal of nitrate and dissolved oxygen is achieved by either passing return activated sludge through an anoxic zone (where there is no free oxygen but nitrate and nitrite may be present) prior to recycling it to the sewage works' inlet, or by using a large internal recycle of mixed liquor to reduce the overall concentration of nitrate (Figure 103). This process is sometimes called the anaerobic–oxic or A–O process.

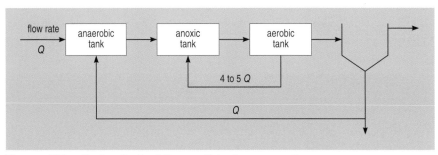

Figure 103   Cycle of mixed liquor; Q is the sewage flow rate

A variation of the A–O process is the PhoStrip® process (Figure 104). Here the phosphorus, rather than being removed in the form of a sludge, is withdrawn as a phosphorus-rich supernatant which can be chemically treated. Some of the waste activated sludge from the secondary

Supernatant: the clear liquid above a precipitate which has just settled out.

sedimentation tank is sent to an anaerobic phosphorus stripper. The phosphorus is released into the supernatant while the sludge is returned to the aeration basin. The supernatant is chemically treated with, say, lime to precipitate out the phosphorus. This can be sold as a resource.

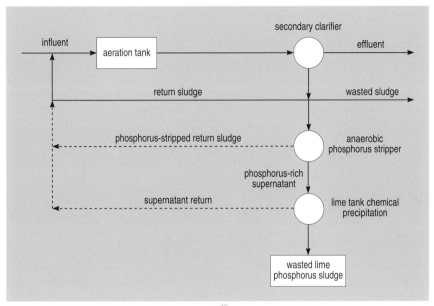

Figure 104 Schematic of the PhoStrip® process

The anaerobic tank, with a long retention time of 8–10 hours, conditions the mixed liquor so that it is able to take up the phosphorus in the aeration basin.

Since the process is continuous with only 10–15% of the total effluent passing through the anaerobic tank, only a small proportion of the flow is treated with coagulant. The higher phosphorus concentration of the liquid from the stripper makes chemical precipitation much more cost-effective.

Combined nitrogen and phosphorus removal
The Bardenpho® process is one that combines treatment stages for nitrification, denitrification, phosphorus removal and carbonaceous oxidation (Figure 105). The wastewater enters an anaerobic zone, where the mixed liquor is conditioned for phosphorus uptake. From there, it goes to an anoxic zone where denitrification takes place. Next it enters an aeration tank where carbonaceous oxidation, nitrification and luxury uptake of phosphorus occur. From here, it goes to an anoxic tank where denitrification takes place. Finally, the effluent goes to a small aerobic tank so that anaerobic conditions do not develop in the final sedimentation tank (this would result in the loss of absorbed phosphorus by the bacterial cells).

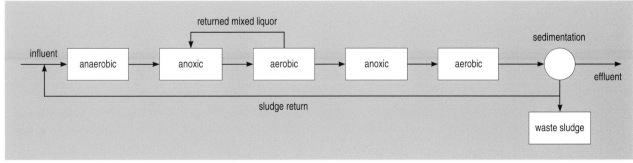

Figure 105 Schematic of the Bardenpho® process

9.10.2   Non-biological methods of removing nitrogen and phosphorus

While biological methods are the most economical, other options are available for removal of N and P. Nitrates remaining in the effluent after secondary treatment can be removed using ion exchange or reverse osmosis. These methods were described in Section 3.8.1.

Phosphorus in the orthophosphate form is easily precipitated using chemicals such as lime, aluminium sulphate, ferric chloride or ferric sulphate. The residual organic phosphorus and polyphosphates are removed by adsorption on to the precipitate. This is the cheapest and most effective means of phosphorus removal.

The reactions of orthophosphate with lime, aluminium sulphate and ferric chloride are:

Lime: $5Ca^{2+} + 3PO_4^{3-} + OH^- \rightleftharpoons Ca_5 (PO_4)_3 OH$ (hydroxyapatite)

Aluminium sulphate: $Al_2(SO_4)_3 \, 14H_2O + 2PO_4^{3-} \rightleftharpoons 2AlPO_4 + 3SO_4^{2-} + 14H$

Iron(III) chloride: $FeCl_3 + PO_4^{3-} \rightleftharpoons FePO_4 + 3Cl^-$

SAQ 74

A sewage works treating 100 000 $m^3 \, d^{-1}$ of domestic effluent plans to incorporate biological phosphate removal. Calculate the amount of P this unit operation will have to remove each day if the P level in the outflow from the plant is not to exceed 2 mg l^{-1}.

9.11   Advanced wastewater treatment

Even after tertiary treatment an effluent could still contain impurities (such as trace organics and pathogens) which might cause problems in the receiving water or interfere with a future use of the receiving water. The methods used to remove these impurities are usually classified under advanced wastewater treatment (AWT).

Some of the typical AWT processes are:

1   *Adsorption using activated carbon.* Adsorption on activated carbon may be used for the removal of residual non-biodegradable organic substances such as pesticides, or for the removal of compounds causing colour, taste and odour.

2   *Reverse osmosis.* Reverse osmosis can be used to remove all the suspended solids and pathogens present in tertiary-treated water. The process also removes any high molecular weight solutes present.

3   *Disinfection.* In many countries (e.g. in southern Europe and in the Middle East) the reuse of treated sewage for irrigation of trees and bushes, fodder crops, and crops that have to be cooked prior to eating (e.g. potatoes, onions) is encouraged. Disinfection of the treated effluent is carried out to render it free of pathogens. Typically, tertiary-treated effluent of 10/10 standard is treated with chlorine. The chlorine added will initially be consumed by any ammonia present, and then a free residual will develop. In instances where treated sewage is discharged into the sea, disinfection is often carried out to prevent pathogens reaching bathing areas. Microfiltration membranes have been used for the removal of bacteria and viruses. Disinfection by UV

is also practised. In order to protect the environment from potentially harmful compounds produced as by-products of chemical disinfection, the Environment Agency in England and Wales prefers non-chemical methods of eliminating pathogens, such as UV radiation.

SAQ 75

(a) When is tertiary treatment likely to be required for the final effluent from a sewage works?

(b) If the effluent from a sewage works has to be improved in terms of BOD and SS, but there is little space for construction at the works, which of the tertiary treatment processes could be selected?

SAQ 76

Which of the following statements about sewage effluent would be applicable after its treatment?

A It will contain at most 30 g m^{-3} of suspended solids and have a BOD of 20 g m^{-3}.

B It will conform to standards depending on the needs of the watercourse receiving it.

C It will not be a risk to public health.

D It will be potable.

E It will not contain any polluting substances.

F It will not contain any suspended solids or toxic chemicals or have a BOD.

SAQ 77

Complete the following diagram on sewage treatment.

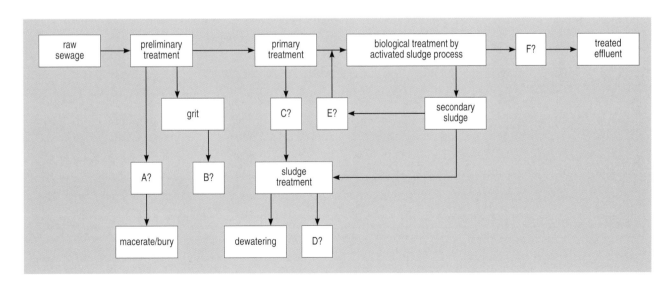

9.12 Summary

The aims of sewage treatment are to reduce the content of biodegradable material in the sewage, and to eliminate any toxic materials and pathogenic organisms present in the effluent.

Sewage treatment by the traditional mechanical/biological method can include some or all of the following processes: screening, grit removal, comminution, primary sedimentation, biological oxidation and secondary sedimentation. In biological oxidation, bacteria convert the soluble and colloidal organic matter into new cell material. This cell material is removed as sludge in the secondary sedimentation tank. The effluent after biological treatment and sedimentation should be of 30/20 quality or better, i.e. with suspended solids content not exceeding 30 g m^{-3} and BOD not exceeding 20 g m^{-3}.

Industrial effluents generally have a wider range of wastewater characteristics than domestic sewage and may contain toxic and refractory components. With appropriate pretreatment, industrial effluents can often be treated together with domestic sewage, resulting in cost savings and more effective control of pollution. In situations where the volume and/or the pollution load of the industrial effluent is high, it has to be treated on its own.

Activated sludge units and biological filters are the main types of bioreactor in wastewater treatment. Many variants of the two exist, each with advantages for a particular wastewater or situation. The greatest potential for cost-effective treatment and safe reuse of sewage might be in waterless sanitary disposal systems but first these have to gain public acceptance. Such systems are unlikely, however, to be feasible in urban areas.

Tertiary treatment may be carried out when a particularly high quality effluent is required. The suspended solids (and associated BOD) concentration is reduced using processes such as microstraining, sand filtration, settlement, and grass plots. Elimination of ammonia, nitrates and phosphates can be achieved with biological systems. A variety of non-biological means is available for elimination of these substances. These include:

for ammonia	air stripping
	breakpoint chlorination
for nitrates	ion exchange
	reverse osmosis
for phosphorus	precipitation using lime, aluminium sulphate, ferric sulphate or ferric chloride

Further purification of the treated effluent is possible using advanced water treatment techniques such as activated carbon adsorption, reverse osmosis and disinfection.

10   SLUDGE TREATMENT AND DISPOSAL

10.1   Introduction

Sludge is the product that arises as a result of removing solids from, and reducing the BOD of, sewage and trade wastes using the various treatment processes we discussed earlier. While the liquid part of sewage can be treated satisfactorily, the treatment and disposal of sludge presents the greatest problems for pollution control. Unsatisfactory methods of disposal can lead to further pollution. Sludge treatment and disposal may represent up to 50% of the total cost of sewage treatment.

10.2   Sludge production and sludge characteristics

Sewage sludge is a direct result of the presence of solids in suspension and an indirect result of the biological treatment of dissolved and emulsified organic matter. The volume of sludge generated in sewage treatment is 1–2% of the volume of sewage treated.

The sludge separated during the treatment processes is an evil-smelling, highly putrescible, thick liquid containing a considerable quantity of water. Table 30 indicates how much sludge may be expected from each treatment process per head of population.

Table 30   Quantity and water content of sludge generated in different operations in wastewater treatment

Source of sludge	Quantity (kg per head per day)	Water content (%; wet basis)
Primary sedimentation	1.1	95.5
Biological filters:		
Low-rate filters	0.23	93.9
High-rate filters	0.30	94.0
Activated sludge unit	2.4	98.5

EXERCISE

How many kilograms of dry solid matter are produced per head per day from primary sedimentation sludge?

ANSWER

From Table 30, primary sedimentation sludge has a water content of 95.5%, i.e. for every 1 kg of sludge, 0.955 kg is water. So out of 1.1 kg of sludge per head per day, the quantity of dry solid matter is given by

$$(1 - 0.955)\,(1.1) = 0.0495 \text{ kg}$$

EXERCISE

What volume of sludge is produced per day from an activated sludge process in a sewage treatment works serving a town of 20 000 population? Take the sludge density as 1200 kg m^{-3}.

ANSWER

For a town of 20 000 the total quantity of sludge from the activated sludge process is

$$(20\ 000)\ (2.4) = 48\ 000 \text{ kg d}^{-1}$$

This is equivalent to a volume of

$$\frac{48\ 000}{1200} = 40 \text{ m}^3 \text{ d}^{-1}$$

Note the comparatively high water content or low percentage of solid matter contained in activated sludge. This is a result of the complicated nature of activated sludge and the interaction of the forces between its particles. The organic component of sewage sludge consists of proteins, carbohydrates and fats which are produced by the human population as a result of its eating habits.

The sludge produced in sewage treatment will have a wide range of constituents. A combined sewerage system collects solids from hard surface areas and this slightly affects the amount of sludge generated. A particular contribution comes from grit that is spread on roads during frosty weather. Although grit removal is incorporated early on in the system, not all the grit is removed and some inevitably passes on to appear in the sludge. Sludge contains 20–30% mineral matter (on a dry basis), most of which is grit. The composition of sludge is also affected by the trade effluents discharged into the treatment works. There may be inorganic material from metal industry wastes, or organic matter from slaughterhouses and distilleries.

The amounts and characteristics of solid matter in trade effluents vary, despite the limits that are placed on the suspended solids, BOD, metals, etc., when a consent is given to discharge wastes to a sewer. Sludge can also contain toxic material which has been removed from the sewage during treatment and it is this toxic material which restricts the use of sludge as a soil fertilizer or conditioner. Heavy metals in particular can end up in the sludge, either through precipitation or adsorption onto the microbial flocs.

Before disposal, the sludge will require treatment.

10.3   Methods of treatment

Table 30 showed that over 90% of sewage sludge is water; thus, before disposal can be considered, the sludge leaving the works should be dewatered to reduce the volume and weight of material for disposal. The dewatering also helps to prevent the sludge from decomposing and creating unpleasant odours. To improve the efficiency of dewatering it is often necessary to include a preliminary conditioning stage to release as much of the bound water as possible and to allow the solids to agglomerate. There are several such conditioning processes which can be used. The method chosen will depend on the characteristics of the sludge.

The sludge can be thickened by coagulation, flocculation and sedimentation. Chemicals such as aluminium sulphate, iron salts, lime and polyelectrolytes can be used as coagulants (as for water treatment, see Section 3.3). Thickening takes place in a tank equipped with a slow-moving paddle or a set of tines (prongs). Sludge settles and supernatant is drawn off. The coagulants used are costly but the increase in solids content of the thickened sludge can make up for the extra cost involved.

Another method of conditioning the sludge for ease of dewatering involves heat treatment. The sludge is heated to 175–230 °C under high pressure (1000–2000 kPa). Under these conditions, the water that is bound within the sludge is released.

After the preliminary conditioning, the sludge can be further treated to increase the solids content by dewatering.

The traditional method of dewatering sludge is by air-drying on open beds. These drying beds consist of large areas (0.5 m^2 per person served by the sewage treatment works) usually surfaced with sand or ash and enclosed by low walls. The beds are filled with wet sludge to a depth of approximately 0.2 m and left until the sludge (cake) is dry enough (20–50% solids content) to be removed by hand or by mechanical methods. This method of treatment is entirely dependent upon the weather. During the summer the sludge may be fit for removal after two weeks, but in the winter it may be months before the sludge can be removed. Drying beds often give rise to offensive smells. The main argument advanced for their continued use is that they require only a small labour force using automatic means (or a shovel) for lifting and conveying the sludge cake. They are usually only found in small rural works.

Other methods of dewatering use mechanical systems and include pressure filtration, vacuum filtration and centrifuging. These were detailed in Section 3.12. The extracted water, high in BOD and suspended solids, is directed to the treatment works inlet.

Sludge can also be composted with household refuse to form an organic manure. This hasn't been popular because the resulting manure often contains broken glass and other debris, and it is unsuitable if the sludge contains toxic waste such as heavy metals. However, manuring is one method of disposal (see Section 10.4).

Many wastewater treatment plants use anaerobic digestion prior to dewatering and disposal (Figure 106). Here, thickened sludge in an airtight tank is partially broken down by anaerobic bacteria to release methane and carbon dioxide. The digester contents are heated to 35 °C and completely mixed. Heating of the sludge in the digester takes place by pumping the sludge through a coil contained in a hot water tank. Alternatively, hot water can be pumped through coils positioned in the digester itself. The retention time is 15 days or less. The output from the digester goes to a second unheated tank where separation of the digested solids from the liquor takes place.

In the digester, the complex organic material is first broken down by enzymes into simpler molecules. The digestion process occurs in two steps:

$$\text{raw sludge} \xrightarrow{\text{acid-forming bacteria}} \begin{array}{l}\text{volatile fatty acids}\\\text{carbon dioxide}\\\text{biomass}\\\text{hydrogen}\\\text{ammonium salts}\\\text{sulphides}\end{array} \xrightarrow{\text{methane-forming bacteria}} \begin{array}{l}\text{methane}\\\text{carbon dioxide}\\\text{small amounts of } H_2, N_2\\\text{and other gases}\end{array}$$

In the first step, acid-forming bacteria (such as *Clostridium* spp. *Peptococcus* spp., *Desulphovibrio* spp., etc.) convert the organic material in the sludge to volatile fatty acids (such as acetic, propionic and butyric

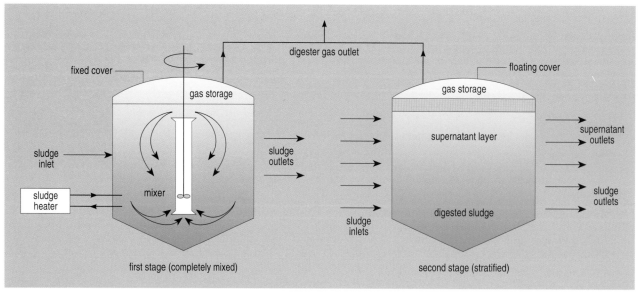

Figure 106   Schematic of the anaerobic digestion process

acids) and other compounds. In the second step, methane-forming bacteria (e.g. *Methanobacterium* and *Methanobacillus* spp.) transform the volatile fatty acids to methane and carbon dioxide. Many of the methane-forming organisms identified in anaerobic digesters are similar to those found in the stomachs of ruminant animals and in organic sediments taken from lakes and rivers.

The methane gas comes out of the digester with carbon dioxide in the proportions 65–70% CH_4 and 30–35% CO_2 and can be used as an energy source. In small treatment plants, the gas is usually used to heat the digester contents to maintain the temperature at 35 °C. Any surplus can be used to heat the offices and laboratories at the treatment plant. Small amounts of H_2, N_2 and other gases may also emerge from the digester. Where there are several digesters producing an appreciable quantity of gas, electricity generation is often carried out, with the surplus being sold to the utility companies.

The pH of the digester should be controlled at about 7.0 since the rate of methane production slows down below this value. Adequate alkalinity (1000–5000 g m^{-3} as $CaCO_3$) is required to buffer the sludge. Toxic material input should be controlled, e.g. heavy metal concentration should not exceed 1 g m^{-3}.

Sludge can be introduced continuously or intermittently. The stabilized sludge (the **biosolids**) has a total solids content 35–40% lower in volume compared with the input. It is not malodorous and is smoother and darker in comparison with the input sludge. Pathogenic organisms are much reduced in number.

In anaerobic digestion, organic nitrogen compounds are broken down to ammonia and ammonium salts, giving much increased concentrations of nitrogen in the liquid phase. This increases the immediate availability of nitrogen to crops if the wet sludge is used as a manure and soil conditioner on agricultural land.

The supernatant from digesters is highly polluting with a high BOD, COD and ammonia, together with a strong colour, and can be a problem. Normally it is returned to the works inlet for treatment. This is usually done at night when the incoming sewage flow is low and the plant is underloaded.

Note that you will also meet the subject of anaerobic digestion in Block 4: *Wastes management* and Block 6: *Air quality management*.

SAQ 78

List the conditions favouring anaerobic decomposition of sludge.

10.4   Methods of disposal

Sludge, in the UK, may be spread on land (land application), dumped in sludge lagoons, buried, composted with household refuse, dumped in landfill sites or incinerated. Up till the end of 1998, sludge was allowed to be dumped at sea, and this was the disposal route for about 30% of the sludge generated in the UK. Purpose-built vessels used to take sludge from the large cities such as London, Manchester, Glasgow and Belfast and dump it, usually outside the 3-mile territorial limit. At the Third North Sea Conference in 1990, a decision was made to stop all sea disposal of sludge by 1998.

In 2005, some 69% of sludge was applied on agricultural land, and 9% was used for land reclamation or restoration. The remainder was landfilled or used in other ways, such as in composting.

10.4.1   Land application

Traditionally, sludge is spread on agricultural land where it is beneficial as a soil conditioner. This disposal method requires large areas of land, and suitable weather conditions.

The value of sludge as a fertilizer is not high since it contains on average only 2.3% nitrogen, 1.3% phosphate and 0.3% potassium as potash. This is insignificant compared with the nutrients applied each year as artificial fertilizers. However, the organic matter in sludge forms a humus which can be a useful soil conditioner. Most sludge is produced in large urban areas and it can be extremely expensive to transport it to farming areas where it is given free to farmers. A further practical difficulty is that farmers only require sludge at certain times of the year, whereas it is produced all year round. The amount of agricultural land able to take sludge is also limited.

Nevertheless, land application has been identified as the *Best Practicable Environmental Option* for sewage sludge. But health scares in recent years (e.g. salmonella, BSE, *Cryptosporidium*, etc.) have raised concern over the safety of recycling sludge to agricultural land. This unease led to a Steering Group, chaired by ADAS (Agricultural Development Advisory Service), comprising representatives of the UK water industry, the major supermarket chains and various Government agencies. This Steering Group formulated the ADAS Sludge Matrix (Table 31), which defines the type of sludge allowed for various crops. This is seen as an effective means of combining good environmental practice and the protection of consumer health.

Table 31   The ADAS matrix for the safe application of sewage sludge to agricultural land

Type of crop	Untreated sludge	Digested sludge	Advanced treated sludge (5)
Fruit	No	No	No (6)
Salad	No	No	No (6)
Vegetables	No	No (1)	Yes (6) (7)
Horticulture	No	No	Yes
Combinable and animal feed crops	No (2)	Yes (3)	Yes
Grass	–	–	–
Silage	No	Yes (3)	Yes
Grazing	No	Yes (3) (4)	Yes
Maize	–	–	–

Guidance notes

(1) Field vegetables

Field vegetables may form part of an arable rotation to which digested sludge is applied, subject to the following:

• a period of 12 months must elapse between the application of digested sludge for the arable crop and harvest of the following field vegetable crop;

• where the field vegetable crop may be eaten raw, application must be made at least 30 months before harvest.

(2) Combinable and animal feed crops (e.g. wheat, field beans, oilseed rape)

Where a field is returning to a rotation which may include field vegetables, the periods specified in (1) above shall apply.

(3) Digested sludge

The application of digested sludge to these crops will be permitted and the water industry has put in train a research programme to provide the necessary assurances that food safety is not compromised.

(4) Grazing

Digested sludge may be deep injected into grassland used for grazing subject to (3) above.

(5) Advanced treated

To include heat treated and other methods of treatment (e.g. sludge pasteurization, mesophilic anaerobic digestion, thermophilic anaerobic digestion, composting, lime stabilization of liquid sludge, liquid storage and dewatering and storage. These treatments significantly reduce the potential health hazards from salmonella and viruses).

(6) EU Directive

In accordance with the Regulations (SI 1989 No. 1263) which implement EU Directive (86/278/EEC) and the 1996 DoE Code of Practice for the Agricultural Use of Sewage Sludge, sludge may not be applied to growing fruit and vegetable crops within 10 months of harvest.

(7) Regulations

In accordance with the regulations referred to in (6) above, sludge may not be applied within 10 months before harvest, if crops are normally in direct contact with soil and may be eaten raw.

Many urban sewage works process a significant amount of industrial waste in addition to household waste. As a result, toxic materials (e.g. toxic metals) concentrate in the sludge and restrict its application to land. The use of sewage sludge on land is now strictly controlled by EU Directive

86/278/EEC. This Directive provides two alternative means of controlling sludge application to land. One method is to state the maximum quantities of sludge (as tonnes dry matter) that can be added to a unit area of soil each year, while at the same time staying within the limits set for heavy metals in the sludge. The second method is to use the limit value quoted for the amount of heavy metals which may be added annually to agricultural land, based on a ten-year average. It is the second method which has been adopted in the UK.

The disposal of sewage sludge would be greatly facilitated if the concentration of heavy metals in it could be reduced. This can be achieved by strict trade effluent control. This approach is now being pursued more vigorously not only for inorganic pollutants but also for some organic pollutants.

SAQ 79

Under what conditions can digested sludge be applied to grazing land?

10.4.2   Incineration

Incineration will destroy any toxic organic compounds present in the sludge and leave the toxic metals unaffected (except those which are volatile) in the non-combustible ash. The main gain in incineration is the large reduction in the volume of waste to be disposed of, along with the elimination of the nuisance from biological decomposition. Incineration still leaves the ash (some 25–40% of the incoming load on a dry basis) to be disposed of and this can have high polluting qualities. The gaseous effluent from the incinerator will also have to be treated (using methods described in Block 4: *Wastes management*) to meet the required standards for emission. Even with all these considerations, incineration is seen by many as the most practicable alternative to sea dumping of sewage sludge. London has opted for this and built two large sludge incinerators at Beckton and Crossness.

Other current methods of sludge disposal include:

1   dumping in large sludge lagoons or sludge beds;

2   dumping in trenches which are then filled in with soil;

3   dumping of dewatered and dried sludge on selected landfill sites.

The first method can cause objectionable smells because the sludge dries slowly. In the third method, the quality of the material to be discharged with regard to smell, groundwater pollution, and space and transport requirements, is of crucial importance. Where the quality is acceptable, method 3 is not likely to add significantly to the problems already arising from the presence of refuse.

It is worth noting that all the methods considered depend on the availability of land.

SAQ 80

What effluents would you expect from an incineration plant?

SAQ 81

Which treatment processes in a sewage treatment works give rise to sludge?

SAQ 82

(a) What volume of sludge is produced per day from a sewage treatment works with primary sedimentation and a low-rate biological filter which serves a town of 100 000 population? Take the sludge density as 1000 kg m^{-3}.

(b) What volume will be produced from primary sedimentation with an activated sludge process?

SAQ 83

What are some of the benefits of treating sludge by anaerobic digestion?

10.5   Summary

In a sewage treatment works, the main sidestream products, apart from screenings and grit, are the various forms of sludge. Treatment and disposal routes depend on the volume and characteristics of the sludges produced.

Sludge treatment and disposal represents up to 50% of the total cost of sewage treatment.

The supernatant from sludge dewatering represents a significant load of recycled suspended solids and BOD to the treatment works. The effects of the final disposal methods and return flows from sludge treatment can have major implications.

Methods of sludge treatment include thickening with mechanical dewatering (after conditioning with chemicals or heat), air drying, composting and anaerobic digestion. Methods of disposal currently used include land application, sale as compost, burial in trenches or landfill sites, and incineration. There are strict guidelines in the form of a safe sludge matrix produced by ADAS, for the use of sludge on agricultural land.

11 AGRICULTURAL POLLUTION

11.1 Introduction

One often hears news reports of fish kills and other mishaps occurring due to farm effluents entering watercourses. The effects of N and P-rich run-off from fields in contributing to eutrophication have been discussed in Chapter 7, but the whole activity of farming can be seen as potentially damaging to the environment unless controls are put in place. Air pollution and solid waste related to farms will be covered in Block 6: *Air quality management* and Block 4: *Wastes management*, respectively. Here we will concentrate on the aqueous aspects.

11.2 The control of agricultural pollution

Agricultural pollution, accounting for about 11% of pollution incidents in the UK, can arise from a well-defined source (referred to as a point source earlier in Section 6.1) such as a pesticide store or from diffuse (or non-point) sources such as a field. Both of these categories will now be considered, together with the possible control measures.

11.2.1 Point sources

On a farm, where several different activities can be taking place, the main point sources of pollution include the following:

slurry tanks or pits (slurry being defined as the excreta produced by livestock, or a mixture of such excreta, bedding and water resulting from washing out of pens, or yards, generally with 4–15% dry matter);

silage effluent tanks;

pesticide and fertilizer stores or handling areas;

uncovered exercise or feeding areas;

wastewater storage tanks;

dungsteads;

fuel oil tanks.

Pollution prevention is best achieved by ensuring that each potential point source is properly sited, designed, constructed and managed, the aim being to contain the pollutants and prevent their uncontrolled release to the environment. For instance, bunding is required for all chemical storage drums. Foremost among the measures would be that the walls and base of any containment structure should be impermeable to the liquid being held.

Point sources of pollution should be sited as far from watercourses as possible (at least 10 m away), and below any water sources on the site. The ground conditions should be appropriate, i.e. slurry pits should be sited in low-permeability soils, or on an artificial liner.

Slurries

Approximate excreta rates for different animals are given in Table 32. The excreta contains micro-organisms such as salmonella, toxin-producing *E. coli* and campylobacter, and could even contain *Cryptosporidium*. These are all serious contaminants which should be prevented from entering potential drinking water sources. It must be remembered that washwaters from animal houses, bedding and run-off from farmyards are routinely mixed with excreted wastes and directed, as slurry, to the slurry pit. Hence these additions must be considered when sizing the pit. The pit must be big enough to hold at least 4 months' slurry unless a safe year-round disposal system is available.

Table 32   Approximate excreta production for different animals

Type of livestock	Body weight (kg)	Excreta (l d^{-1})	Approx. % dry matter in excreta
Dairy cow	500	41	10
Pig	50	4.0	10
Broiler	2	0.04	60
Duck	2	0.03	12
Laying hen	2	0.11	25
Turkey	7	0.17	23

EXERCISE

A farmer wants to design a slurry pit to contain the excreta from his broiler house where there are 400 chickens, for a period of 4 months. He also wants to direct rainwater from the farmyard (50 m × 30 m) into the same pit in order to dilute the waste and make it pumpable. If the long-term average rainfall for the 4-month period is 120 mm, calculate the minimum size of pit required.

ANSWER

Volume required for excreta

$$= 400 \text{ broilers} \times 0.04 \frac{1}{\text{broiler} \cdot \text{day}} \times 120 \text{ days} \times \frac{1}{1000} \frac{\text{m}^3}{1} = 1.92 \text{ m}^3$$

Volume of run-off

$$= 50 \text{ m} \times 30 \text{ m} \times \frac{120}{1000} = 180.00 \text{ m}^3$$

Total $= 181.92 \text{ m}^3$

Therefore, the minimum volume of pit required is 182 m^3.

Silage effluent
Silage is cattle food produced by fermenting grass, cereals or maize. These materials can be fermented in silos, in wrapped and sealed bales, or in field heaps. Figure 107 shows a typical walled silo and baled silage.

A strong, corrosive effluent is produced, with maximum flow occurring within two days of putting the material in the silo. This silage liquor should not be able to pass through the silo base, and the base should have channels around it to collect it, if it leaks out. The base and the channels should be resistant to the corrosive effects of the silage effluent (it can dissolve concrete!).

The amount of effluent depends on how wet the material is when put into the silo (Table 33). The amount produced from grass can be minimized by wilting it to 25% dry matter or more before putting it into the silo. With cereals and maize, little effluent is produced provided they are harvested at the correct stage of maturity.

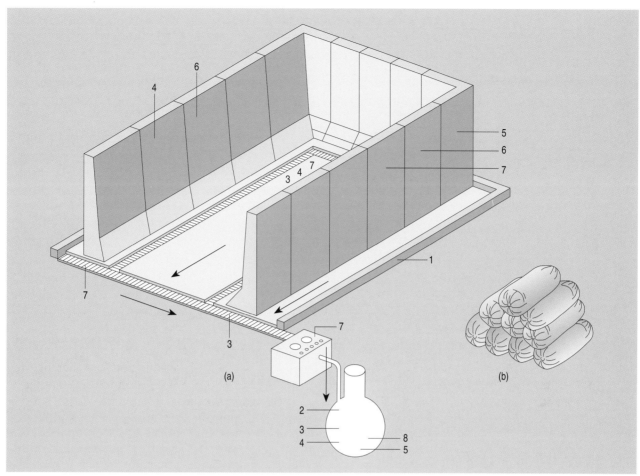

Figure 107 (a) A walled silo. Key: 1, Base must extend beyond walls and include a perimeter drainage channel. 2, Effluent tank capacity (20 litres/cubic metre of silo capacity – up to 1500 m³; above 1500 m³, 6.7 litres/cubic metre of silo capacity). 3, The silo base, tank and drains must all be impermeable. 4, Base and walls of silo plus tank and drains shall be resistant to attack from silage effluent. 5, No part of the installation should be within 10 m of a watercourse. Field silage should not be made or stored within 10 m of a watercourse or 50 m of a protected water supply source. 6, Silo walls must be designed to BS 5502, Part 22. 7, Silo, tank and drains must be capable of lasting for 20 years (with routine maintenance). 8, Below-ground effluent tanks must be capable of lasting for 20 years without maintenance. The Environment Agency will expect a certificate to confirm suitable design and construction. (b) Baled silage

Table 33 Approximate volumes of effluent produced from grass silage

Dry matter content of grass (%)	Effluent per tonne of silage (litres)
16	220
18	170
20	130
22	90
26	40
30	0

Since rainwater that falls onto a silo will add to the amount of effluent, a roof is advisable. If necessary, the effluent can be pumped from a small underground tank to a larger tank above ground.

The effluent from any baled silage has to be disposed of safely. Maturing and storing silage in field heaps without an impermeable base or walls is allowed provided the site is suitable, i.e. the risk of causing pollution of underground or surface waters is very low.

SAQ 84

A dairy farmer with 600 head of cattle is considering constructing a slurry pit to contain animal wastes produced over 4 months, together with rainwater run-off from his farmyard, some 80 m × 20 m in size. The annual rainfall in the district is 560 mm. He also intends to store silage effluent in the same pit. The farmer has 50 ha of grassland from which an average yield of 12 t ha^{-1} is expected, at 22% dry matter. Estimate the minimum volume of pit required.

Pesticides

Pesticides entering watercourses harm aquatic life, and may pose a threat to drinking water sources. You will recall that the EU limits for pesticides in drinking water are stringent.

Pesticides stores should be built from fire-resistant materials and be located in a position where there is minimal risk of polluting watercourses or groundwater.

The store should be able to contain the contents safely if they leak or are spilt. The floor should be impermeable and should either be below ground level to form a sump, or there should be a door-sill and walls that do not let liquid pass through. This facility should be able to hold the store contents plus at least an extra 10% (or an extra 85% if the store is in an environmentally sensitive area).

All mixing, filling and washing operations should be carried out in an area designated and constructed for the purpose, such that spillages cannot escape from the area and contaminate soil, groundwater or surface water.

Small spillages can be soaked up with absorbent material, e.g. sand. Disposal of used absorbents should be through a licensed waste disposal operator.

If a major spill occurs, the liquid should be contained and the Environment Agency contacted immediately for advice.

After spraying, all the equipment used should be washed and rinsed. The contaminated water can be reused in making up pesticide solutions later. If not, it can be applied to untreated crop areas, or disposed of via a licensed waste disposal operator.

Empty containers should be first cleaned following the instructions on the label. Then, the containers should be crushed, or holes made in them so that they cannot be reused. They should then be stored in a secure location until they can be disposed of at a licensed disposal site. Containers for hydrogen cyanide gassing powders or aluminium, magnesium or zinc phosphides should not be rinsed because these will give off dangerous gases if they get damp. These containers should be sent to a licensed waste disposal operator.

Sheep dip

Sheep dip is very toxic, and extremely small amounts can cause the death of fish and other aquatic life. Dipping facilities should be not less than 10 m from any watercourses and drains, and not less than 50 m from springs, wells or boreholes.

Dipping baths should not have a drain hole. There should be 'draining-off pens' for sheep to stand in after dipping. The floor of the pen should be impervious, and have a slope of at least 1 in 60, so that surplus dip drains back to the dipping bath. The sheep should be kept in the draining-off pens for about 5–10 minutes after dipping to allow complete drainage of surplus dip. Freshly dipped sheep should not be allowed into a watercourse or wetland area.

The containers for sheep dip concentrate should be cleaned when the dip is being prepared so that the rinsing liquid can be used to dilute the dip.

After cleaning, the containers should have holes put in them, or be crushed so that they are non-reusable. They can then be disposed of as non-hazardous industrial waste at licensed disposal sites.

Fertilizers

Bags of fertilizer should not be stored within 10 m of a watercourse. The same rule applies to tanks of fluid fertilizers. The tank should be resistant to corrosion from the fertilizer, and should be put in a location where the chance of a vehicle hitting the tank is as low as possible. Protective barriers may need to be put at the filling and emptying points of the tank.

Fuel oil storage

Oil, if it enters rivers or streams, can, as mentioned in Section 7.4.2, drastically affect the diffusion of oxygen into the water. For this reason, bunding is required to contain any spillage from above-ground fuel tanks or oil drums when more than 1500 litres is stored. There are different sizes for bunds where fuel is stored in drums, a single tank or several tanks; for example, with a single tank, the bund should be big enough to hold the tank's contents plus an additional 10%.

Figure 108 shows the essential features of such a bund. The tank should be located away from any drains, and should have protection from vehicles. There should be sand (or another suitable absorbent) available nearby to soak up any spillages.

Below-ground tanks should be inside a masonry or concrete chamber. They should only be used if there is no risk that leaks could pollute groundwater.

With all the storage facilities described, it is important that regular inspections are undertaken for detection of any corrosion or leaks. Repainting and resealing have to be carried out to maintain the integrity of the structures.

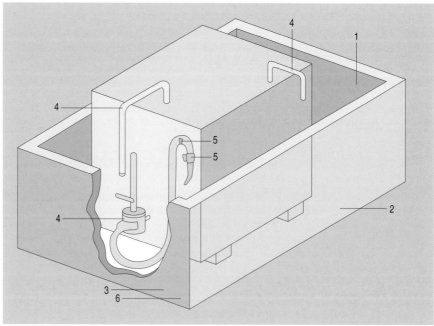

Figure 108   Bunding of an oil storage tank. Key: 1, Fuel oil storage must be surrounded by a bund with a capacity of either 110% of the capacity of the largest tank or 25% of the total capacity of multiple tanks and/or drums and/or barrels, whichever is the larger. 2, Bund and base must be impermeable (e.g. no internal drains or drains hole) and made to last for 20 years (with routine maintenance). 3, Every part of fuel store must be within bund. 4, Taps and valves must point downwards and be shut and locked when not in use. 5, Flexible pipes must be fitted with an automatic closure valve and shall be locked within the bund when not in use. 6, No part is to be within 10 m of a watercourse that fuel oil could enter if it were to escape.

11.2.2   Diffuse (non-point sources)

The main pollutants of concern from diffuse sources are nitrogen, phosphorus and soil. The effects of these on watercourses have been discussed in Chapter 7. Some management practices to minimize the input of these components are listed in Tables 34 and 35.

Table 34   Effective management practices for controlling nitrogen and phosphorus from cropland

Practice	Description
Application of nutrients at correct rate	Application of nutrients to match crop needs
Correct timing of nutrient application	Application should correspond to plant needs
Appropriate method of nutrient application	Fertilizers or slurries should be bonded or incorporated where consistent with other crop management practices
Crop rotation	Incorporation of regimes to assist in reducing nitrogen addition
Cover crops	Planting of cover crops to use up residual nutrients, thus eliminating leaching
Pond	Construction of a water impoundment to trap sediment and any run-off which might contain nitrogen and phosphorus

Table 35 Effective management practices for reducing losses of eroded soil

Practice	Description
Contour cultivation	Planting on the contour of the land, reducing run-off, nutrient and soil losses
Strip cropping	Planting alternating strips of row crops and close-growing crops (such as cereals). Run-off is filtered and infiltration is increased
Grass or vegetable filter strips	A permanent grass strip at the base of a slope filters particulates and increases infiltration
Terrace	Construction of terraces to reduce slope length and run-off velocity. Run-off is reduced and infiltration is increased
Diversion	Construction of a narrow channel perpendicular to the field slope, which diverts run-off to areas where it can be managed
Windbreaks	Belts of trees or shrubs to decrease wind velocities and reduce erosion potential

11.2.3 Local environmental risk assessment for pesticides (LERAP)

Everyone who uses pesticides has a legal responsibility under the Control of Pesticides Regulations 1986 (as amended) to take all reasonable precautions to safeguard the environment, and, in particular, to avoid the pollution of water.

Some pesticides are toxic to fish and other aquatic organisms, and buffer zones are necessary to ensure that while spraying with these, none enters a watercourse. The buffer zone is the area within which directly applied spray must not be allowed.

The buffer zone for ground crop sprayers is 5 m from the top of the river bank (Figure 109). For hand-held sprayers, the distance is 1 m.

The buffer zone for dry ditches is 1 m.

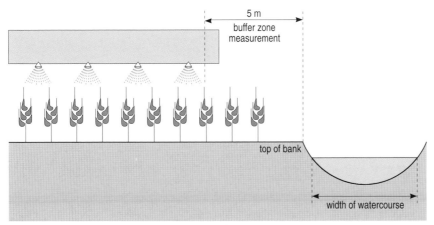

Figure 109 The buffer zone for ground crop sprayers

For certain pesticides applied by ground crop sprayer, there is a legal obligation to carry out and record the results of a local environmental risk assessment for pesticides (LERAP). By carrying out a LERAP, users may be able to reduce the size of the buffer zone required. This can come about due to one or more of the following factors:

(a) the size of the watercourse – the impact of spray drift fall-out is reduced as the size of the watercourse increases, because of dilution;

(b) a reduction in the dose applied, thereby reducing the amount of pesticide in the spray drift;

(c) use of low-drift spray equipment to reduce the amount of spray drift produced during application.

Pesticides washed off crops are also a concern, especially if they enter rivers which are a source of drinking water. Integrated pest management (IPM) is a strategy whereby chemical and biological controls are implemented to enhance the effective use of pesticides, thereby reducing pollution risks.

11.3 Land application of wastes

Land application is the most economical way of treating agricultural wastes. This method also recycles valuable nutrients and organic matter, and is an environmentally sustainable way of disposing of the waste. To reduce the risk of polluting groundwater, wastes should not be applied within 50 m of a spring, well or borehole that supplies water for human consumption, or for use in farm dairies.

The high strength of animal wastes especially makes land disposal preferable to treatment in an effluent treatment plant. The rate of application has to be controlled such that the soil does not become anaerobic.

11.3.1 Rate of application

The soil system on which agricultural wastes are applied can be viewed as a fixed film biological reactor, with millions of microbes in place. Waste spread on the surface of soils is aerobically degraded if applied at an acceptable rate, taking into account the aeration status of the soil (dependent on its structure, texture and moisture content) and the temperature and strength of the waste.

The solid fraction of organic wastes contributes BOD, while the dissolved components confer a COD to the wastes. The liquid portion of the wastes can, by its nature, move deep into the soil, where oxygen may be lacking.

On well-aerated soils (e.g. light texture, free-draining sands and loams) total oxygen demand loadings of 56–112 $kg\ ha^{-1}\ d^{-1}$ have been used.

11.3.2 Hydraulic considerations

The rate at which liquid wastes are applied to soils is critical. Application rates that are greater than the rate at which water will infiltrate the soil will result in surface ponding, surface run-off and thus transport of the pollutants, possibly to a watercourse.

The infiltration rate for a given soil will be influenced by the characteristics of the applied waste, the tendency of the soil surface to seal, the soil moisture content, and the type of vegetation present. On-site measurements are needed to arrive at a design for a disposal site, as such characteristics are very site specific.

Another factor to consider is the amount of waste applied at a given instance. Applying wastes in quantities greater than the retention capacity of the soil will result in leachate being generated, and thereby the possibility of groundwater contamination. The moisture retention or storage capacity of a soil is often referred to as the available water capacity. Table 36 shows typical values for available water capacity for different soils in terms of depth of moisture retained per unit depth of soil.

Table 36   Typical available water capacities for various soil types

Soil type	Available water capacity (mm m^{-1})
Coarse-textured loamy sands, loamy fine sands	83
Medium-textured very fine sandy loams, loams and silt loams	166
Fine-textured sandy clays, silty clays and clays	192

EXERCISE

Estimate the water capacity of a piece of land (15 m × 45 m) where the soil is a course-textured loam of depth 1.2 m.

ANSWER

Available water capacity (from Table 36) = 83 mm per m

$$= 0.083 \text{ m per m}$$

Depth of soil = 1.2 m

Area of land = 15 m × 45 m = 675 m^2

Therefore, available water capacity $= 0.083\dfrac{\text{m}}{\text{m}} \times 1.2 \text{ m} \times 675 \text{ m}^2$

$$= 67.23 \text{ m}^3$$

SAQ 85

Estimate the area required to dispose of 25 m^3 of farm effluent with a COD of 18 000 mg l^{-1} each week over the period April–August, when crop uptake of water and nutrients will be active, permitting a loading rate of 115 kg ha^{-1} d^{-1}.

Assume the 25 m^3 is applied to land in two equal batches each week, i.e. 12.5 m^3 on each occasion.

SAQ 86

If the soil in SAQ 85 is a medium-texture loam 1.4 m in depth, estimate the available water capacity, and estimate the number of applications before any leachate is produced.

11.3.3   Nutrients

The preceding considerations of the organic and hydraulic capacities of a given soil define its short-term assimilative capacity but long-term considerations have to take into account the nutrient application rate. The wastes should be applied at rates that supply the nutrient needs of the crops. This is due to the fact that organic wastes rarely contain the major plant nutrients (these being N, P and K) in the relative proportions required by plants. Inorganic fertilizers often have to be used with organic wastes to meet the nutrient needs.

Table 37 gives typical nutrient uptake rates for N and P for different crops, and can be used to arrive at a waste application rate for a given crop after consideration of existing nutrients in the soil. The waste should be applied as close as possible to the time when maximum crop growth, and thus maximum N and P uptake, occurs.

Table 37 Typical uptake rates for N and P for a variety of crops

Type of crop	Nitrogen uptake $(kg\ ha^{-1})$	Phosphorus uptake $(kg\ ha^{-1})$
Alfalfa	504	39
Reed canary grass	350	36
Sweet clover	177	18
Barley	70	17
Corn	174	19
Soya beans	105	12

The wastes should be applied when the crops require the nutrients, but practical considerations associated with agricultural production (such as soil conditions and the weather) may constrain the precise time when the wastes are applied. For example, application of waste when soils are saturated results in the spreading equipment damaging the soil. Pollution from run-off is also highly likely. Similarly, the application of wastes during the wet season increases the chances of pollution from run-off.

Limiting values for nutrient loadings (in order to prevent any excess from polluting waterways) are based either on the N or the P values of the waste. For surface waters, algal blooms are the problem of concern and these are more easily controlled by limiting the P level in the water. On the other hand, aquifers as sources of drinking water are protected by limits on nitrates (or nitrogen) applied to the land.

11.4 Anaerobic digestion

The alternative to land application of organic waste is its treatment through anaerobic digestion in lagoons. Retention time is typically 12–30 days. Very often animal slurries have their larger solids removed and are diluted down from 5–15% solids to 1–2% solids before digestion. After the lagoons have lost most of their volume due to solid deposition, they are pumped out and the slurry is spread on land. To minimize complaints of odour, the slurry is often injected into the soil.

11.4.1 Odours

The major impact of the land application of farm wastes is that of odours. This aspect is covered in greater detail in Block 6: *Air quality management*. Odours arise from the waste storage area due to the anaerobic decomposition of the organic matter in the waste. When the wastes are applied to land, the odorous compounds escape to the atmosphere and hence affect the public.

Lagoons holding the wastes should have adequate oxygen in order to ensure aerobic conditions. In the case of anaerobic lagoons, the crust that sometimes forms prevents odours escaping. Straw has also been used as a cover for anaerobic ponds to reduce escape of odours.

To prevent odours escaping to the land, the waste can be injected beneath the surface of the soil. Other ways in which the nuisance factor of land spreading of waste can be reduced include: avoiding spreading on weekends and holidays, avoiding spreading when the prevailing winds are in the direction of population centres, and avoiding the use of techniques that atomize the waste and disperse it into the atmosphere.

11.5   Farm waste management plans

The Environment Agency (in England and Wales) encourages farmers to produce a farm waste management plan, in order to reduce the risk of farm wastes polluting watercourses.

The plan identifies:

1   the volume and type of all the wastes produced on the farm;

2   the periods during which the wastes are produced;

3   the amount of land available for spreading the wastes on;

4   the amount of storage required for periods when safe disposal is not possible (say, due to rainy weather, or when nutrient uptake by crops is low).

The plan contains the following:

(a) a map showing where and when land is available for spreading, identifying vulnerable watercourses, land drains, springs and wells. Spreading should be avoided within 10 m of a ditch or watercourse, and 50 m of a water source such as a spring, well or borehole;

(b) a listing of all the areas of risk, taking into account soil type, slope, rainfall, and cropping constraints;

(c) an indication of the method of application and a description of the management and maintenance of the disposal systems required throughout the year;

(d) a contingency plan for dealing with unforeseen accidents and breakdowns.

SAQ 87

What sort of provisions do you think might be in the contingency plan in (d) above?

SAQ 88

Select the true statement from the following:

A Though the pollution from farms can be categorized into two types (point and diffuse), containment methods are appropriate for both.

B Wilting grass before putting it into a silo ensures that minimal silage effluent is produced.

C The safest way to store fuel oil on a farm is underground.

D The buffer zone width when pesticides are applied using a ground crop sprayer is a mandatory 5 m.

E Organic farm wastes are ideal for fertilizing crops as they contain all the required nutrients in the appropriate proportions.

F For aesthetic reasons, the crust formed on the surface of anaerobic lagoons is best removed.

11.6 Summary

Some 11% of pollution incidents are attributed to agriculture. The origin can be point sources (such as leakage of silage effluent, pesticides, wastewater, slurry or oil) or diffuse sources such as run-off from fields. There are guidelines for the containment of potentially polluting material.

Nitrogen, phosphorus, soil and pesticides are the substances of concern with regard to run-off from fields. Effective farm management practices, including farm waste management plans, help to minimize any impact.

The land application of agricultural and animal wastes is the most economical way of disposing of this type of waste. Soil loading rates and nutrient uptake by plants are the major considerations in calculating application rates. Environmental impacts, such as odour generation, should also be considered.

APPENDIX I: EUROPEAN UNION DRINKING WATER DIRECTIVE (98/83/EC)

The revision of the WHO Guidelines for Drinking-Water Quality led to the revision of the European Community Drinking Water Directive in 1998. The number of parameters in the new EU Directive is significantly less than in the old. The Directive covers all water for domestic use and water used by the food industry where this affects the final product (and thus consumers' health). It does not apply to water used for agricultural purposes, natural mineral water or medicinal waters.

There are 53 parameters in the new Directive, compared with 67 in the old. Amongst these are 13 new parameters. The parameters will be reviewed at least every five years.

The major changes to the original directive are as follows:

1   faecal coliforms are replaced by *Escherichia coli*, and *Pseudomonas aeruginosa* is to be measured in bottled waters;

2   antimony is reduced from 10 to 5 $\mu g\ l^{-1}$;

3   lead is reduced from 50 to 10 $\mu g\ l^{-1}$;

4   nickel is reduced from 50 to 20 $\mu g\ l^{-1}$;

5   disinfection by-products are included;

6   radioactivity is considered;

7   ten potential carcinogens are taken into account.

The new Directive splits the quality parameters into two categories: Mandatory and Indicator.

Mandatory parameters

For tap water, there are two microbiological and 26 chemical parameters (Tables A1 and A2). Instead of guide levels and maximum admissible concentration (as in the old Directive), there are now parametric values.

Table A1   Microbiological parameters

Parameter	Parametric value (number/100 ml)
Escherichia coli (*E. coli*)	0
Enterococci	0

The following applies to water offered for sale in bottles or containers:

Parameter	Parametric value
Escherichia coli (*E. coli*)	0/250 ml
Enterococci	0/250 ml
Pseudomonas aeruginosa	0/250 ml
Colony count at 22 °C	100/ml
Colony count at 37 °C	20/ml

Table A2   Chemical parameters

Parameter	Parametric value	Unit	Notes
Acrylamide	0.10	µg/l	Note 1
Antimony	5.0	µg/l	
Arsenic	10	µg/l	
Benzene	1.0	µg/l	
Benzo(a)pyrene	0.010	µg/l	
Boron	1.0	mg/l	
Bromate	10	µg/l	Note 2
Cadmium	5.0	µg/l	
Chromium	50	µg/l	
Copper	2.0	mg/l	Note 3
Cyanide	50	µg/l	
1,2-dichloroethane	3.0	µg/l	
Epichlorohydrin	0.10	µg/l	Note 1
Fluoride	1.5	mg/l	
Lead	10	µg/l	Notes 3 and 4
Mercury	1.0	µg/l	
Nickel	20	µg/l	Note 3
Nitrate	50	mg/l	Note 5
Nitrite	0.50	mg/l	Note 5
Pesticides	0.10	µg/l	Notes 6 and 7
Pesticides – Total	0.50	µg/l	Notes 6 and 8
Polycyclic aromatic hydrocarbons	0.10	µg/l	Sum of concentrations of specified compounds; Note 9
Selenium	10	µg/l	
Tetrachloroethene and Trichloroethene	10	µg/l	Sum of concentrations of specified parameters
Trihalomethanes – Total	100	µg/l	Sum of concentrations of specified compounds; Note 10
Vinyl chloride	0.50	µg/l	Note 1

Note 1:   The parametric value refers to the residual monomer concentration in the water as calculated according to specifications of the maximum release from the corresponding polymer in contact with the water.

Note 2:   Where possible, without compromising disinfection, Member States should strive for a lower value.
For the water referred to in Article 6(1)(a), (b) and (d) [see below], the value must be met, at the latest, 10 calendar years after the entry into force of the Directive. The parametric value for bromate from five years after the entry into force of the Directive until 10 years after its entry into force is 25 µg/l.

Article 6
Point of compliance
1 The parametric values set in accordance with Article 5 shall be complied with:
a) in the case of water supplied from a distribution network, at the point, within premises or an establishment, at which it emerges from the taps that are normally used for human consumption;
b) in the case of water supplied from a tanker, at the point at which it emerges from the tanker;
c) in the case of water put into bottles or containers intended for sale, at the point at which the water is put into bottles or containers;
d) in the case of water used in a food production undertaking, at the point where the water is used in the undertaking.

Note 3:   The value applies to a sample of water intended for human consumption obtained by an adequate sampling method at the tap and taken so as to be representative of a weekly average value ingested by consumers. Where appropriate, the sampling and monitoring methods must be applied in a harmonized fashion to be drawn up in accordance with Article 7(4). Member States must take account of the occurrence of peak levels that may cause adverse effects on human health.

Note 4   For water referred to in Article 6(1)(a), (b) and (d), the value must be met, at the latest, 15 calendar years after the entry into force of this Directive. The parametric value for lead from five years after the entry into force of this Directive, until 15 years after its entry into force is 25 µg/l.

Member States must ensure that all appropriate measures are taken to reduce the concentration of lead in water intended for human consumption as much as possible during the period needed to achieve compliance with the parametric value.

When implementing the measures to achieve compliance with that value, Member States must progressively give priority where lead concentrations in water intended for human consumption are highest.

Note 5:   Member States must ensure that the condition that [nitrate]/50 + [nitrite]/3 $\leq$ 1, the square brackets signifying the concentrations in mg/l for nitrate (NO_3) and nitrite (NO_2), is complied with and that the value of 0.10 mg/l for nitrites is complied with ex-water treatment works.

Note 6:   'Pesticides' means:
           – organic insecticides,
           – organic herbicides,
           – organic fungicides,
           – organic nematocides,
           – organic acaricides,
           – organic algicides,
           – organic rodenticides,
           – organic slimicides,
           – related products (*inter alia*, growth regulators)
           and their relevant metabolites, degradation and reaction products.
           Only those pesticides which are likely to be present in a given supply need be monitored.

Note 7:   The parametric value applies to each individual pesticide. In the case of aldrin, dieldrin, heptachlor and heptachlor epoxide the parametric value is 0.030 µg/l.

Note 8:   'Pesticides – Total' means the sum of all individual pesticides detected and quantified in the monitoring procedure.

Note 9:   The specified compounds are:
           – benzo(b)fluoranthene,
           – benzo(k)fluoranthene,
           – benzo(ghi)perylene,
           – indeno(1,2,3-cd)pyrene

Note 10:   Where possible, without compromising disinfection, Member States should strive for a lower value.
           The specified compounds are: chloroform, bromoform, dibromochloromethane, bromodichloromethane.
           For the water referred to in Article 6(1)(a), (b) and (d), the value must be met, at the latest, 10 calendar years after the entry into force of this Directive. The parametric value for total THMs from five years after the entry into force of this Directive until 10 years after its entry into force is 150 µg/l.
           Member States must ensure that all appropriate measures are taken to reduce the concentration of THMs in water intended for human consumption as much as possible during the period needed to achieve compliance with the parametric value.
           When implementing the measures to achieve this value, Member States must progressively give priority to those areas where THM concentrations in water intended for human consumption are highest.

Indicator parameters

This is a new concept. Generally speaking, the parametric values (PVs) for these parameters are not based on health considerations and are non-binding. When the PVs are exceeded, remedial action is only necessary if a Member State judges there to be risk to health. Most of the indicator parameters are included in the list of parameters to be analysed in check monitoring. This has the aim of providing information on the organoleptic and microbiological quality of supplied water, as well as on the effectiveness of treatment. The indicator parameters are listed in Table A3 below. A fair number of the existing EU standards have been turned into indicator parameters in the new Directive, or omitted altogether.

The Department for Environment, Food and Rural Affairs, however, proposes to retain most of the existing EU standards as binding limits. This means, for instance, that standards for aluminium, iron, manganese, colour and turbidity intended to prevent the supply of discoloured water, will be retained.

Table A3   Indicator parameters

Parameter	Parametric value	Unit	Notes
Aluminium	200	μg/l	
Ammonium	0.50	mg/l	
Chloride	250	mg/l	Note 1
Clostridium perfringens (including spores)	0	number/100 ml	Note 2
Colour	Acceptable to consumers and no abnormal change		
Conductivity	2500	μS cm^{-1} at 20 °C	Note 1
Hydrogen ion concentration	$\geqslant$ 6.5 and $\leqslant$ 9.5	pH units	Notes 1 and 3
Iron	200	μg/l	
Manganese	50	μg/l	
Odour	Acceptable to consumers and no abnormal change		
Oxidizability	5.0	mg/l O_2	Note 4
Sulphate	250	mg/l	Note 1
Sodium	200	mg/l	
Taste	Acceptable to consumers and no abnormal change		
Colony count at 22 °C	No abnormal change		
Coliform bacteria	0	number/100 ml	Note 5
Total organic carbon (TOC)	No abnormal change		Note 6
Turbidity	Acceptable to consumers and no abnormal change		Note 7
Radioactivity:			
Tritium	100	Bq/l	Notes 8 and 10
Total indicative dose	0.10	mSv/year	Notes 9 and 10

Note 1:   The water should not be aggressive.

Note 2:   This parameter need not be measured unless the water originates from or is influenced by surface water. In the event of non-compliance with this parametric value, the Member State concerned must investigate the supply to ensure that there is no potential danger to human health arising from the presence of pathogenic micro-organisms, e.g. *Cryptosporidium*. Member States must include the results of all such investigations in the reports they must submit under Article 13(2).

Note 3:   For still water put into bottles or containers, the minimum value may be reduced to 4.5 pH units. For water put into bottles or containers which is naturally rich in or artificially enriched with carbon dioxide, the minimum value may be lower.

Note 4:   This parameter need not be measured if the parameter TOC is analysed.

Note 5:   For water put into bottles or containers the unit is number/250 ml.

Note 6:   This parameter need not be measured for supplies of less than 10 000 m^3 a day.

Note 7:   In the case of surface water treatment, Member States should strive for a parametric value not exceeding 1.0 NTU (nephelometric turbidity units) in the water ex-treatment works.

Note 8:   Monitoring frequencies to be set later in Annex II.

Note 9:   Excluding tritium, potassium-40, radon and radon decay products; monitoring frequencies, monitoring methods and the most relevant locations for monitoring points to be set later in Annex II.

Note 10   1   The proposals required by Note 8 on monitoring frequencies, and Note 9 on monitoring frequencies, monitoring methods and the most relevant locations for monitoring points in Annex II shall be adopted in accordance with the procedure laid down in Article 12. When elaborating these proposals the Commission shall take into account *inter alia* the relevant provisions under existing legislation or appropriate monitoring programmes including monitoring results as derived from them. The Commission shall submit these proposals at the latest within 18 months following the date referred to in Article 18 of the Directive.

2   A Member State is not required to monitor drinking water for tritium or radioactivity to establish total indicative dose where it is satisfied that, on the basis of other monitoring carried out, the levels of tritium of the calculated total indicative dose are well below the parametric value. In that case, it shall communicate the grounds for its decision to the Commission, including the results of this other monitoring carried out.

APPENDIX 2: WATER SERVICE COMPANY CONSENT TO DISCHARGE

ANGLIAN WATER SERVICES LIMITED

NOTICE OF DIRECTION VARYING THE CONDITIONS ATTACHING TO A CONSENT TO THE DISCHARGE OF TRADE EFFLUENT ISSUED PURSUANT TO: WATER INDUSTRY ACT 1991

To

of

('the Trader')

the owner/occupier of

('the said premises')

SEE NOTE 2	ANGLIAN WATER SERVICES LIMITED ('Anglian Water') under their powers in the above Act HEREBY DIRECT that as from the 1 September 1994 the conditions attaching to the Consent given on 1 March 1976 shall cease and the Consent to discharge the trade effluent from the said premises into the public sewer shall be subject to the following conditions.
Nature and composition	1. The trade effluent discharged shall be of the following nature and composition: WASTEWATER FROM WASHING VEGETABLES.
Sewer affected	2. The sewer into which the trade effluent shall be discharged is the public foul sewer (hereinafter called 'the sewer') situated at
Maximum quantity to be discharged in any day.	3. The volume of trade effluent shall not exceed 2400.0 cubic metres in any period of 24 hours from midnight.
Maximum rate of discharge.	4. The rate of discharge of trade effluent shall not exceed 100.0 cubic metres per hour.
Matters to be eliminated prior to discharge to the sewer.	5.(a) There shall be eliminated from the trade effluent before it is discharged into the sewer:

(i)   Petroleum spirit and other volatile or flammable organic solvent.

(ii)   Calcium carbide.

(iii)   Sludges arising from the pre-treatment of the trade effluent before discharge to the public sewer.

(iv)   Waste liable to form viscous or solid coatings or deposits on any part of the sewerage system through which the trade effluent is to pass.

(v)   Substances of a nature likely to give rise to fumes or odours injurious to persons working in the sewers through which the trade effluent is to pass.

(vi)   Halogenated hydrocarbons unless specified in 5(b).

(vii)   Halogen substituted phenolic compounds unless specified in 5(b).

(viii)   Thiourea and its derivatives unless specified in 5(b).

(ix)   Substances listed in Schedule 1 of the Trade Effluent (Prescribed Processes and Substances) Regulations 1989; at a concentration greater than the background concentration (See Appendix II to this Direction for the listing of Prescribed Substances).

(x)   'Waste' as defined in the Disposal of Waste (Control of Beet Rhizomania Disease) Order 1988(45) namely, waste obtained from the processing of any imported raw potatoes, beets, carrots, celery or celeriac, leeks, turnips or swedes (other than those from which all traces of soil or other growing medium have been removed by washing or otherwise in the exporting country) but not including:

a)   waste obtained by or following a process which will kill *Polymyxa betae*, the vector of Beet Rhizomania Disease, or

b)   water which has been freed from solid waste

(b)   The trade effluent shall not contain any of the substances listed below in a concentration expressed as milligrams per litre greater than that stated:

Suspended solids	1000
Chemical oxygen demand (after one hours quiescent settlement)	2000
Oil and grease (expressed as non-volatile matter extractable by 40° / 60° petroleum ether)	100
Sulphate (expressed as SO_4^{2-})	1000

Temperature   6.   The trade effluent shall have a temperature not higher than 45 °C.

Acidity or alkalinity   7.   The trade effluent shall have a pH value not less than 6.0 or greater than 10.0.

Payment   8.   The trader shall pay to Anglian Water for the trade effluent discharged into the sewer (a) a sum calculated in accordance with the provisions contained in Appendix I hereto together with (b) the amount of any expenses additional thereto which Anglian Water may from time to time incur in connection with the reception and disposal of the trade effluent. All sums payable to Anglian Water under this condition shall become due and payable on demand.

Entry and samples   9.   The trader shall permit Anglian Water's duly authorised representatives to inspect, examine and test at all reasonable times any works and apparatus installed in connection with the trade effluent.

Inspection chamber   10.   The Trader shall provide and maintain if required by Anglian Water an inspection chamber or manhole in a suitable position in connection with each pipe through which the trade effluent is being discharged and such inspection chamber or manhole shall be so constructed and maintained by the Trader as to enable duly authorised representatives of Anglian Water readily to take samples at any time of what is passing into the sewer from the said premises.

Measurement and determination of discharge   11.   The Trader shall provide and maintain if required by Anglian Water a notch gauge and continuous recorder and/or some other approved apparatus suitable and adequate for measuring and automatically recording the volume, rate of discharge and nature of the trade effluent to the satisfaction of Anglian Water in connection with every pipe through which the trade effluent is being discharged.

12. If the said measuring apparatus ceases to register or measure correctly then, unless otherwise agreed, the quantity of trade effluent discharged into the sewer during the period from the date on which records of the volume of the trade effluent discharged into the sewer were last accepted by Anglian Water as being correct, up to the date when the said measuring and recording apparatus again registers correctly, shall for the purpose of any payment to be made to Anglian Water be based on the average daily volume of the trade effluent discharged during the period of one month preceding the date on which the said records were last accepted as aforesaid or during the month immediately after the said measuring and recording apparatus has been corrected, whichever is the higher.

Records

13. The Trader shall provide records in such form as Anglian Water may require of the volume, rate of discharge, nature and composition of trade effluent discharged into the sewer and these shall be available at all reasonable times for inspection by duly authorised representatives of Anglian Water. Copies of such records shall be sent to Anglian Water on demand.

Changes to processes

14. The occupier(s) of the said premises shall forthwith give to Anglian Water notice in writing of any change or proposed changes in the flow, the process of manufacture or nature of the raw materials used or of any other circumstances which may alter the nature and composition of the trade effluent or may result in permanent cessation of the discharge.

Duly authorised to sign on this behalf

Signed ....

Quality Standards Manager

Dated this .... day of ....

NOTE

Your attention is drawn to the right to appeal to the Director General of Water Services conferred by Section 126(1) of the Water Industry Act 1991 which reads as follows:

'The owner or occupier of any trade premises may

(a) within two months of the giving to him under subsection (5) of section 124 of a notice of a direction under that section; or

(b) with the written permission of the Director, at any time, appeal to the Director against the direction.'

NOTE 2

This direction is issued following amendment(s) to:

a) COMPANY NAME

AND b) SECTION 5a) AND 5b) LIMITS

APPENDIX I

The sum referred to in Condition 8 of this Consent shall be calculated as:

(i) a minimum charge determined by Anglian Water

    or

(ii) a charge fixed in accordance with any charges scheme made from time to time by Anglian Water

(iii) a charge per cubic metre calculated by the following formula:

$$C = R + (V \text{ or } VB \text{ or } VM \text{ or } M) + \frac{Ot}{Os} B + \frac{St}{Ss} S$$

Where:

C	=	Total cost per cubic metre for treatment and disposal of the trade effluent.
R	=	Reception and conveyance charge per cubic metre.
V	=	Volumetric and primary treatment charge per cubic metre chargeable for those trade effluents discharged to a sewage treatment works where there is no biological treatment.
VB	=	As for V, but where there is biological treatment.
VM	=	Treatment and disposal charge for sea outfalls per cubic metre of trade effluent.
M	=	Treatment and disposal charge for designated sea outfalls per cubic metre of trade effluent.
Ot	=	The strength of settled trade effluent as determined by an oxidation parameter.
B	=	Biological oxidation charge per cubic metre of settled sewage.
St	=	The suspended solids content of the trade effluent in milligrams per litre.
Os	=	The mean strength of settled sewage at Anglian Water's sewage treatment works as determined by an oxidation parameter.
Ss	=	The mean suspended solids content of sewage at Anglian Water's sewage treatment works in milligrams per litre.

A P P E N D I X II

Trade Effluent (Prescribed Processes and Substances) Regulations 1989

Prescribed Substances – Schedule 1

Mercury and its compounds	Dichlorvos
Cadmium and its compounds	1, 3-Dichloroethane
Gamma-hexachlorocyclohhexane	Trichlorobenzene
DDT	Atrazine
Pentachlorophenol	Simazine
Hexachlorobenzene	Tributyltin compounds
Hexachlorobutadiene	Triphenyltin compounds
Aldrin	Trifluralin
Dieldrin	Fenitrothion
Endrin	Azinphos-methyl
Carbon tetrachloride	Malathion
Polychlorinated biphenyls	Endosulfan

ANSWERS TO SELF-ASSESSMENT QUESTIONS

SAQ 1

A is correct.

SAQ 2

B is correct.

SAQ 3

D is correct.

SAQ 4

(a) Ammonium (ion)
(b) Nitrogen (molecule)
(c) Hydroxide (hydroxyl) (ion)
(d) Nitrate (ion)
(e) Magnesium chloride (molecule – strictly, an ionic compound)
(f) Bicarbonate (ion)
(g) Carbon dioxide (molecule)

SAQ 5

$$\text{Volume of 1 mm diameter raindrop} = \frac{4}{3}\pi\left(\frac{0.5}{10^3}\right)^3 \text{m}^3$$

$$\text{Mass of 1 mm diameter raindrop} = \frac{4}{3}\pi\left(\frac{0.5}{10^3}\right)^3 \times 998 \text{ kg}$$

$$\text{Surface area of 1 mm diameter raindrops} = 4\pi\left(\frac{0.5}{10^3}\right)^2 \text{m}^2$$

$$\text{Ratio of mass to surface area} = \frac{\frac{4}{3}\pi\left(\frac{0.5}{10^3}\right)^3 \times 998 \text{ kg}}{4\pi\left(\frac{0.5}{10^3}\right)^2 \text{m}^2}$$

$$= \frac{1}{3}\left(\frac{0.5}{10^3}\right) \times 998$$

$$= 0.166 \text{ kg m}^{-2}$$

Carrying out similar calculations for the 3 mm raindrops, we get

$$\text{Mass of 3 mm raindrops} = \frac{4}{3}\pi\left(\frac{1.5}{10^3}\right)^3 \times 998 \text{ kg}$$

$$\text{Surface area of 3 mm raindrops} = 4\pi\left(\frac{1.5}{10^3}\right)^2$$

$$\text{Ratio of mass to surface area} = \frac{\frac{4}{3}\pi\left(\frac{1.5}{10^3}\right)^3 \times 998}{4\pi\left(\frac{1.5}{10^3}\right)^2}$$

$$= \frac{1}{3}\left(\frac{1.5}{10^3}\right) \times 998$$

$$= 0.499 \text{ kg m}^{-2}$$

Thus, the large drop has a larger ratio of mass to surface area.

SAQ 6

Surface freshwater available from:

Freshwater lakes	125×10^{12} m^3
Rivers	1.7×10^{12} m^3
Total	126.7×10^{12} m^3

As a percentage of the total water resource available ($1\,383\,794.7 \times 10^{12}$ m^3)

$$= \frac{126.7 \times 10^{12}}{1\,383\,794.7 \times 10^{12}} \times 100$$

$$= 9.156 \times 10^{-3}\ \%$$

which is less than 0.01% – this is a very small amount indeed!

SAQ 7

Total volume of water on Earth $= 1\,383\,794.7 \times 10^{12}$ m^3

Volume of river water $= 1.7 \times 10^{12}$ m^3

$$\text{River water fraction} = \frac{1.7 \times 10^{12}}{1\,383\,794.7 \times 10^{12}}$$

$$= 1.2 \times 10^{-6}\ \text{m}^3$$

i.e. 1.2 millionths of the total available water.

SAQ 8

The components are: rainfall, evapotranspiration, run-off, abstraction of surface water, infiltration to groundwater storage, inflow and outflow of groundwater between the aquifer and other areas or the sea, and the change in groundwater storage due to abstraction.

SAQ 9

Option **D** is best, but option **E** is also valid.

SAQ 10

(a) Dense vegetation reduces the rate of surface run-off and thus increases infiltration. However, the effect will be offset to some extent by interception, whereby a large proportion of the precipitation stays on the leaves of the vegetation and evaporates.

(b) Water runs rapidly off steeply sloping land surfaces so there is little time for significant infiltration to occur.

(c) Cultivated land is in general subject to greater amounts of infiltration, unless the land is sloping, when the effect will be as in (b).

(d) Tarmac, concrete and roofing surfaces are relatively impermeable, so that roads and buildings promote run-off and reduce infiltration.

SAQ 11

C. Only if the wind is strong enough to cause turbulence will it result in an increase in the rate of oxygen transfer across the water–air interface; otherwise it will not significantly affect the rate of transfer. The atmosphere contains approximately 21% oxygen by volume so there is always plenty of oxygen in the air immediately above the interface, even when the air is not moving.

SAQ 12

In warm weather when aquatic plants are growing rapidly, their photosynthetic processes usually result in a diurnal variation in the concentration of dissolved oxygen; it is high during the day and low at night. During summer days, the water may become supersaturated with dissolved oxygen, especially during the afternoon. After sunset, the oxygen-producing phase of photosynthesis ceases and the concentration of dissolved oxygen declines, generally reaching its lowest levels just before dawn. Variations of up to 10 g m^{-3} have been recorded in 24 hours.

The oxygen demand as a result of bacterial decay of leaves and other organic matter that have fallen into the water means that levels of dissolved oxygen will also be very low in the autumn.

SAQ 13

E is true.

A 'Sewage fungus' is a mixture of different species of bacteria, fungi, algae and protozoa.

B Oxygen does not react with water but with the substances contained in the water.

C *E. coli*, although common in animals and humans is not pathogenic.

D High pH values correspond to low H$^+$ or alkaline conditions. From Equation (1) (describing the bicarbonate–carbonate equilibrium), this will mean a decrease in hydrogen ions and thus the equilibrium moves to the right, increasing the concentration of carbonate.

SAQ 14

According to Equation (1), the removal of carbon dioxide by plants causes the reaction to shift to the left to compensate. The concentration of hydrogen ions then drops and so the pH rises.

SAQ 15

For the sea water to be saturated, the dissolved oxygen concentration at 8 °C

$$= 11.84 - (35 \times 0.0697) \text{ g m}^{-3}$$

$$= 11.84 - 2.44 \text{ g m}^{-3}$$

$$= 9.40 \text{ g m}^{-3}$$

But the sample is only 30% saturated. Thus dissolved oxygen present

$$= 9.40 \times \frac{30}{100} \text{ g m}^{-3}$$

$$= 2.82 \text{ g m}^{-3}$$

SAQ 16

Species		Points scored
Mayfly nymph	Baetidae	4
Snails	2 families	$3 \times 2 = 6$
Leeches	2 families	$3 \times 2 = 6$
Fly larvae	Chironomidae	2
	Culicidae	1
True worms	3 families	$1 \times 3 = 3$
Total		22

The BMWP score is 22. The low score and the absence of clean water indicators signifies that the effluent discharge is having a detrimental effect on the river quality.

SAQ 17

Look at the diagram for the River Tees and go to 11 km on the scale given. (You will need to use a ruler to determine the exact spot.) Then draw a vertical line until you reach the top of the figure showing salinity. The top depicts the salinity at the surface. The value is between 19 g and 25 g per 1000 g of water. You will have to use a ruler again to determine the exact value.

For the salinity at 3 m depth, draw a horizontal line at the 3 m mark, until it hits the vertical line that you first drew. The point of intersection between the two lines gives the salinity, at 3 m depth, 11 km from the mouth of the river.

You will have to repeat the exercise for part (b) for the River Thames using the bottom diagram but for a distance of 36 km from the mouth of the river.

(a) 19.6 g and 25.6 g per 1000 g of water, respectively.

(b) 20.2 g per 1000 g of water at surface and also at 3 m depth.

SAQ 18

$$\text{Retention time} = \frac{\text{volume}}{\text{flow rate}}$$

$$= \frac{\text{depth}}{\text{minimum settling velocity}}$$

$$= \frac{4}{0.4 \times 10^{-3}} = 10\,000 \text{ s (2.8 hours)}$$

$$\text{Flow rate} = \frac{\text{volume}}{\text{retention time}}$$

$$= \frac{\text{area} \times \text{depth}}{\text{retention time}}$$

$$= \frac{700 \times 4}{10\,000} = 0.28 \text{ m}^3 \text{ s}^{-1}$$

SAQ 19

$$\text{Maximum flow} = 0.25 \times 60 \times 60 \times 24 \text{ m}^3 \text{ d}^{-1}$$

$$= 21.6 \times 10^3 \text{ m}^3 \text{ d}^{-1}$$

$$\text{Weir overflow rate} = \frac{\text{maximum flow per day}}{\text{effective weir length}} \text{ m}^3 \text{ m}^{-1} \text{ d}^{-1}$$

Therefore

$$\text{Effective weir length} = \frac{\text{maximum flow per day}}{\text{weir overflow rate}} \text{ m}$$

$$= \frac{21.6 \times 10^3}{350} \text{ m}$$

$$= 61.7 \text{ m}$$

In this case, a suspended trough 31 m long would provide the weir length required.

SAQ 20

A and **C**. Possibly **B**, depending on the nature of the suspended material.

SAQ 21

Slow sand filter

Advantages: a very efficient physical, chemical and bacterial filter; produces water of consistent quality.

Disadvantages: expensive to build and maintain; takes up a large area; since efficiency depends on microbial growth, the temperature and speed of flow must be carefully controlled.

Rapid gravity filter

Advantages: fast; relatively cheap to install and operate; occupies less space than an equivalent flow slow sand filter.

Disadvantages: water has to be treated with coagulant before being passed through the filter; may not produce water of a satisfactorily high bacteriological quality, especially from heavily polluted water.

SAQ 22

This will lead to an increase in the absorption of heat energy.

SAQ 23

Chlorination

Advantages: cheaper than ozone; results in a residual effect to protect the water in the distribution system.

Disadvantages: does not kill all viruses; is not effective against spores and protozoa; can result in trihalomethanes being produced.

Ozonation

Advantages: acts in a short time and kills all bacteria, spores and viruses; reduces taste, colour and odour; does not produce trihalomethanes.

Disadvantages: The major one is that there is no residual germicidal effect, i.e. the water is not protected against subsequent contamination in the distribution system. Ozone can produce bromates if bromine is present, and these are toxic. Finally, ozone production requires complex equipment, and is expensive.

SAQ 24

C is correct.

SAQ 25

A False. There are four zones. The missing zone is the sludge zone.

B False. Discrete particles settle ahead of flocculent particles.

C False. The maximum flow rate allowed is $0.24 \text{ m}^3 \text{ s}^{-1}$. This is because

$$\text{Surface loading rate} = \frac{\text{maximum flow rate}}{\text{area of surface of tank}}$$

Therefore

$$\text{Maximum flow rate} = (\text{surface loading rate}) \times (\text{area of surface of tank})$$

$$= (30 \text{ m}^3 \text{ m}^{-2} \text{ d}^{-1}) \times (14 \times 50) \text{ m}^2$$

$$= 21\,000 \text{ m}^3 \text{ d}^{-1}$$

$$= \frac{21\,000}{60 \times 60 \times 24} \text{ m}^3 \text{ s}^{-1}$$

$$= 0.24 \text{ m}^3 \text{ s}^{-1}$$

D False. The colloids and the micro-organisms carry a negative charge.

E False. The ion exchange resin will be represented by R*Cl where R* is the complex resin base. The equation for its action will be

$$\text{R*Cl} + \text{NaNO}_3 \longrightarrow \text{R*NO}_3 + \text{NaCl}$$

F True.

G False. Only a granular activated carbon can be regenerated.

SAQ 26

$$\text{Relative molecular mass of H}_2\text{SiF}_6 = 2 + 28 + (6 \times 19) = 144$$

and

$$6F = 114$$

$$\text{Therefore, fluoride ions in 1000 kg H}_2\text{SiF}_6 = \frac{114}{144} \times 1000 \text{ kg} = 791.67 \text{ kg}$$

$$\text{Fluoride ions added per day} = 791.67 \text{ kg}$$

$$\text{Fluoride ions added per second} = \frac{791.67 \times 10^6}{24 \times 60 \times 60} \frac{\text{mg}}{\text{s}}$$

$$= 9.16 \times 10^3 \text{ mg s}^{-1}$$

$$\text{Fluoride ions added per litre} = \frac{9.16 \times 10^3}{15\,000}\,\text{mg l}^{-1}$$

$$= 0.61\,\text{mg l}^{-1}$$

$$\text{Original concentration of fluoride ions} = 1.0 - 0.61\,\text{mg l}^{-1}$$

$$= 0.39\,\text{mg l}^{-1}$$

SAQ 27

The four processes are:

- multistage flash distillation;

- reverse osmosis;

- electrodialysis;

- solar distillation.

SAQ 28

If the 4.5-litre container has to be filled in 30 seconds, the flow rate has to be 9 litres a minute.

SAQ 29

The mass diagram is plotted in Figure 110. Maximum surplus in volume supplied V_1 is 300 m^3 at 6.00 a.m. Maximum deficit in volume extracted V_2 is 200 m^3 at 8.00 p.m.

So the equalizing storage $= V_1 + V_2 = 500$ m^3.

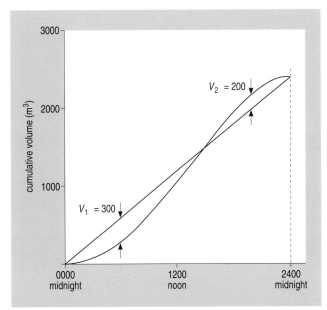

Figure 110 Mass diagram for SAQ 29

SAQ 30

A 1, 2 and 3

B 1 and possibly 3

C 4

SAQ 31

Original water demand $= 50\ 000 \times 130 \times 3 = 19.5 \times 10^6$ l per day

$= 19.50$ megalitres per day

New water demand $=$ water demand of 10 000 single-person households

$+$ that of 10 000 households with two persons

$+$ that of 40 000 households with three persons

$= (10\ 000 \times 211) + (10\ 000 \times 154 \times 2) + (40\ 000 \times 3 \times 130)$

$= (2.11 \times 10^6) + (3.08 \times 10^6) + (15.6 \times 10^6)$

$= 20.79 \times 10^6$ litres per day

$= 20.79$ megalitres per day

The increase will be $20.79 - 19.50 = 1.29$ megalitres per day

SAQ 32

A household size of three gives a per capita consumption of 130 l/head/day and that with an occupancy of two gives a figure of 154 l/head/day.

So, one extra person results in a reduction in per capita consumption of 24 litres and we can say that the average occupancy rate is between 2 and 3.

We have a reduction of 18 litres (from 154 to 136 litres). This will be due to an additional

$$\frac{1}{24} \times 18 = 0.75 \text{ person}$$

So, the average occupancy rate $= 2.75$

SAQ 33

Canada, the USA, Japan and Australia have high per capita consumption rates. One reason is the widespread use of water-hungry appliances such as dishwashers in these countries. Another might be the use of jacuzzis and swimming pools within homes and watering gardens in dry climates.

SAQ 34

Hair, scum, sand, grit, faecal coliforms, grease, oil (from face creams, etc.)

SAQ 35

Light would encourage the growth of algae.

SAQ 36

The reason it might be true is because milk has an extremely high BOD (as high as 140 000 g m^{-3}) and a 10 m^3 batch will exert a very high BOD loading (calculated below) on the river.

$$\text{BOD loading due to milk} = 10 \text{ m}^3 \times 140\,000 \frac{\text{g}}{\text{m}^3}$$

$$= 140 \times 10^4 \text{ g}$$

$$= 1400 \text{ kg} - \text{a very high figure!}$$

SAQ 37

C and **D**.

A is false because low concentrations of organic pollutants can serve as nutrients for the river organisms.

B is false because pollutants can be carried into rivers.

E is false because antibiotics can also cause mutagenicity and also bring about allergic responses.

SAQ 38

Option **D**.

A   Depletion of oxygen occurs due to the activities of decomposers.

B   Only in eutrophication are plant nutrients present, and these will usually encourage plant growth.

C   This contradicts Figure 54.

E   Applies only to organic pollution.

SAQ 39

Options **B** and **E**.

A   Heavy organic loads on a watercourse can cause permanent damage to the water in the vicinity of the effluent outfall.

C   Concern has arisen regarding fish farm effluents mainly because they contain antibiotics.

D   The toxicity of all substances depends on concentration. Some substances are essential to diet in low concentrations but can be toxic in high concentrations.

SAQ 40

B and **E** are the only correct statements.

A   False, because there may be synergistic effects.

C   False, because fish spawning is also disrupted.

D   Certain strains of *E. coli* (e.g. *E. coli* O157 H) are pathogens, and can cause fatalities.

F   False, because the discharge of natural oestrogens, often at high levels, due to the use of contraceptive pills, will still contribute to the problem.

SAQ 41

Cholera	bacteria
Poliomyelitis	virus
Typhoid	bacteria
Bilharzia	helminth
Anthrax	bacteria
Cryptosporidiosis	protozoa
Tuberculosis	bacteria

SAQ 42

(a) From Equation (3), the ultimate oxygen demand of the diluted sample is

$$L_u = 7.6 - 1.3 \text{ g m}^{-3}$$

$$= 6.3 \text{ g m}^{-3}$$

(b) The principle of mass conservation applies. If x is the 'concentration' of oxidizable material in the original effluent then

$$(1)(x) = (1 + 49)(6.3) \text{ g m}^{-3}$$

$$x = 315 \text{ g m}^{-3}$$

SAQ 43

From Equation (4) the dissolved oxygen concentration C_t after 14 hours or 0.58 days is given by

$$\frac{C_t - 2.3}{8.0 - 2.3} = e^{-(0.2)(0.58)} = 0.89 \text{ g m}^{-3}$$

$$C_t = 2.3 + (5.7)(0.89) \text{ g m}^{-3}$$

$$= 7.4 \text{ g m}^{-3}$$

SAQ 44

$$\text{BOD}_5^{20} = L_u \left(1 - e^{-5k}\right) \text{ g m}^{-3}$$

or

$$L_u = \frac{\text{BOD}_5^{20}}{\left(1 - e^{-5k}\right)} \text{ g m}^{-3}$$

$$= \frac{150}{\left(1 - e^{-2}\right)} \text{ g m}^{-3}$$

$$= 174 \text{ g m}^{-3}$$

SAQ 45

Material	BOD_5^{20}	BOD_5^{20}/L_u
1	19.95	0.998
2	49.66	0.993
3	92.75	0.713
4	183.58	0.918
Overall	345.87	0.865

SAQ 46

(a) The BOD–time curve is shown in Figure 111.

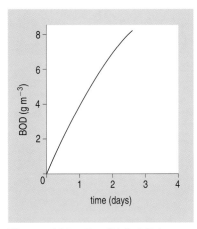

Figure 111   For SAQ 46(a)

(b) From Equation (6), a plot of BOD_t versus $(1 - e^{-kt})$ should give a straight line through the origin of slope L_u. This is shown in Figure 112, from which $L_u = 12.9$ g m^{-3}.

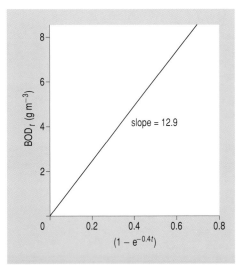

Figure 112   For SAQ 46(b)

(c) $BOD_5^{20} = 12.9\left(1 - e^{-2}\right)$ g m^{-3}

$\phantom{BOD_5^{20}} = 11.2$ g m^{-3}

SAQ 47

The BOD:COD ratios are as follows:

Domestic sewage = 250:500 = 1:2 or 0.5:1

Pulp mill effluent = 25 000:76 000 = 1:3.04 or 0.33:1

This shows that a greater proportion of the domestic sewage is biodegradable, in comparison with pulp mill effluent.

SAQ 48

A   False. Physical parameters are the manifestations of pollutants and are useful in characterizing the general nature of pollutants.

B   False. While clean freshwaters are generally low in chloride, sewage or sewage-like pollution increases chloride concentrations. The chloride levels vary in different groundwaters depending on the geochemical nature of the aquifer and the intrusion of sea water.

C   True. These parameters are all related through the carbonate, bicarbonate, carbonic acid system.

D   False. The Hazen scale is based on the colours produced by specific substances in water, but the presence of a particular colour does not imply that those substances are necessarily present. Other substances may produce similar colours.

E   False. Human operators are used in some water treatment plants to detect the presence of odoriferous compounds.

SAQ 49

Of those listed, only the BOD and TOC tests give a measure of organic matter.

(a) Option **B**, the BOD test, because the organic matter in dairy wastes is biodegradable.

(b) Option **C**, the much more severe TOC test, because the organic matter in petroleum refinery effluent is not easily biodegradable due to the presence of toxic components such as cyanides and heavy metals.

SAQ 50

(a) Since this is extremely unlikely, we suspect something in the water has killed the bacteria that are normal inhabitants of river water, or that the test was not carried out properly.

(b) This is evidence that faecal pollution is present and it is possible that pathogens are also present.

SAQ 51

An intake point for a water treatment plant or a fish farm.

At a discharge point of an effluent treatment plant, particularly one treating industrial effluent.

SAQ 52

We have 250 m^3 of sewage:

$$\text{Density} = \frac{\text{mass}}{\text{volume}}$$

So

$$\text{mass} = \text{density} \times \text{volume}$$

$$\text{Mass of sewage} = 1000 \, \frac{\text{kg}}{\text{m}^3} \times 250 \, \text{m}^3$$

$$= 2.5 \times 10^5 \, \text{kg}$$

Sewage is up to 98.5% water:

$$\frac{98.5}{100} \times 2.5 \times 10^5 = 246\,250 \, \text{kg}$$

The remaining 1.5% (3750 kg) is made up of 70% organic material and 30% inorganic material.

$$70\% \text{ of } 3750 \, \text{kg} = \frac{70}{100} \times 3750 = 2625 \, \text{kg}$$

This consists of

$$65\% \text{ protein} = 1706.25 \, \text{kg}$$

$$25\% \text{ carbohydrate} = 656.25 \, \text{kg}$$

$$10\% \text{ fats} = 262.5 \, \text{kg}$$

30% is inorganic (grit, metals and salts). This would be 1125 kg.

SAQ 53

Option **A**. Sewers may receive the flow from several underground drains so they should be larger. The pipe materials and jointing are usually similar for both drains and sewers as there are the same constraints on both. Also, both drains and sewers are laid to exploit gravity wherever possible. Finally, note that although a distinction has been drawn in this text, in common usage the terms 'drain' and 'sewer' are interchangeable.

SAQ 54

All differ except **C**.

A The diameter of a rising sewer main will be smaller since it is designed to flow full.

B The pressure in a part-full pipe is just local atmospheric pressure. A rising main flowing full is under a pressure greater than atmospheric because of the pump pressure.

D A gravity sewer slopes downwards. A rising sewer main, as its name suggests, slopes upwards.

E The flow velocity in a rising main will be higher for a given flow rate than in a gravity sewer, because of the reduced flow area (since the diameter of the rising main would be smaller than that of the gravity sewer). Both have gradients, but a gravity sewer slopes downwards while a rising main slopes upwards.

SAQ 55

Domestic and industrial effluent flow

$$= 20\,000 \times \frac{250}{1000}\,\text{m}^3\,\text{d}^{-1}$$

$$= 5000\,\text{m}^3\,\text{d}^{-1}$$

Infiltration rate $= 0.2 \times \text{DWF}$

Then $\text{DWF} = 5000 + 0.2\,\text{DWF}$

Therefore $0.8\,\text{DWF} = 5000$

$$\text{DWF} = \frac{5000}{0.8}$$

$$= 6250\,\text{m}^3\,\text{d}^{-1}$$

Maximum flow to treatment plant will be $3 \times \text{DWF} = 3 \times 6250$

$$= 18\,750\,\text{m}^3\,\text{d}^{-1}$$

SAQ 56

From Table 25, volume of sewage generated per day

From factories $= 10\,000 \times 70$ litres $= 700\,000$ litres

From offices $= 6000 \times 50$ litres $= 300\,000$ litres

Total $= 1\,000\,000$ litres

$$= 1000\,\text{m}^3\,\text{d}^{-1}$$

SAQ 57

A combined sewerage system will collect grit, sand, oil and rubbish from roads and paved areas. This can lead to increased wear of equipment in the sewage treatment works and also cause problems with the disposal of the resulting sludge. Oil can affect treatment of the sewage and can also cause blockage in filter cloths used in sludge presses. The flows arriving are much more variable in a combined system and this can complicate treatment as well as necessitate storm overflows and storm tanks. Combined systems also need bigger sewers. However, a separate system needs more pipe-laying.

SAQ 58

A   False. In situations where a high proportion of grit is present, comminutors are placed after the grit removal system.

B   True.

C   False. Biological filters require final humus settling tanks.

D   False. Only the bacteria would reduce the BOD of the settled sewage.

E   True.

SAQ 59

Option **C**. The ratio of surface area to unit volume of the filter medium is most important since this determines the extent to which oxidation will take place.

Options **D** and **E** are secondary considerations.

Option **A** can be relevant in choosing between plastic and conventional media.

It is also important that the medium does not deteriorate significantly while being used.

SAQ 60

$$\text{Mass of BOD applied to filter} = 1200 \times \frac{180}{10^3}$$

$$= 216 \text{ kg BOD d}^{-1}$$

$$\text{Volume of filter bed} = \pi \times 20^2 \times 1.8$$

$$= 2262 \text{ m}^3$$

$$\text{Organic loading rate} = \frac{216}{2262}$$

$$= 0.095 \text{ kg BOD m}^{-3} \text{ d}^{-1}$$

$$\text{BOD removal rate} = 1200 \times \frac{(180 - 20)}{10^3}$$

$$= 192 \text{ kg BOD d}^{-1}$$

SAQ 61

$$\text{SVI} = \frac{\text{settled volume of sludge} \left(\text{ml l}^{-1} \right)}{\text{mixed liquor suspended solids} \left(\text{g l}^{-1} \right)}$$

$$= \frac{280 \text{ ml l}^{-1}}{1.05 \text{ g l}^{-1}}$$

$$= 267 \text{ ml g}^{-1}$$

This sludge would have a tendency not to settle and could possibly be carried over in the effluent.

SAQ 62

(a) From mass balance on aeration unit (Equation 8),

$$X = \frac{Q(L_i - L_e)}{k_a V}$$

$$= \frac{(1000)(0.25 - 0.02)}{(0.3)(250)} \text{ kg m}^{-3}$$

$$= 3.07 \text{ kg m}^{-3}$$

(b) There are two alternatives:

1   Divert some of the entering sewage into temporary storage to await repair of the primary treatment plant, or

2   Increase the concentration X of activated sludge in the aeration tanks by recirculating a larger quantity of sludge in the return loop (see Figure 80). This action is also likely to require increased aeration to cope with the increased organic loading rate in the tanks.

This second option would not be possible with a biological filter. It is this additional flexibility in operation that gives activated sludge plants an important advantage.

SAQ 63

Activated sludge process	Biological filter
Treated effluent quality can be controlled through the sludge recycle in the event of a poorer quality influent entering the works.	Treated effluent quality not easily controlled.
Fly nuisance is avoided.	Flies can be a problem.
Negligible loss of head in effluent flow.	Significant loss of head in effluent flow.
Low space requirement.	Significant space requirement.
Requires continuous attention.	Requires little attention.
Energy consumption high.	Energy consumption low.
Can be upset by surges in flow or high organic loading.	Can tolerate surges in flow and high organic loading.
Noisy.	Quiet.
Limited nitrification.	Nitrification efficiency high.
Relatively complex to monitor and control.	Simple to monitor and control.
Vulnerable to toxics.	Not so vulnerable to toxics.

SAQ 64

Industrial activities	Pollutants	Pretreatment options
Ceramic works	china clay	sedimentation
Distillery	spent grain	microstraining
Chicken processing plant	oil and fat	flotation
Electroplating works	chromium(VI)	chemical reduction (to chromium(III))
Copper mining	acid mine waters	neutralization

SAQ 65

(a)

Concentration of trade effluent (%)	Percentage inhibition
20	8.2
40	18.2
60	38.2
80	44.1
100	55.5

(b) The EC_{50} is estimated to be about 90% (Figure 113).

(c) The concentration of the trade effluent that will result in 15% inhibition of biological activity is 33.6% (Figure 113). This is equivalent to roughly one volume of trade effluent being mixed with two volumes of domestic sewage (assuming the latter doesn't contain any toxics).

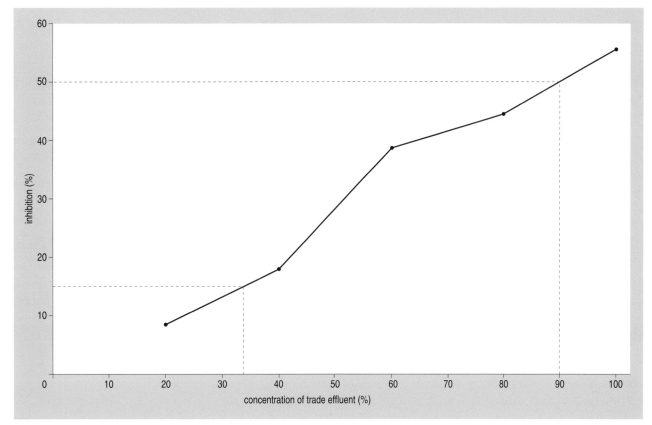

Figure 113   For SAQ 65

SAQ 66

The desert area in the immediate vicinity of the oil wells was where the research team scanned for suitable micro-organisms.

SAQ 67

Total BOD input per day to plant

$$= 1100 \frac{mg}{l} \times 32\,000\,m \times 1000 \frac{1}{m^3} = 352 \times 10^8\,mg$$

Per capita BOD $= \dfrac{352 \times 10^8}{540\,000}\,mg = 0.6519 \times 10^5\,mg$

$\qquad = 65.19\,g$

SAQ 68

(a) It is able to do so because it holds a much higher concentration of biomass.

(b) No micro-organisms and, therefore, no pathogens at present. No suspended solids either.

(c) Because the system is enclosed.

SAQ 69

$$Q = 72 \times \frac{150}{1000} = 10.8\,m^3\,d^{-1}$$

$C_o = 230\,mg\,l^{-1} = 230\,g\,m^{-3}$

$C_1 = 20\,mg\,l^{-1} = 20\,g\,m^{-3}$

$k_1 = 0.08\,m\,d^{-1}$

$$A = 10.8 \left(\frac{\ln 230 - \ln 20}{0.08\,m^2} \right)$$

$$= 10.8 \left(\frac{5.4381 - 2.9957}{0.08\,m^2} \right)$$

$$= 10.8\,(30.53)\,m^2$$

$$= 329.72\,m^2, \ \text{say} \ 330\,m^2$$

SAQ 70

(a) Septic tank or rotating biological contractor.

(b) Contact stabilization.

(c) Waste stabilization ponds; possibly reed beds.

(d) Deep Shaft process; possibly pure oxygen activated sludge process.

(e) Rotating biological contactor (a septic tank would not be appropriate as the effluent would not soak away easily).

(f) Oxidation ditch; possibly rotating biological contactor.

(g) Reed beds; possibly waste stabilization ponds.

(h) Pure oxygen activated sludge process; possibly Deep Shaft process.

(i) Vitox System.

(j) Membrane bioreactor.

SAQ 71

Treatment stage	Pollutants removed
(a) Biological aerated filter	BOD and SS
(b) Reed beds	Particulates, organics and metals
(c) Addition of hydrogen peroxide to groundwater	H_2S
(d) Passage through a GAC column	Hydrocarbons
(e) Ultrafiltration membrane	Particulates and micro-organisms (pathogens)
(f) Reverse osmosis unit	Salts, to reduce hardness and salinity

SAQ 72

B. Grass plots, lagoons and reed beds are all likely to remove nitrogen and phosphorous as well.

SAQ 73

D Air stripping.

In nitrification, ammonia is converted to nitrate. In denitrification, nitrates are converted to nitrogen gas. In the oxidation ditch system, nitrification (and denitrification) takes place. In breakpoint chlorination, the ammonia is oxidized to nitrogen gas.

SAQ 74

Typical inlet P level in domestic sewage $= 8$ mg l^{-1}; 10% of this will be removed in primary settlement.

This leaves 7.2 mg l^{-1}.

If final level is to be 2.0 mg l^{-1}, then 5.2 mg l^{-1} has to be removed.

If the effluent flow is 100 000 m^3 d^{-1}, this is $100\,000 \times 10^3$ l d^{-1}.

So, in one day, the amount of P that has to be removed is

$$5.2 \, \frac{mg}{l} \times 100\,000 \times 10^3 \, \frac{l}{d} \times \frac{1}{10^6} \, \frac{kg}{mg} = 520 \text{ kg d}^{-1}$$

SAQ 75

(a) Tertiary treatment will be required where the discharge consent conditions are stricter than the 30/20 standard set by the Royal Commission. This could be because it is not possible to achieve an 8:1 dilution in the receiving watercourse.

(b) To conform with requirements of the EU Urban Waste Water Treatment Directive, if space is at a premium then a possible choice is microstraining or rapid sand filtration.

SAQ 76

Option **B**. The 30/20 standard is not always enforced since greater pollution loads are considered to be acceptable in some circumstances. Where a watercourse is used for direct abstraction for domestic and industrial supplies as well as effluent discharge, the treatment may aim for a higher standard. Higher standards will of course apply if the dilution is less than 8:1.

SAQ 77

A Screenings.

B Grit disposal – possible use in road gritting if grit is well washed.

C Primary sludge.

D Anaerobic digestion.

E Return activated sludge.

F Tertiary treatment if required, e.g. further settlement or use of grass plots, etc.

SAQ 78

A temperature of 35 °C.

pH of 7.0.

Adequate alkalinity (1000–5000 g m^{-3} as $CaCO_3$)

Minimal toxic material (e.g. heavy metal content should be less than 1 g m^{-3}).

SAQ 79

When it is injected into the ground, and food safety is not compromised.

SAQ 80

(a) Wastewater from toilets and showers.

(b) Scrubber effluent from treatment of acid gases.

(c) Quench waters from cooling of bottom ash.

You will learn about (b) and (c) later in the course.

SAQ 81

Sludge is generated in primary and secondary sedimentation in biological filter and activated sludge systems. In primary sedimentation it is the solid matter in the incoming crude sewage that is removed, while in secondary sedimentation it is the biomass produced in the biological oxidation stage that is separated. Sludge is also produced where chemical precipitation of phosphates is carried out.

SAQ 82

(a) From Table 30, quantity of sludge from primary sedimentation and low-rate filter

$$= 1.1 + 0.23 = 1.33 \text{ kg person}^{-1} \text{ d}^{-1}$$

Total volume per day from town treatment works

$$= \frac{1.33 \times 100\,000}{1000} \text{ m}^3 \text{ d}^{-1}$$

$$= 133 \text{ m}^3 \text{ d}^{-1}$$

(b) From Table 30, quantity of sludge from primary sedimentation and activated sludge process

$$= 1.1 + 2.4 = 3.5 \text{ kg person}^{-1} \text{ d}^{-1}$$

Total volume per day from town treatment works

$$= \frac{3.5 \times 100\,000}{1000} \text{ m}^3 \text{ d}^{-1}$$

$$= 350 \text{ m}^3 \text{ d}^{-1}$$

which is almost three times the amount for the low-rate filter process.

SAQ 83

35–40% reduction in total solids content of sludge.

Production of methane gas which can be used as a fuel for heating.

Removal of offensive odours from sludge.

Reduction in number of pathogenic organisms present in sludge.

Breakdown of organic nitrogen compounds in sludge to ammonia or ammonium salts, increasing the availability of nitrogen to crops when the wet digested sludge is applied to land.

SAQ 84

Volume required for excreta

$$= 600 \text{ head} \times \frac{41 \text{ litres}}{\text{head} \cdot \text{day}} \times 120 \text{ days} \times \frac{1}{1000} \times \frac{\text{m}^3}{\text{litres}}$$

$$= 2952 \text{ m}^3$$

Volume required for rainwater

$$= 80 \text{ m} \times 20 \text{ m} \times \frac{560}{1000} \text{ m} \times \frac{4}{12}$$

$$= 298.67 \text{ m}^3$$

Volume required for silage effluent

$$= 50 \text{ ha} \times 12 \frac{\text{t}}{\text{ha}} \times \frac{90}{1000} \text{ m}^3$$

$$= 54.0 \text{ m}^3$$

Total $= 3304.67 \text{ m}^3$

Therefore, minimum volume of pit $= 3305 \text{ m}^3$

SAQ 85

The COD load of the effluent will be

$$25 \text{ m}^3 \times 18\,000 \frac{\text{g}}{\text{m}^3} \times \frac{1}{1000} \frac{\text{kg}}{\text{g}}$$

$$= 450 \text{ kg}$$

The effluent is applied in two batches of 225 kg

1 ha can take 115 kg each day

Therefore, area required for each application is $225 \text{ kg} \times \dfrac{1 \text{ ha}}{115 \text{ kg}}$

$$= 1.96 \text{ ha}$$

SAQ 86

$$1.96 \text{ ha} = (1.96 \times 100 \times 100) \text{ m}^2 = 19\,600 \text{ m}^2$$

Water capacity of land is $19\,600 \text{ m}^2 \times 166 \dfrac{\text{mm}}{\text{m}} \times 1.4 \text{ m} \times \dfrac{1}{1000} \dfrac{\text{m}}{\text{mm}}$

$$= 4555.04 \text{ m}^3$$

If each application is 12.5 m^3, the theoretical number of applications before leachate is produced

$$= \frac{4555.04}{12.5}$$

$$= 364.4, \text{ say, } 364$$

SAQ 87

Plans to block land drains should pollutants, such as slurry, enter them. This should be by the use of wooden boards.

Plans to contain spillages of oil in watercourses. Again, wooden boards or, better, booms, would be required.

Pesticides or oil which escaped could be captured by adsorbents.

Minor spillages could be removed by a vacuum device. Leaking silos could be repaired by quick-drying concrete.

Means of contacting the relevant authority (the Environment Agency, SEPA, the Environment and Heritage Service).

Means of contacting downstream landowners and water abstracters, e.g. water companies.

SAQ 88

A False – it is not practicable to prevent run-off reaching a water source.

B True.

C False – while this may be true from the point of view of vehicle damage, it is more prudent to store oil above ground where any leakages can be easily seen and dealt with.

D False – this width may be reduced after considering the risks posed for a particular situation, following LERAP.

E False.

F False – this crust helps to maintain the pond in an anaerobic state, and also keeps odours trapped within the pond!

REFERENCE

Porteous, A. (2000) *Dictionary of Environmental Science and Technology*, 3rd edition, John Wiley & Sons (T210 Set Book).

ACKNOWLEDGEMENTS

Grateful acknowledgement is made to the following sources for permission to reproduce material in this block:

Text

Pages 36–37: Edwards, R. 'WWF blames fish farms for poison algae', *The Sunday Herald*, 17 September, 2000. Courtesy of the Scottish Media Group; *Pages 239–242:* Council Directive 98/83/EC of 3 November 1998 on the Quality of Water Intended for Human Consumption, *Official Journal of the European Communities*; *Pages 243–247: Consent to the Discharge of Trade Effluent*, May 1992, with permission from Anglian Water Services Ltd.

Figures

Figure 1: Courtesy of Centre for Science and Environment, New Delhi; *Figure 4(a):* © Gerard & Margi Moss: Still Pictures; *Figure 4(b):* © David M. Denis/Oxford Scientific Films; *Figure 15:* Courtesy of The Centre for Ecology and Hydrology, Windermere; *Figure 17(a):* © Paul Kay/Oxford Scientific Films; *Figures 20, 21, 23 & 28:* Hall, T. & Hyde, R. A. *Water Treatment Processes and Practices.* Reproduced courtesy of WRc Plc. www.wrcplc.co.uk; *Figure 27:* Klei, H. E. & Sundstrom, D. W. (1979) *Waste Water Treatment*, Prentice-Hall, Inc.; *Figure 29:* From *Water Treatment*, PCI-Water; *Figure 30:* Courtesy of Dept. of Water and Sanitation in Developing Countries (SANDTEC) EAWAG; *Figures 32, 77 & 90:* Courtesy of Biwater Treatment Ltd; *Figure 33:* 'Fluoride concentrations in water supplies', *Digest of Environmental Statistics*, Chapter 3 *Inland Water Quality and Use*, December 2001, DEFRA. Crown copyright is reproduced under Class Licence Number C01W0000065 with the permission of the controller of HMSO and the Queen's Printer for Scotland; *Figures 34–36:* Overman, M. (1976) *Water*, Aldus Books Ltd; *Figure 39:* Courtesy of Howard Humphries & Partners Ltd; *Figure 40:* Courtesy of Tendring Hundred Water Services Ltd; *Figures 42, 65 & 69:* Burberry, P. (1992) *Environment and Services: Mitchell's Building Series*, Longman Group; *Figure 46:* Courtesy of Parliamentary Office of Science and Technology; *Figure 48:* Courtesy of RMC Concrete Products (UK) Ltd; *Figure 49:* Courtesy of and available from Construction Resources 020 74502211; *Figure 50:* © 2000 David Williams, djwilliams@bigfoot.com; *Figure 51:* Courtesy of Thames Water; *Figure 56(a) & (d):* © Institut Pasteur/CNRI/Science Photo Library; *Figure 56(b) & (c):* © Eye of Science/Science Photo Library; *Figure 56(e):* © CNRI/Science Photo Library; *Figure 62:* Courtesy of Lovibond Water Testing; *Figures 64 & 65:* Courtesy of Millipore; *Figures 66 & 67:* Taken from technical literature, Amtox; *Figure 71:* Courtesy of Suresh Nesaratnam; *Figure 73:* Courtesy of James & Attwood Ltd; *Figure 74:* Courtesy of Yeomans Chicago Corporation; *Figure 78:* Courtesy of WRc Plc.; *Figure 81:* Courtesy of Simon Hartley Ltd; *Figure 84:* Courtesy of Strathkelvin Instruments Ltd; *Figure 87:* Courtesy of Wimpey Construction Ltd; *Figure 88:* Courtesy of BOC; *Figure 89:*

ICI Bio Products; *Figure 92:* Membrane Bioreactor Technology, Biomembrat. Wehrle Werk AG; *Figure 95: The Chemical Engineer*, 14 March, 1991. Reproduced with permission from the Institute of Chemical Engineers; *Figure 96:* Courtesy of The National Botanic Garden of Wales, www.gardenofwales.org.uk; *Figure 97:* Reproduced with permission of BSI, under licence no. 2002SK/0250. Complete standards can be obtained from BSI Customer Services, 389 Chiswick High Road, London, W4 4AL. (Tel: 020 89969001); *Figures 98, 99, 101 & 104:* Kieley, G. *Environmental Engineering*, © 1997 McGraw-Hill International, with permission of the McGraw-Hill Companies; *Figures 107 & 108: Farm Waste Regulations*, courtesy of the Environment Agency.

Tables

Table 6: 'Water abstracted in England and Wales in 2003 for various uses', www.defra.gov.uk. Crown copyright is reproduced under Class Licence Number C01W0000065 with the permission of the Controller of HMSO and the Queen's Printer for Scotland; *Table 31:* 'ADAS Matrix: the food and water industry in agreement', *Wastes Management*, December, 1999; *Table 32:* Adapted from Grundy, (1980) *Tackling Farming Waste*, Farming Press, Ipswich; *Table 33: Farmyard Wastes and Pollution*, Courtesy of TEAGASC, Agricultural & Food Development Authority; *Tables 34–36:* Adapted from Kieley, G. *Environmental Engineering*, © 1997 McGraw-Hill International, with permission of the McGraw-Hill Companies.

Every effort has been made to contact copyright owners. If any have been inadvertently overlooked, the publishers will be pleased to make the necessary arrangements at the first opportunity.

INDEX